There Go The Ships

Marshall Meek.

There Go The Ships

by

MARSHALL MEEK

To Nigel

With best wishes

Marshall Meek

The Memoir Club

First published in 2003 by
The Memoir Club
Whitworth Hall
Spennymoor
County Durham

British Library Cataloguing in
Publication Data.
A catalogue record for this book
is available from the
British Library.

ISBN: 1 84104 045 2

Any views expressed are those of
the author, and do not necessarily
represent those of the MOD.

All efforts have been made to obtain permission
for reproduction from copyright holders.
The author regrets any omission.

Typeset by George Wishart & Associates, Whitley Bay.
Printed by CPI Bath.

For Elfrida, Hazel, Ursula, Angela and all those 'that go down to the sea in ships'.

So is this great and wide sea, wherein are things creeping innumerable, both small and great beasts. There go the ships: there is that leviathan whom thou hast made to play therein.

Psalm 104

Contents

Part VI: Professional Interests

Part VII: Last Entries in the Log

List of Illustrations

Foreword

by

The Lord Greenway

MARSHALL MEEK'S distinguished career as a naval architect encompasses two stints in both shipbuilding and maritime research separated by a quarter of a century with the celebrated Liverpool shipowner Alfred Holt (Blue Funnel Line).

It spans a period during which shipping underwent a revolution every bit as far-reaching as when steam replaced sail. Perhaps the greatest change was the advent of containerization, a novel and more secure mode of transport which dramatically reduced cargo-handling time in port and allowed ships to spend more time at sea earning money.

On becoming Holt's chief naval architect in 1961, Marshall broke away from the conservative designs of his predecessor with his attractive passenger/livestock liner *Centaur*. His subsequent and highly acclaimed *Priam* class of advanced cargo liners were just entering service when fate decreed that he would be chosen to design the world's first purpose-built deep-sea containerships for Overseas Containers Limited, a consortium of British shipowners engaged in the Australian trade. *Encounter Bay* and her sisters, and the larger and faster *Liverpool Bay* class which followed for the Far East service, were standard-setters and ensured Marshall a place in shipping history.

With British shipping declining as the 1970s wore on, he returned to shipbuilding as technical director of British Shipbuilders. His time with Holts had given him firsthand experience of the efficiency of modern Japanese shipbuilding techniques but he was unable to convince the die-hards in the UK industry, where practices were not much altered from his wartime apprenticeship days at Caledon, to adapt to new methods, and his frustration at seeing the industry wither is palpable.

His career culminated in tenures as executive deputy chairman of British Maritime Technology, where he was involved with undersea technology for the offshore industry as well as ships, and as president of the Royal Institution of Naval Architects. In addition his expert knowledge has been called upon in a number of maritime *causes celèbres* such as the inquiry into the loss of the *Derbyshire*, the capsize of the *Herald of Free Enterprise* and the prolonged saga of the 'Short-Fat versus Long-Thin' warship controversy.

All this and more is covered in this story of quiet achievement and the same attention to detail that typified Marshall's work now enables us to share and enjoy his recollections of past events and the personalities that went with them. At the same time it is also a very human story, that of a man sustained by a strong faith and supportive family who, despite his undoubted successes, has never lost sight of his commitment to the common good.

House of Lords

Acknowledgements

BECAUSE I WANTED my memoir to be something of a historical record as well as a personal narrative, I consulted at various stages both family members and kind former business colleagues. They have devoted more time and critical thought to my maunderings than I deserve. I thank most warmly my sister Martha and brother Max; Ray Adams, Bob Brown and Dave Tucker of Blue Funnel days; George Ward from the BSRA and NMI era; Charles Betts on warship affairs; and most of all Elfrida who supported the venture from the start, and applied the final, authoritative adjustments. In addition she and our daughters Ursula and Angela quite miraculously made sense of my manuscript. The fact that my editor Jane Olorenshaw was the presence hovering over the entire effort was my ultimate reassurance. Lord Greenway, man of the sea, has given my offering a final benediction. I am more than content – I am deeply indebted and grateful to all.

PART I

Shipbuilding

CHAPTER 1

Apprenticeship

'VILLY,' said Mrs Bingham to her ever attentive husband, 'Villy, why not have Marshall in das drawing office?' Villy was William Bingham, assistant chief draughtsman at the Caledon shipyard, Dundee. Mrs Bingham was Hannah, German in thought, word and deed – and appearance (and this was in late 1942 when Britain and Germany were casting high explosive on one another with utmost venom). And Marshall was me. The occasion was one where my older sister, Martha, studying at Dundee Training College to be a teacher, was being entertained one Sunday by the kindly Mr and Mrs Bingham. They had considerately enquired concerning her younger brother, who apparently had been showing a certain restiveness while in the sixth form at Bell-Baxter School in Cupar, Fife. I have no particular recollection of how that unhappy state was being expressed but it was apparently sufficient to indicate that, having achieved a batch of Scottish 'Highers' in the fifth year, I was not too pleased to be continuing at school in the sixth. University had not been considered, presumably because with one member of the family already being supported at college, there was not the resource to fund another. We had never even heard of what is now called the 'gap year'. After all, it was wartime and there was an unspoken reality about life and work. So it was that I finished school at the age of seventeen after one term in the sixth form of a good school, but one which was at that time very strongly slanted to the arts and to a lesser extent science. Entries to the higher grades of the civil service were seen as the hallmark of success. I understand all that has changed now. But at that time the concept of joining the engineering profession was beyond their comprehension. Although engineering as a profession was not so well defined then as it is now, that is what I was doing by becoming an apprentice in the drawing office of a small but progressive Scottish shipyard.

I was accompanied by my father by bus firstly from Auchtermuchty where I was born and brought up, to Cupar, and then to Dundee by train on Saturday 19 December 1942, that is, the day after the school term finished. My father had found lodgings for me near the shipyard and there I spent the first night I had ever been away alone from home. I particularly remember seeing some unfortunate body being carted away on a handcart by the police as we waited on the platform at Cupar. Whether inebriated, incapacitated, or what, I do not know, but it added to the general state of rather miserable apprehension. I started in the drawing office, complete with stiff collar, cuff links and trilby on Monday 21 December. Draughtsmen were superior staff and dressed accordingly. Naturally I worked on the 25th. The only concession to Christmas was that Henry Main, the corpulent but genial and competent managing director, came through the office to shake our hands and wish us a Merry Christmas. My family, knowing that I would have left home by Christmas day, celebrated the event the week before. In our family we tended to celebrate Christmas rather than the traditional Scottish Hogmanay.

The drawing office was typical of its day. About twenty-five or thirty draughtsmen working at drawing boards all of them some 3 metres long or more. Today a similar drawing office would have none, only ranks of computers. Nearly all men, they adopted different stances at the drawing boards. Some stood on wooden stools to reach the far side of the plans they were working on. Ken Shaw was Scottish National Heavyweight Boxing champion. He failed to advance his career further after Freddie Mills considerably altered his lineaments. Ken, who was a most amiable character, was wont to lie flat on his board as he drew, with his heels in the air. It was not long before I started to suffer from fallen arches, never having had to stand for so long; so much so that I consulted the family doctor. He advised standing mid-foot on the fireplace kerb. It was quite a happy place to work, and most of the chaps helped each other along, because after all it was wartime and a reasonable sense of urgency prevailed.

The youngest apprentice depended on the one next above him to show him the ropes. I was very favoured to have Kenny Constable to guide me along, wheezing as he did so. He suffered badly from asthma. There were several duties for the new apprentice which Ken was half ashamed to tell me about. They included ensuring there was soap and toilet rolls in the 'bog' (where the smokers were to be found). Also one I did not enjoy much, mainly because it involved visiting the assistant foreman joiner, was when the wartime black-out blinds that covered the large north-facing glass roofs came off the slides they ran on. It was my job to close and open them. Bob Poulson found it tiresome to have to put up ladders to put them right, and took it out on the unfortunate youngest apprentice.

From all these draughtsmen came plans which produced blueprints. My duties included delivering the steady flow of these blueprints to the appropriate departments in the yard so a fair bit of walking was involved. To this day I recall the noise and the semi-darkness of the platers' shed with the hydraulic punches knocking out the rivet holes, the growling of the bending machines as they shaped the bilge shell plates, the clanging of plate on plate as they were lifted around. By comparison the joiners' shop was much more peaceful with a lovely smell of wood. Above the joiners' shop was the mould loft where the 'lofting' was, quite naturally, carried out. Here you saw the actual shape of the ship's hull marked out and 'scrieved' on to portable floor-boards. From 'moulds' – or templates taken from these, the platers were able to bend the ship side frames to shape and 'expand' the difficult curved areas of shell plating. In one corner of the joiners' shop was the model maker, where the smell of glue pervaded. He was the quietest of all, almost totally deaf, and produced a beautiful model for almost every ship built, such as I would love to possess today. Quite his best was a very large model of the *Glenearn* which sat in pride of place in the main entrance hall. Every fitting, cargo block, rope, winch, or windlass was silver-plated. I was to know more of the famous *Glenearn* class of cargo liners and their owners before very long.

The reaction of the various foremen to the arrival of the juvenile drawing office apprentice when he arrived with a newly issued plan was intriguing. If it was a 'modified' plan, meaning a revision of one previously issued, the foreman plater could be explicit and unpleasant. It probably meant he had to try and correct something he had already committed into cold steel, or he would have to find or wait for a new steel plate and start again. The foreman blacksmith was always considerate and kind when he took delivery of the 'rails and stanchions' plan or the 'mast fittings'. He would even have a little talk with the innocent-faced junior, which was very cheering. Bob Poulson just looked slightly sardonic as if anything emanating from the drawing office must be suspect.

One of the most fatuous duties was to accompany, every so often, two of the most foulmouthed and foulminded little men employed by the Dundee Harbour Authority. They came to measure up the ground space occupied by various bits and pieces belonging to the shipyard but which for convenience were dumped on their land outside the yard gates. The junior apprentice had the job of supposedly checking their figures on behalf of the shipyard. In the grimmest of weather we would record in sodden notebook the square footage of every steel plate, angle bar, bollard or spare anchor lying about and tally it up. The shipyard paid rental on this basis. As the spaces between the assorted hardware were completely useless there was no reason at all to be so precise in this miserable charade of accurate estimating.

There was the incessant noise of riveting. I have often wondered how many deaf people there were then or later because no one wore any protection and the riveters were using pneumatic hammers all day long. The foreman riveter was a suitable persona for the trade – big and crude, Po Thomson by name, and a known and respected poacher. There must have been, however, some official recognition of his countryside abilities because he was entrusted at least once to take an honourable shipowner on a weekend rough shoot. Sir Edmund Watts had three ships being built in the yard and was therefore worthy of some special hospitality. Unfortunately on the day one of his ships was being launched he turned up heavily bandaged. Apparently, in negotiating a stile during the shoot Po had inadvertently filled the back of his neck with lead shot. There seemed to be no ill feelings or repercussions as far as I could detect.

The bowler hat was everywhere. Like all foremen Po wore his, but at a jaunty back-of-the-head angle. As tradition had it, the bowler was needed to protect the wearer from red-hot rivets 'accidentally' dropped from above. I suspect Po had so many land on his that his skull was inured and the bowler was unnecessary. I forget just when I felt I was qualified to wear one. It certainly was not until I had finished my apprenticeship, but wear one I did for many years particularly during my visits to shipyards as a representative of a major shipowner. Otherwise there would have been little respect. I remember in particular lunching at the John Brown Shipyard senior dining room during the 1960s. The anteroom contained at least forty identical bowlers around the walls.

Our plans were either drawn on tracing paper and then transferred in ink to the more durable bluish 'linen'; or they were, more seldom, drawn direct on to the linen. For the latter the draughtsman had to be more proficient with his printing pen and his linesmanship. For the former, there was the tracing office, a rather private female sanctuary, where the temperature always seemed to be five or more degrees higher than in the drawing office, the aroma was different, and you had to have a pretty good reason for entering at all. Plans when complete were stored in the 'safe', a little room with heavy lockable doors and without ventilation, where Sidney held sway. Sidney was mostly helpful but could be highly irascible if plans were mislaid, usually by him. The back of the safe was the place where dark deeds of retribution were enacted between adverse drawing office parties. Running it during any absence of Sidney was another job for the youngest apprentices. Yet another was to run the print room in any absence of Chrissie. Chrissie was an exceptionally nice, quiet, long-suffering girl who churned out the blueprints. The print room was of course quite dark most of the time and lit only by the ever-traversing brilliance of the carbon arc as the print paper passed under it. The place stank of the chemicals used in fixing the print. And there were rollers over which the prints passed on their way to the drying end. The plans were often 3 or more metres long (which was why we needed the long drawing boards) and for some reason, any time I had to run the wretched place, they had an innate proclivity to wind themselves round the hateful rollers, rather than pass over them. That generated alarming thoughts that the whole war effort was being held up while I, usually with some other kind help, had to lift out the rollers, stinking with chemicals, unwrap and start all over again.

Yet there were compensations for the junior apprentice, like the privilege of attending on the platform at launches. The duty was to hold the champagne bottle (or whatever was used during wartime in lieu) until the lady sponsor was ready to pronounce the traditional words 'I launch this ship so and so and may God bless her and all who sail in her', and then hand over the bottle on its length of rope so that she could proceed to smash it against the ship. Remarkably there was a launch the very first day I started, and I was taken first thing that morning by the taciturn design office manager, Alex Allardyce, to help check out the final measurements of the launch ways. I had never seen a large ship before, let alone one at such frighteningly close quarters. She was Ship No. 400. In a shipyard the number matters, not the name, which is only divulged towards the time of the launch. She was in fact *Norman Monarch* and she was sunk in war service shortly after. In my trepidation at climbing over the launch platform rail to hold the end of the measuring tape I inadvertently stood on a roll of the bunting being used to decorate the platform, and made a dirty footprint. Bob Poulson (of course!) was not pleased. At the actual launch ceremony I managed to perform my little duty but then made the mistake of joining in the three hearty cheers as the ship started off down the slipway. My taciturn friend at my elbow was quick to remind me my job was to retrieve the bottle's remains and stow away the silver cord and not stand there cheering as if I was somebody.

To leap ahead thirty years for a moment, I recall the next time I felt similar concern, having by that time witnessed dozens of launches and naming ceremonies. An offshore supply boat for Ocean Inchcape, one of our subsidiary companies, built by the Van der Giessen shipyard was being named as she lay alongside the quay in Rotterdam. The lady sponsor had made two abortive attempts to break the bottle. At the third, and amid mounting concern, she used extra force, the rope broke and with a sickening plop the bottle went directly into the deep. I shared the immediate and awful premonition that the ship must therefore be in some way doomed. Peter Van der Giessen, the managing director, simply turned to his launch manager and said 'Next bottle'.

I was not junior apprentice for long. Jimmy Young arrived and I was glad to see the more menial tasks handed over. Jimmy had a certain 'air' and dignity about him. He was 'English' and had arrived on a sort of fast track where there was some specific encouragement given to certain rather upper-class types to enter shipbuilding. They seemed to come from 'English' public schools. It was really because of him that I went eventually to university and qualified as a naval architect. Jimmy (who was quietly known as 'the Count' by apprentice colleagues) let it be known after a few months that he was headed for university. He actually did go, but after I myself graduated some years later and had returned to the shipyard to complete my apprenticeship, there was Jimmy. Apparently having failed repeatedly in his first year at college he had been kicked out. As the shipyard's very first graduate I was invited, or perhaps required, to lecture at the Dundee Technical College night classes. Students there studied for their Higher National qualification and Jimmy, having failed to progress at university, was now trying for his Higher National. Jimmy stuck to it and very pleasantly heeded my lectures without harbouring any ill will towards me. As far as I know Jimmy might well still be there. Clearly he was not meant to be a naval architect. But it was when my parents heard that he was heading for university that they started to think I should go too. So before my first year of apprenticeship was complete I had been accepted by the engineering faculty at Dundee. This did not mean I was finished with the shipyard or the drawing office – far from it. Without thinking too much about it I had applied to the civil engineering faculty, fancying the idea of building great bridges, or dams, or railways. When Henry Main the managing director heard of this he called me in. I was instructed, in quite a kindly fashion, to re-apply for the naval architecture course and the company could then accommodate my course within my apprenticeship. Looking back, this was really rather considerate. He assured me this would ensure some real success in life. Whether he was right I leave to the judgement of my readers but it meant that in due course I became the first home-grown graduate within the company. There was one other graduate in the office when I returned from university, a Pole called Baginski, who had escaped at the beginning of the war and being older, had already acquired a degree. But he did not stay long in the shipyard and neither did I in the end. I shall revert to the reasons for the failure of British shipbuilding to survive in the late 1970s but I believe the lack of graduate-level people even at the time I write about was just one of the failings.

My colleagues in the drawing office were really very tolerant of me, a part-timer and student, whose university term time counted as valid apprenticeship compared with their steady slog of five full years at the drawing board. I remember their names to this day, many of them carved on my set-square in the way we did for each other – and I still use it. Willie Bingham took over from the chief draughtsman, Davy Black soon after I joined. Davy was really rather blind and young apprentices used to take a deep breath when opportunity offered, and make blatant and rude signs to him from the other end of the office. One was never quite sure whether he was that blind or not. Willie Bingham was from Belfast. He had toiled in the famous Workman Clarke shipyard until it went broke in the 1930s depression. Its staff were to be widely scattered after that. Jimmy Gardner was leading hand and on the very first day, and indeed in the very first hour of my starting in the office, on hearing I came from Auchtermuchty in Fife he demanded of me 'why...! I had not gone to Burntisland Shipyard' which was in my native Fife, rather than to Dundee. The forcefulness and expletive nature of his approach was really rather unsettling to one of my disposition and background. I never did understand the logic of his welcome but under that carapace of hostility he turned out to be a most kind and helpful colleague who was to guide me very soon in the very first bit of structure I ever drew out and then saw being made in the yard – an engine-room skylight. A relatively small item, but for me a landmark.

The set-square carries other names. Eric Milton, a nice chap, lame in one leg, who would bravely go a cycle run pedalling with one foot, and later became a very successful Church of Scotland minister in Glasgow; Bob Pattullo, who eventually became head of Vickers experiment tank at St Albans; Jimmy Abbot, from a family of famous singers and who tried to teach me with minimal success to swim in the local baths, became a Lloyd's Register surveyor, as did Harry and Bill McQueen; Malcolm Smith, who did beautiful printing on his plans, and with whom I used to go for a walk at lunchtime and quite happily never say a word, also bound for Lloyd's Register; Jimmy Grewar, who became a teacher locally. It can be gathered that many passed through the drawing office on their way elsewhere.

It was not only the drawing office that exported talent. Shortly to depart was McDonald the foreman joiner who enjoyed a tremendous elevation when he became foreman at John Brown's shipyard on the Clyde. My friend, assistant foreman Poulson, naturally benefited and was promoted. With the satisfaction of running one of the biggest joiners' shops anywhere, turning out furniture for the prestigious Cunarders and the like, McDonald achieved his pinnacle of success. Andy Boyack and Jimmy Fearns lived amongst leather-bound order books and catalogues. They did the selecting and purchasing of all the outfit needed on the ships, except the steel materials. Requirements for steel, which was naturally the biggest item, were handled by one or two seniors who were privileged to enter orders for steel plates and sections in a special series of black books. These disappeared at regular intervals for the orders to be processed elsewhere in the building. It was when I was helping one of these seniors that I discovered the importance of the number 'two', not only in ordering the steel but in nearly every other aspect of ship production. Because a ship is, or should be, symmetrical about its fore and aft centre-line one usually only deals with one half of the ship and then multiplies by two at the end. If you forget the 'two' there tends to be big trouble. Willie Fearns, brother of Jimmy, was of long standing and did the major structural drawings such as the plan of 'pillars and girders' which provided the skeleton of the whole internal structure of the ship.

Sam Sweet became assistant chief draughtsman to Willie Bingham. He was a tiny man who used to rub a tiny hand over a very bald and shiny head, and was reputed to be able to sneak up on you from under the drawing board. I once greatly appreciated an unsolicited compliment from him that has stayed with me. He described a plan I had prepared as 'beautiful', and he meant it. I was unfamiliar with such terminology. It was, I thought, a straightforward setting out of a bunker arrangement for a ship that was changing over from coal burning to oil burning and needed new structure to accommodate the oil. I had never thought I was producing anything beautiful, but the inadvertent success opened my eyes to what can be real draughtsmanship, and I am therefore grateful.

Caledon shipyard turned out good ships of many types, but mainly cargo ships either of the tramp type like *Norman Monarch*, or cargo liners, the higher-class jobs such as were built for Alfred Holt & Company of Liverpool, often known as the Blue Funnel Line. That famous shipping company held a large chunk of Caledon shares and hence many of its ships were built there. I was later to work for AH & Co. for twenty-five years and it was the most satisfying time of my life. Up till about the time I entered shipbuilding, ships' structure had been mainly riveted. Welding was just becoming accepted. Also coal had been the principal fuel, but oil was becoming more common – hence the oil bunker designs I referred to. Something like 450–500 feet was the upper limit of length of ship at Caledon, and so size was limited. Only shipyards like John Browns or Fairfields on the Clyde could at that time build the really big ships in Scotland. It did mean, however, that at Caledon we got varied experience, instead of being stuck with a *Queen Mary* or *Empress of Canada* for years at a time. Draughtsmen at these large yards reputedly spent months and almost years on the same plan, whereas we were given a run round all the drawing office sections, always starting with steelwork and structure, but also covering such as piping work. Here Ernie Lloyd reigned and sat (often asleep) by an open window breathing pure tar and oil fumes from the refinery next door. Or the derrick and cargo gear section where Dave Drummond was leader, reckoned to be a grump, with a wooden leg. Supposedly careless younger draughtsmen walking behind his back would endeavour to casually swing their wood and ivory scales which were in constant use, so that the spring controlling his wooden leg was hit and became dislodged, with regrettable results.

The ships were built in our yard with no less than six parallel berths. They were launched freely into the wide Tay estuary, which practice was unlike that in many other narrower rivers where heavy drag chains had to be used to control the speed into the water. Building procedure was based on laying the keel plates and then the bottom plating, erecting the side frames and adding the shell (or hull) plating, plate by plate and strake by strake. Likewise the decks, all within a cradle mesh of scaffolding uprights and ladders. The engines and machinery were inserted after launch at a separate berth up river under 'the big crane'. Then the ship was fitted out back at the shipyard. All this was to change in the next few years and it was to be foreign shipyards that led the change away from multiple berths, concentrating on only one, or perhaps two at the most, and accepting the discipline of sticking to the schedules and programmes that had then to be enforced. Before this change the work-force moved from one berth to another rather like what happens with your local jobbing joiner or builder who always finds some other pressing or convenient job to fit in as well as yours. I am surprised to this day to read in quite authentic records that such and such a shipyard had six or seven berths or whatever, using the number of berths to denote shipyard size and output. It is just like saying that the local grocer's store had five or six counters as a measure of its commercial success. It was what passed over the counter, or over the berth, and the time it took that mattered. Together with the reduction in berths came the concept of building in much larger sections or units, prefabricated away from the berth and even away from the shipyard, and all brought together on the berth in a carefully scheduled sequence. Caledon was not alone in being slow to adapt.

The shipyard had over 2,000 employees when I joined. Before World War II the UK built over half the world's total of merchant ships. For the cognoscenti this meant 1.874 million gross tons. In 1946 just after the end of the war we were still building over 52 per cent of the world's ships. By the time I re-entered shipbuilding in 1979 the percentage of British ship completions was down to 3 per cent. Today our percentage is so small as to be negligible. I find it difficult to believe that change of this magnitude should happen over my working life in ships, but it has.

CHAPTER 2

Into ship design

MY FIRST YEAR at university started within a year of my sister's helpful introduction to Willie Bingham. Dundee University was at that time a college of St Andrews. That was before the fecund growth in universities all over the country. Dundee now has two universities. The first year in the faculty of engineering was common to the four Scottish universities that existed at that time, and obviously it suited me to continue there. Then I had to go to Glasgow for the rest of my naval architecture course. I suppose I could have gone to Newcastle upon Tyne which was an alternative, but presumably the idea of going outside Scotland never crossed anybody's mind. Glasgow normally did a 'sandwich' course, four years instead of the more usual three, half the year at university classes, half back in industry. However it was wartime and the university decided to cram the academic year in engineering into two sessions, i.e. the industry period was virtually squeezed out. Add to that the fact that only one fail and one re-sit was allowed before you were chucked out, and it will be realized that university life was no joyride. In fact it was sheer hard graft and probably rightly so when so many of one's contemporaries were out on the battle lines. Coupled with that, I had to return to the shipyard for such few weeks as were available between sessions. Under these pressurized circumstances it may not be surprising that I finished my degree course in 1946 before I was twenty-one. What is more surprising perhaps is that I acquired a BSc in engineering with 2nd class honours in naval architecture.

Back in the shipyard, in due course I reached my five-year mark. Like all apprentices finishing their 'time' I received a beautiful instrument box made by the joiners' shop (I was now on good terms with Bob Poulson) in which to store my accumulated tools of the draughtsman's trade – set-squares, scales, compasses, erasing shield, the multitude of 'curves' so peculiar to the ship draughtsman. I am sorry to say I never really put it to good use because I moved on from being a draughtsman shortly afterwards and achieved an ambition – I entered the ship design office. Thrusting young draughtsmen generally saw three avenues of advancement beyond the drawing office. Either they wanted to become part of the yard management as an 'outside' or ship manager, looking after the ships on the berth or fitting out, and perhaps advancing to management of the yard itself; or moving out altogether to the highly desirable and select realms of surveyor to Lloyd's Register of Shipping or other classification society; or following the ship design route. I was now on this last alternative. It was the design of ships that was to give me so much satisfaction from then on. I was to become a real naval architect, one of that smallish, rather close, always friendly and slightly superior profession.

The design and estimating office was next door to the drawing office, the quickest and most dangerous entry being through Sidney's sacrosanct safe, although that involved ducking under the shelf-counter arrangement at each door. There were only four or five people there. John Liddle was in charge and was also chief estimator. To him fell the perilous job of costing the ship as it was designed and submitting the price to the shipowner. Noel Adams was naval architect. My principal recollection of him was being told 'Marshall, you are in too much of a hurry'. This because I had, in my enthusiasm to see my calculations turned into a ship design, made some error or other. The pleasure in developing a 'lines plan' for my own first ship, a small tanker, remains with me. This plan delineates the shape and size of the ship, and therein lies a great part of the naval architect's expertise. The lines plan will ensure that the ship has enough buoyancy to carry its own weight plus the cargo; that it will float level fore and aft with the centre of buoyancy in the right place; and it will, most importantly, float level transversely but with enough capability to ensure it will not capsize under the influence of waves or wind or wrong cargo loading. My tanker was so important to me that I used to cycle back to the office of a summer's evening, after having my tea, to put in an hour or two of unpaid overtime. The method of working was very different from that in a similar office today. The slide rule and the measuring scale of boxwood and ivory were all important. You had either the conventional push-pull slide rule where you carried a 6-inch version in your pocket (it needed better eyesight) or the more usual 12-inch job on the desk. Or more professionally still, you had a Fuller barrel slide rule. This was hand-held or on a stand and it rotated, and because of the greater length of the spiral scale round the barrel, it could achieve greater accuracy. Naval architecture calculations are intensively repetitive and were exceedingly time-consuming when done manually like this.

Today the computer rules, and the biggest change to the science and art of naval architecture is that it is now very easy to calculate and recalculate. In my day, if for example you found you had not enough transverse stability to ensure adequate resistance to capsizing, you would probably increase the beam (or the width) of the ship. This was a major decision because it meant a mass of recalculations. Today it is done very easily by computer. Yet the basic necessity for understanding the principles of naval architecture stand, however clever you may be with a computer. I got involved a year or two ago with one well-known UK shipping company whose ship proved seriously defective on delivery. The naval architect in the shipyard had fed in the wrong figures based on wrong assumptions at the design stage. His final calculations, all computer calculated, formed an impressive and well-laid out presentation. But the ship had to be taken very quickly out of service after it was built, cut in two, and have a very large portion of extra hull added, together with other measures like adding buoyancy chambers underwater, to correct both the carrying capacity and the stability. The computer does not think; the naval architect must.

Another well-used instrument in my day was the integrator, a mechanical device which traversed the drawing board on a heavy steel rail. A pointer was tracked round the 'lines' of the ship and after reading various micrometer scales and doing a few calculations you could have not only the area traced out by the pointer but also its 'centre'. This, after repeated moves, eventually gave for example, the volume or displacement of the ship, and also its centre of buoyancy, which is a fairly fundamental requirement. A few years ago I was visiting the Swan Hunter shipyard on the Tyne and there on the wall was an integrator mounted on a plaque. It was an 'antique', superseded by the computer.

I enjoyed my first launching plan and its associated calculations once I was settled in the shipyard design office. The sliding of a ship down the launch ways and its transference from land into the water has always been one of the bigger engineering transactions performed by man. It is quite possible that a large ship may weigh 25,000 tonnes or more, although it is more common in modern large shipyards for such ships to be built in a dock and floated out rather than be launched, which is rather unspectacular. The traditional launch is much more exciting; it carries a sort of latent risk and spawns a ghoulish anticipation that something may go wrong. Once the triggers retaining the vessel on the ways are released on the command of the lady sponsor on the platform up front, the ship (usually) starts to slide. As the aft end leaves the support of the launch ways the ship 'hogs' until the buoyancy of the aft end takes effect. It bends upward at the middle. This imposes severe strains on the bottom of the ship and concentrated pressure on the seaward end of the launch ways. As the stern enters the water and buoyancy takes effect the strains are reversed. The ship 'sags'. It bends upwards at the ends more and more until the fore end, which is specially supported by the cradle called the fore poppet, drops off the end of the ways and with a little curtsey (usually) she is afloat. What impressed me was how sensitive the exercise was to the depth of water at the end of the launch ways. Because the River Tay into which we launched is a wide estuary at that point, the effect of the wind was very noticeable. With a good strong east wind the water level increased and could easily provide an additional six inches or more over the end of the ways. This has a very marked and beneficial effect on the stresses on the ship's hull and on the speed with which the vessel reaches flotation. The sooner the better, not only for the lady sponsor and the shipyard manager but also for the stressed structure of the ship itself.

I had soon become aware that there was a special aura attaching to the Blue Funnel Line of Liverpool, otherwise known as Alfred Holt & Co. The company, because of its shareholding in the Caledon shipyard, had built many ships there which, like all AH and Co. ships, were named after Greek heroes from Homer's *Odyssey*. As can be imagined shipyard workers and dockers developed their own derisive renderings of names such as *Autolycus* and *Euryades* and *Philoctetes*. The *Telemachus* was part-built when I joined Caledon, and was followed by *Rhexenor* and *Stentor* when I returned from university. There were to be many more, and especially a remarkable series known as Holt's '*A*' Class, the building of which ran for years. These cargo liners were the cream of British merchant shipping and, even during wartime when there was great urgency to produce tonnage, they received special care and attention in the building. Willie Bingham described them to me, during his one-to-one teaching sessions on ships and shipbuilding, as of 'a disgustingly high standard'. They always took longer to build than more commonplace ships. I was to come to the realization shortly that this veneration of all things Holt was wholly appropriate.

During these years in Dundee I stayed in lodgings. Mrs Rae, my first landlady, soon tired of the chore and I found a berth at Miss Lockhart's house almost overlooking the shipyard. My diaries started at this time and were originally intended to record for my concerned mother how I was being fed during these difficult wartime years. Hence copious references to dinner and tea content (being lunch and evening meals respectively). My family find it hard to believe me today when I quote my records on certain days – 'had real eggs', and even, 'had cake today'. My bicycle was important, and was accommodated in Miss Lockhart's hall. I went home every second weekend, crossing first on the *Fifie*, the much loved ferry crossing over to Newport in Fife. The Tay Road Bridge had not even been thought of. Then cycling, with a case of dirty laundry on the carrier, the eighteen miles to Auchtermuchty. Otherwise it would have meant train to Cupar and bus from there. With a starting pay of eighteen shillings per week, and a payment to Miss Lockhart of thirty-five shillings I had to conserve the funds provided by my father that I depended on. It was the fact that even though I was working, my parents were still having to pay out for me, that encouraged them to feel they might as well pay out for my going to university.

I did two years in the design office and then looked for a change. At the end of 1948 as I shall explain, I had an interview with the British Shipbuilding Research Association and got a job as assistant naval architect from January 1949. But I leave my description of my time in research till later and continue with my experience in shipbuilding; because I came back into the industry in January 1979 exactly thirty years later. What a change I found, and for the worse!

CHAPTER 3

Back to shipbuilding

BY 1978, after I had been with Alfred Holt-Blue Funnel in Liverpool for quarter of a century, it had become obvious that that famous shipping company was moving away from shipping into other business. Chairman Sir Lindsay Alexander was sympathetic when I received, out of the blue, an invitation to become technical director at the recently established nationalized British Shipbuilders and accepted. During the acrimonious run-up to the nationalizing of the industry, Tony Benn, Secretary of State for Industry (or was it 'Technology' in those enthusiastic white-hot days?) had decreed that its headquarters must be outside London. The choice lay between Liverpool and Newcastle upon Tyne, the latter being eventually chosen. So it meant a move for my family. When I told friends we were going to Newcastle they genuinely thought I meant Newcastle under Lyme. The other, greater Newcastle on the River Tyne was beyond general comprehension, for it was over the Pennines. Such is the rift and lack of knowledge that exists between East and West, as well as between North and South in our little country.

By now my wife Elfrida and I had three daughters, all in their teens, although Hazel the oldest was studying in London at that time. When we put the proposition of a move to them they were all quite happy about it, almost as if we all felt we had done a reasonable stint on Merseyside. We had no knowledge of the North East, although for years I had been making regular visits to Vickers shipyard at Walker on the Tyne during the building of about ten Blue Funnel ships. These visits meant only rather miserable and uninteresting train journeys, after a day's work, between Liverpool and Newcastle; or slow flights in DC3 aircraft with ice forming on the inside of the windows in winter, and a night in the Station Hotel. So I had developed no particular familiarity with the region and certainly had no experience of the curiously haunting and lonely beauty of Northumberland which now means so much to us.

We found a very suitable house at Tranwell Woods three miles west of Morpeth and fifteen miles north of Newcastle, and there settled into our own five acres of Northumberland. With only a short break in 1985–6 when we were in Hampshire, we were to enjoy it for the next sixteen years – hard work in looking after house and garden but a great period of family life. Both Hazel our oldest and Ursula our middle daughter were married from there.

There was no difficulty in arranging a helicopter to land in the garden to take Hazel and Arthur away after their celebration in the grounds. There was a distinct feeling of seclusion and togetherness in 'The Woods' as we locals called it; with folklore attaching to the old wartime Tranwell aerodrome along the road where many friends had learned to drive over the old runways; and still whispers of secret MOD installations somewhere around. George Snaith, director of research and a helpful colleague at my new office, warned me that drainage and septic tanks were a problem in the area (true, but manageable); that deer were another (true and less manageable); and that we should watch out for opencast mining (true, but the mines came and went, not too close by, in less than two years.) When I went for my morning jogging session I had to pass the homes of Kevin Keegan and Steve Cram. I hoped they did not see my laborious and breathless progress.

Although the headquarters of the new British Shipbuilders was in Jesmond in Newcastle where I was based, there was also an office in Knightsbridge, a necessity for contact with the Department of Industry and also for marketing purposes. And because successive chairmen almost perforce lived in the South, the Knightsbridge office virtually became another HQ. Recently retired Admiral Sir Anthony Griffin was the first chairman of British Shipbuilders, a naval gentleman in the finest traditions. He made a point of calling on every new member of staff as they joined. Unfortunately there was a lack of empathy between him and his chief executive Michael Casey who was a very senior civil servant from the Department of Industry. The story went that they did not really speak to each other. I could never prove or disprove this, but it was an ominous portent for the future. When I joined roughly a year after vesting day there was a very reasonable feeling that something could be made of the industry, in spite of all the troubles that had increasingly pressed down on it since I was at Caledon shipyard in the 1940s. There was a sense that Government was in support and that with a fair wind in the market place we could make something out of an outfit that had lost a lot of respect in the eyes of the public. When my ailing old Uncle Willie heard I was going back to shipbuilding he quoted Kipling:

> Or watch the things you gave your life to, broken,
> And stoop to build 'em up again with worn out tools.

Actually, not all the tools were worn out. There were some quite modern establishments in the massive set-up that was British Shipbuilders with its more than 80,000 employees, like Sunderland Shipbuilders or the warship yards at Barrow and Scotstoun. A bigger problem was the people, both in top management and in the yards. I shall try to explain why, when I left five years later, all had gone wrong.

The formation of separate divisions within British Shipbuilders was not organized as such until 1980 but the scene can best be appreciated by looking at these divisions. Merchant shipbuilding was the largest. It represented 44 per cent of the total activity on vesting day, but was down to less than 30 per cent when I left at end of 1983. Warship building was 30 per cent of activity at the outset and rose to over 40 per cent over the same period, but this was only because of the reduction in merchant ships. The other divisions – offshore, ship repair and engineering – were all smaller and made up the other 25 per cent. We have to remember the awful years previously when the UK sank from building half the world's merchant ships at the end of World War II to the mere 2 or 3 per cent which was all that the 30,000 people in the merchant division could achieve. Many who are around today will recall the reporting in the 1960s and 1970s of lunatic demarcations between the various trades in the shipyards, ('who should bore the holes?'); the sheer negativism of the trade unions, where the boiler-makers must at all times come out tops in the union pecking order; the arguments about pennies per hour differences; and how many minutes less per week could be squeezed out of the companies. If half the time and energy spent arguing with shop stewards and unions had been devoted to improving methods of building the ships we would not have ended up the way we did.

There were eleven individual merchant shipbuilding yards within BS in 1982 and six warship yards. I soon discovered that one big problem lay in the relationship between these companies and headquarters. All these yards had been accustomed to conducting their own business and the bosses of each were loath to relinquish their autonomy. Yet the financial assistance that was needed, and was forthcoming from Government at the start, had naturally to be processed through headquarters. This required staff in the finance department. Headquarters also needed a central marketing department and various others such as personnel and legal. My technical department was one of them. The individual yards were not averse to calling the 130 or so staff at headquarters an 'overhead', and the whole set-up as an ivory tower – or worse. And so a sort of tension was generated. I remember Derek Kimber, the managing director of Austin & Pickersgill, sounding off one evening to some of us on these lines. Professor John Caldwell of Newcastle University was one of those in the group and in his usual thoughtful and deferential way he asked Derek what would have happened if BS had not been formed and A&P, as it was known, had had to exist on its own. Derek could only gulp, and in a rather less stentorian tone admit they would have gone under – as would most of the others.

The trouble was that the advantages of having a central direction were never either appreciated or exploited because there was not enough understanding of the business either by the chairman or the chief executive, and not enough muscle or guts to make the individual shipyard barons conform. When Sir Robert Atkinson, who had a somewhat keener knowledge of the industry had become chairman, he once told a few of us, in a state of frustration, that the attitude of the managing directors of the shipyards was simply 'give me the money and leave me alone'. I fear he was right, and also that one of the greatest weaknesses of all was that the leaders of the industry were either so uninterested or so busy with internal troubles that they had totally neglected to observe how ships were being built more efficiently in other more successful countries around the world, and emulate them.

A few examples. I have already said that the Caledon shipyard in Dundee worked on six berths at any one time, and this was typical. Shipyards in Japan, which was our first major competitor, were cutting down the number of berths, even in the early 1960s. They accepted the discipline of having to be organized so that work continued without interruption on one, or at the most, two building berths. Ships on these one or two berths had then to be pushed out steadily and quickly so as not to disrupt the yard's output. I always had the feeling that the British enjoyed building their ships, taking plenty of time, watching them grow. I recall observing a workman at Fairfields yard as he stopped on his way past the slipway just to stare at and admire my containership being built on the berth. Other countries just wanted to deliver the ships and make money.

When I was with Blue Funnel in Liverpool in the early 1960s we built two cargo liners with Mitsubishi in Nagasaki. They were sisters to five ships being built at Vickers Walker yard on the Tyne and one at John Brown Clydebank. These were almost the first UK cargo liners to be ordered in Japan. The British yards started off in the traditional way, every effort being made to draw the steelwork plans expeditiously and get the first keel sections on the berth. In that way the date of the payment of the first major instalment of the price of the ship, usually based on the appearance of the first blocks of steel structure on the berth, was hastened as much as possible. The Japanese did it quite differently. They painstakingly did their plans first in the form of composite drawings, showing not just the steelwork, but also the arrangement of piping and other services that had to be fitted into these bottom sections. It ensured that all the subsequent cutting of steelwork and fudging to accommodate these services later was avoided. The British yards traditionally got the steel units on the berth, then had to adapt them to take the mass of piping and other services as a later exercise. I showed these composite drawings to Vickers at Walker on the Tyne in the hope they would be interested. John Browns were following the Vickers plans so as to economize on doing their own, a dangerous exercise when the practices within the shipyards were different. There was no interest in either yard. It was obvious there was neither the willingness nor the capability to alter and improve their current practices. They paid dearly for it, both yards going out of business once these ships had been completed – all very late on delivery.

This sorry story is but a confirmation of what Sandy Marshall, one-time chairman of P&O and chairman of Trident Tankers, wrote in his memoirs referring to his experience of the same era. He had been so impressed with Japanese shipbuilding performance with his ships that he suggested to two British shipbuilders that they might consider lending Trident one of their managers to go out to the Mitsui yard in Japan and actually see the developments there. Ross Belch of Lithgows at Greenock took up his offer; but from my own later experience of him he clearly failed to effect the changes that were needed in his yards. The other was Vickers at Barrow (and Walker) where Len Redshaw just dismissed the idea with 'what on earth could we learn from them? – after all we taught them how to build ships in the first place'.

Because the hull of a ship is by nature curvaceous a great deal of the hull plating has to be formed into suitable shape, especially if it is a fast fine-lined vessel. Clearly this involves bending the steel plates in more than one direction to the predetermined shape. Traditionally, this shape was achieved by passing and repassing the steel plates through heavy rollers until they are correctly formed. While I was building these same cargo liners at Nagasaki in the early 1960s, we discovered Mitsubishi were 'line heating' their plates instead of using rollers. This involved repeatedly heating the steel with gas torches, then cooling with water jets along predetermined straight lines so making the material contract to a new shape. We had always taken great care with superintending our ships and we were concerned that this unusual process might change the properties of the steel. After careful thought we imposed a limit of 800 degrees centigrade on the heating, and I think the yard found it difficult to keep to this, but the method was used extensively on our ships. In the early 1980s when I was with British Shipbuilders, a new production department was set up at headquarters under Roger Vaughan, an expert on ship production, to try to get the yards to improve output. One of the new developments brought to their attention by Roger was line-heating – twenty years after we saw it used in Japan.

With Ray Adams, my assistant of many years, I had written a paper for the Royal Institution of Naval Architects in 1969 describing the design and building of these eight ships, and comparing the differences in building methods between the two Japanese and the six British ships. I know it was well used by universities in lectures to students but it did not seem to achieve much in the shipyards. What that paper also showed was that the British shipyards started erecting steelwork on the berth between four and seven months after signing the contract. The Japanese waited for fifteen months, preferring to get their planning well on the way first. The British ships were something like fifteen to nineteen months on the building berth. The Japanese were four to five months. Fifteen years later, during my time with British Shipbuilders, there had been some improvement towards these Japanese levels of construction performance, but not nearly enough. What I found galling was that I had people in my technical department who were familiar with Japanese practices. They had joined me from Liverpool when I moved to Newcastle. These were highly competent men: Ray Adams my closest associate; Bob Brown; Mike Burkett; Howard Jones and others, but neither I nor they were ever asked or given an opportunity to comment or help, such was the rigid and compartmentalized BS set-up.

During World War II Britain was greatly indebted to the US for building so many of the famous Liberty ships – straightforward cargo ships, all based on a British design by a Sunderland shipbuilder. In spite of having to use unskilled labour and the newish technique of welding rather than riveting, they were built in very large numbers and were highly successful. Construction occupied an incredibly short time, because so much pre-planning, standardization and pre-fabrication was done. The record lies with the Richmond shipyard, where one ship was on the berth four days and fifteen and a half hours. She was ready to join her first convoy fourteen days later, and she operated successfully thereafter. While such a schedule is quite impossible and uneconomic in peace time, and ships are far bigger and more complex now, it is still a surprise to me how long it took before our yards realized the benefit of that wartime approach to shipbuilding. To some extent Austin & Pickersgill of Sunderland was the one yard within BS that came anywhere near producing a standard ship. Their *SD14* was produced successfully in more numbers than any other, but it was a fairly primitive vessel and could not save the yard from ultimate demise. Other countries learned much quicker.

My department had several functions as well as advising the board on the technicalities of ships and on concept design. I had to support the general PR department of the Corporation, and found the best way, rather than grimace in front of television cameras, was to write technical papers and articles for magazines and journals and professional institutions. This meant spending almost every evening that I was at home, and at weekends as well, writing. As there was endless travel to Knightsbridge, to shipyards, to clients' offices, life was really rather busy. I just wish there had been more production in the form of orders for ships rather than erudite papers.

In 1973 and again in 1979 we had the oil crises, with savage increases in the cost of fuel. These meant greatly increased costs for everybody and for the first few days after each crisis broke we all drove our cars very slowly on the A1 going in to Newcastle to conserve petrol. We soon forgot and were back to full speed, but we had to pay the price. For ships it was different, for oil fuel is much more important in the operating cost of a ship than petrol is to us in our cars. My department spent a lot of effort in redesigning for lower fuel cost. My marine engineering colleague John Williams was a man of great talent (and still is). Having started life as a seagoing engineer (part of it with Alfred Holt & Co.) he had not only keen engineering abilities but readily took to the commercial scene. He did valuable studies into the economics of ship operation which were most helpful. They showed and quantified what we all suspected – that ship speeds had to reduce to keep ship operation economic. As so often in life strong economic pressures produce urgent solutions. Not only did ship speeds become lower but diesel engine technology made enormous strides to higher efficiency, together with the ability to run at lower revolutions per minute; this in turn provided the lower propeller revolutions at which the propeller itself becomes more efficient; new machinery arrangements including waste heat systems were designed for greater efficiency; the exterior of ships' hulls was made smoother. It can safely be said that for the average ship the fuel consumption in the 1980s was half that of the 1970s, albeit the ship would be running at a lower speed.

Everybody naturally asked if there was an alternative to oil as a fuel. So we looked at coal-burning ships. It was obvious there was a lot of coal around the world but we had to overcome the immediate reaction of – 'We can't go back to that!' Memories of ranks of firemen feeding furnaces in grim conditions of sweat and dust were still fresh in mind. Our research showed that the science of materials handling had moved on over the years, unnoticed by ship designers who were wedded to oil as a fuel. Coal was no different from many other materials. There was plenty of evidence that machinery existed which could easily move coal around a ship without anybody ever seeing the stuff. It could be conveyed even from bunkers at the far end of the ship either mechanically or pneumatically just as oil was pumped. It meant a return to examining steam machinery of course, at a time when the diesel engine had really become the mainstay of ship propulsion. We even found a flourishing company in USA that was prepared to manufacture the old-fashioned reciprocating steam engines as an alternative to steam turbines.

South Africa was one country that had vast coal resources which had been ruthlessly exploited during the period of its isolation. They also wanted a stronger role in world shipping. I went on a round trip of the country in 1983 with a group of fellow engineers from the Royal Institution of Naval Architects and the Institute of Marine Engineers. Our host body was our sister Institution in South Africa. Starting from Johannesburg we looked at the vast opencast mines in the Rand. On seeing the earth's surface being ripped up so implacably I could not help feeling that there must at some stage be a limit to what was taken out of the ground. We saw the long trains of coal wagons set off on their journey to Richards Bay, a brand new port built for exporting coal. It is a steady downhill slope from the mines to sea level three hundred miles away, so the trains run downhill when loaded and return uphill empty – very convenient. We looked at the port itself and saw how the wagons were turned upside down to dump the coal without uncoupling them. From there we did the well-travelled route south by coach, stopping at Port Elizabeth and Durban for talks with the technical institutions, and ending in Capetown with a conference on coal-burning ships. It was all good sensible discussion and pointed to the possibility of seeing coal-burning ships before long. It was not to be. Before we could get started with any firm orders, the oil price came down a bit and the cost advantage for coal was lost. Perhaps we shall have to come back to it some day.

In my shipowning days I had been familiar with ships with fifty of a crew or more. Now, following the success in reducing fuel consumption, came the pressure to reduce crew numbers. This brought a different set of problems. People are not so amenable as diesel machinery, but we had to reduce the number of people on board and achieve lower crew costs to remain economic. Our studies led us eventually to propose centralized control; new communication techniques including satellites; streamlined onboard documentation; and extensive use of shipboard computers for management, stock control and energy saving. We saw it as quite reasonable to reduce the crew for our standard 35,000 tonne deadweight bulk carrier from the then current thirty-three or so to seventeen without prejudicing safety. This trend became the norm everywhere. The pity is that even having done these things British-manned ships were still expensive to run compared with ships with crews of sundry other nationalities. It was a very exciting time in ship design, but unfortunately not reflected in British Shipbuilders' performance in the international shipbuilding market.

An exercise that again had a disappointing ending was the design of large passenger ships. None had been built in UK for some years, but Cunard and some other companies were interested in new passenger tonnage. By this time there existed quite serious misgivings amongst shipowners about British shipyards because of the very obvious poor image created by union troubles and general weakness in production. I found we had to overcome this first before getting into serious talks, trying to point out we were a new company with new management. Cunard were the most interested of the companies and Joe Gratten, their director in charge of new tonnage was very co-operative. But then we found that the bigger shipyards who might have been involved were distinctly cool about re-entering this market. Swan

Hunter were firmly against. They wanted to tread what they saw as the easier lucrative route of specializing in naval vessels. Anybody could see that that market would contract before long and there were already enough warship yards, Yarrow, Vickers and Vospers, to cope with it. Only Cammell Laird showed any real interest and they, to their credit, did put a fair lot of work into quoting for an order. But it was about this time, half-way through my spell of five years with BS that I and my team began to realize the Corporation might be heading for trouble. The merchant shipyards had simply lost confidence and were beginning to lead a double life, keeping up a façade of interest and progress, but in fact unable to manufacture ships competitively. For us at HQ it was most frustrating to be trying to link the central marketing, which was quite active, with yards that would rather not know about anything beyond what they claimed were their own traditional and specialist products.

I was particularly disappointed, for example, in the response of Ross (later Sir Ross) Belch of Scott Lithgow when he was asked to quote for very sophisticated chemical carriers for Pan Ocean of London. Pan Ocean was a joint company of Ocean and P&O and I had already worked closely with them in designing and building such ships in Holland. I always felt they gave British Shipbuilders this sort of last chance because I was there. I was with Ross Belch in his private suite in the Charing Cross Hotel when he telephoned his price to John Maltby of Pan Ocean. The phone was on the mantelpiece. Ross stood admiring himself in the enormous wall mirror, patting his elegant, greying hair into place as he gave a figure somewhere between 25 and 50 per cent above anything Maltby expected. I could hear the gasp at the other end. Ross didn't want nasty complicated ships. Shortly afterwards his shipyard at Greenock closed. Meantime the warship yards were trading on their past successes and the rather more assured route to profit through Ministry of Defence contracts with their soft procurement policies.

I could get another feel for the way things were going through the regular technical directors' meetings which I chaired. These were quite useful because we were all professional engineers, slightly divorced from the responsibility of the actual production in the yards, and there was a common interest in the design and operation of the ships. Yet even here one could sense the tensions. The merchant shipyard directors showed a hesitancy in getting too heavily committed to anything beyond the narrow perceived scope of their companies, although some like Brian Tebbutt of Sunderland Shipbuilders were always willing to take a wider view. The warship yard directors such as Roy Turner of Vickers and Tony Dorey of Vospers were much more forthcoming, vocal and helpful. It was quite obvious that all the shipyards should have had more and better qualified technical staff. I thought back to my days at Caledon shipyard where I was the first graduate to be begotten. There were not to be many more there, although I must mention Stewart Tennant, who was an apprentice a few years behind me. He, a fiery go-ahead Dundonian, has always claimed that he made the tea for me, his senior (although I cannot remember it). A Newcastle University graduate, he moved steadily up after leaving Caledon to become technical director at Harland & Wolff in Belfast. Generally, there were not enough top-class people within British Shipbuilders. Managing directors seemed to economize on technical staff because they were obvious and vulnerable; yet they would suffer gross over-manning in the workshops, and concede to trade union demands regarding staffing levels without obvious demur.

The single common fault running through the whole Corporation was that there was absolutely no recognition of the way foreign shipbuilders, mainly in the Far East, were producing ships more efficiently. The report of the Government-appointed Geddes Inquiry in the mid 1960s was useful and gave a good summary of the position at that time, and also made sensible suggestions for improvement, including a real shake-up of the fabric of the industry. This led to restructurings such as the amalgamation of some Scottish yards into Upper Clyde Shipbuilders. But the basic change in culture that would have led to looking over the horizon to see how others achieved success was never achieved, nor indeed attempted. What was needed was what I and my colleagues had seen, for example at Tsu in Japan, where a completely new shipyard was built in short order in a non-shipbuilding part of the country. While the UK yards, and an ill-informed public it must be admitted, were chuntering on about the ingrained skills of our work-force which were so valuable, the Japanese simply acquired labour 'out of the trees' as our superintendents rather unkindly put it. And they built ships successfully. Geddes himself had described shipbuilding as an assembly industry with no real difference from other building industries, meaning no greater level of skill was involved.

I first visited the world-class Nissan motor car factory at Sunderland in the early 1980s when the shipyards all around, in this biggest of all shipbuilding towns, were having to close. As we watched the dedication of the work-force on the assembly lines and the way they, quite literally, ran from one workstation to another, full of enthusiasm at working for a highly profitable company, the Nissan director taking us round said quietly 'most of them are from the shipyards'. The only time anyone ever ran in a shipyard was in passing through the yard gates on the way home. Somehow, our shipbuilding failed to advance. As late as the 1980s Roger Vaughan took a large contingent of BS staff to study production methods at the Burmeister and Wain shipyard in Copenhagen. It was already too late. Because of the lack of capital to ensure modernization, the feebleness of management, the non co-operation of the unions and the antipathy to the industry now prevalent in Government, there was no hope of success by that time anyway.

When I joined British Shipbuilders they ran a chartered jet aeroplane, which conveyed a nice sense of well-being and style. It was used much between Newcastle and London and chairman Admiral Sir Anthony Griffin obviously enjoyed having it. He drew quite heavily on my time, quite rightly, in support of his marketing efforts on behalf of the Corporation, being much more active than his chief executive in this. The longest trip I made with him and a few others was to Algiers where there was interest from the Algerian Line CNAN in ro-ro vessels such as our Smiths Dock Company on Teesside produced. Hence George Parker, the managing director of that shipyard was there too. George's father was yard manager of the Caledon shipyard when I was serving my apprenticeship. George junior, and his brother Cameron, were well-recognized figures in the marine world, George having previously been a manager at John Brown's shipyard, and Cameron was head of engine-builders Kincaid of Greenock. George achieved wide recognition at the launch of the *QE2* where television displayed him encouraging the vessel down the launch ways by applying his bowler with some force to the front end.

We were entertained by the UK ambassador on arrival and confronted on entry to his home by a large photograph of Dr David Owen, who had recently become Foreign Secretary. The ambassador felt he had to explain quietly that Owen had demanded the photograph be given prominence in all embassies. We had profitable discussions with the shipowners, were further entertained by them, and on the last day visited one of their ferries, when we were each given a large engraved copper tray and a burnous camel-hair coat. The tray was just too big to tuck and hold under the arm and too heavy to hold by the rim. The coat was not in any way needed for warmth. A memory is of the gallant Admiral our chairman, standing on deck in the blazing sun, burnous-attired, copper tray under some control, dripping with sweat and making a sincere farewell speech – in French. Sadly, no orders were forthcoming for BS.

Closer to home, I accompanied him to Trinity House in London to give a presentation to the Elder Brethren on British Shipbuilders' capabilities. They were proposing to order a replacement for their major survey and support vessel *Patricia*. Again there was the layer of suspicion about BS' performance to penetrate, but the Admiral performed convincingly. In the question and answer session that followed he dealt competently with the size of the ship, the question of single screw versus twin, the various machinery arrangements and so on, until I began to feel I was some sort of spare part in the proceedings. Then one of the Elder Brethren (we discovered later he was something of a maverick) asked with singular irrelevance how many quangos British Shipbuilders were involved in. My chairman helpfully and immediately responded – 'Oh, Marshall will deal with that one'. Slightly underhand, I thought, but we got the order this time.

Strictly speaking, I reported not to the chairman, but to John (now Sir John) Parker, who was managing director. John is a Northern Ireland charmer as well as being a very shrewd and competent manager. He had recently moved from Austin & Pickersgill in Sunderland to British Shipbuilders when I joined, and he was always most helpful. John has the most sensitive antennae and I am convinced he knows what I am thinking, and about to say, before I get round to saying it. I think he found the change in chairmanship following the Admiral somewhat irksome so went off to run Harland & Wolff, which was never part of British Shipbuilders. After that came a steady progression to chairman of Babcock International and then Lattice. When I and every single colleague I know learned from the press that John was about to become chairman of Railtrack in the year 2001 there was a unanimous cry from the heart of us all – 'John, please don't!' And at the last minute he didn't. Did the antennae fail for once?

When Robert (later Sir Robert) Atkinson took over as chairman in 1980 there was a distinct change in atmosphere. Gone were the cosy days, there was a tightening of all expenditure, the private aeroplane was discarded, and he decided to economize by becoming both chairman and chief executive. Naturally he was less popular than the Admiral and he did try to instil greater discipline, not afraid to highlight the weaknesses. I was at one meeting to which he invited himself. It was to discuss the use of computers in the companies, a new department having just been established to progress this. Sir Robert was in critical and demanding mode. He wanted to know why, when we were all supposed to be economizing, there were chocolate biscuits with the coffee. The relatively new head of the department could only stammer in reply that he had bought them out of his own pocket seeing the chairman was coming. Which was, in fact, true.

Yet even his efforts were unsuccessful. If anything, there was a hardening of the acrimony between HQ and the individual shipyards. In due course and after the statutory knighthood had been bestowed on Robert Atkinson, Graham Day (later Sir Graham, naturally) arrived as chairman in 1983. Graham, a Canadian, had made his mark at Cammell Laird some years before when, as a lawyer advising the Canadian Pacific Company, he took drastic action over their ships being built in the yard when the unions were proving intractable. He subsequently became chief executive of Cammell Laird and certainly improved things there with his matey but determined style. He had been marked down as one of the triumvirate of Griffin, Griffin and Day (likened to a family solicitors' outfit by some) who were to inaugurate British Shipbuilders on nationalization – Admiral Griffin, Ken

Griffin a trade union representative and Graham. However, during the endless political arguments leading up to nationalization, Graham got fed up and left. Now he came back as chairman, but we suspected with a specific brief from his political masters. I think it must have been something like 'Sort it out – get rid of it if necessary, and we will reward you.' So he sorted it out. It is interesting reading *Upwardly Mobile*, the biography of Norman Tebbit. He was Secretary of State for Industry and therefore Graham's boss at the time, and says 'Robert Atkinson had proved a great disappointment at British Shipbuilders and I was relieved to find Graham Day, a tough Canadian, in charge.' So much for poor Sir Robert's efforts at resuscitating and driving the Corporation towards viability. Sir Graham was the first chairman I ever encountered who was not there to make his company a success. The warship yards were separated out and sent off to find their way in the defence world, which was always going to be an easier vineyard to cultivate than the merchant yards would ever enjoy. The latter were quietly allowed to wither away, and presumably Sir Graham received his just reward. For a fuller explanation of the demise of our shipbuilding industry one can read *The Rise and Fall of British Shipbuilding* by Antony Burton, and also *British Shipbuilding and the State since 1918* by Johnman and Murphy. The narrative and conclusions in both are very much in line with my own. A sorry story. I was relieved when in mid 1984 I was approached, again out of the blue, to take an interest in becoming managing director of NMI, the National Maritime Institute at Feltham, West London, and I was appointed in August 1984.

During these five years with BS our three daughters had grown up and two had flown from Redstacks at Tranwell Woods, which had been a happy home for us all. Ursula the middle one was first to depart and married Rob Wilson, a teacher in Newcastle, and they set up home in Killingworth. Hazel the eldest married Arthur Redpath who is a vet and from a well-known Northumberland farming family. These two have been in so many homes, as Arthur progresses in business, that we seem to pass a house where they have lived every other day. As I write they are in Papworth in Cambridgeshire but proposing now to move to Switzerland for perhaps three years. Angela remained with us until she moved a few years ago to her own house firstly in Newcastle and then in Morpeth. I used to think that we would be at Redstacks only for my years at British Shipbuilders, but it turned out to be much longer, sixteen years, and very happy we were to have it so. I managed to do the garden myself, much of it being woodland, until it all became bigger than we needed. Now on our own, we moved in 1994 further into Northumberland to the village of Rothbury – very much in traditional Northumbrian heartland.

Part II

Beginnings

CHAPTER 4

What went before

I MUST GO BACK to the start line and explain how it came to be that Mrs Bingham suggested to her husband Willie that 'Marshall join das drawing office', and so precipitated me into shipbuilding. I was born into a two-bedroom cottage in the royal burgh of Auchtermuchty in the middle of Fife on 22 April 1925. Drawing my first breath in a place bearing such a name is surely one of my few claims to any sort of fame. My father, who enjoyed the same name as he gave me, was a Dundonian but moved to Fife when his father, again of the same name, retired there in 1912 and built that cottage he himself had designed. Because Dundee lies mainly on two hills, The Law and Balgay Hill, nearly everybody was attracted by the view across the two-mile wide estuary of the River Tay towards Fife with its peaceful green fields and hills which provided such a contrast to the bleak streets and jute mills of the city.

In addition grandmother Meek had relatives in Auchtermuchty. In those days there was regular rail traffic across the recently opened Tay Bridge to Fife. This was especially so on a Sunday when you needed to show a rail ticket and prove you were a 'bona fide' traveller to obtain a drink. One such traveller was Robert Wills whom I knew years later as a nice old man in the Brethren assembly I attended when I worked at the Caledon shipyard. He had been one of the young bloods of his day and while on such a jaunt to Fife had lost his hat in a severe gale as he returned to the station. He spent so long searching for that it he missed the train. This was the train that went down with the bridge when it collapsed under the force of the storm. The event is described unforgettably by William McGonagall:

> Good Heavens! The Tay Bridge is blown down,
> And a passenger train from Edinburgh,
> Which fill'd all the people's hearts with sorrow
> And made them for to turn pale,
> Because none of the passengers were sav'd to tell the tale.
> How the disaster happen'd on the last Sabbath day of 1879
> Which will be remembered for a very long time.

Robert Wills took his escape more seriously. He always valued the days allowed to him thereafter and from that time onwards never omitted any opportunity to evangelize and demonstrate his Christian faith.

MM, Martha and Max at Balgay Cottage, 1932.

Grandfather Marshall Meek was a monumental sculptor with a fair business success behind him. I have by me an invoice addressed to him dated 1893 from the Caledon shipyard for £5. It was for the sale of a derrick crane, surplus to shipyard requirements, for use in his sculptor's yard – some sort of precursor of a later family link with the shipyard. The business was based where the family lived on the slopes of the well-wooded Balgay Hill to the west of the city, and that was why my birthplace in Auchtermuchty was called Balgay Cottage. Grandfather was much respected in Dundee, and had two daughters and two sons by his first wife. After her death he remarried and my father, the oldest of three boys, followed in the steps of grandfather as a sculptor. He attended classes in art and design at the Technical College in Dundee and, quiet and retiring, he read and studied seriously. He was also very active in church affairs, in singing and in mountain walking. After grandfather retired in 1912 he went off to Edinburgh to work with a sculptor and masonry company to widen his experience. Some of his work can still be seen in the magnificent carved stonework, thistles and all, on what were then the offices of the *Scotsman* on the North Bridge of Edinburgh.

I never knew either of these Dundee grandparents because grandmother died in 1920. This left my still unmarried father to look after grandfather until he too died in 1922. At Balgay Cottage my father, who did marry later in that year, ran his own one-man sculptor's business for the rest of his days, from which business he had to support his wife and three children – Martha the eldest, me, and my younger brother Robert, always known as Max. The grandparents' move on retirement from Dundee to Auchtermuchty had been influenced not only by grandfather's attraction to the place but also by grandmother's links. Her lineage is better defined and is easily traced back to the early 1700s through Grays and Ogilvies who had strong Fife connections.

My father served as a sapper in the Royal Engineers in World War I and apparently spurned any idea of advancement, just happy to do his duty and get home. His reminiscences of his time in Flanders were always light-hearted. Like most of his fellow-soldiers he seldom referred to the awfulness he must have gone through. We have a photograph, such as was common at that time, of him with his two brothers all in uniform. Jim the middle one was a wandering Scottish laddie who didn't easily settle. He was in Fiji when war broke out and in his enthusiasm to get involved travelled all the way to New Zealand to join up. As one of the illustrious Anzacs he managed to stay alive through the lethal Dardanelles campaign, but lost a leg in Flanders in the last week of the war. I have some of his postcards sent to his worried parents at that time cheerily advising that 'his stump had been troubling but was healing'. Andrew the youngest son first took up pharmacy but then studied as a doctor, with my father helping financially, and qualified in time to serve in France in the RAMC. He went on to hold successful medical officer's posts in Uganda and Tanganyika, a very special position in those days; whereas Jim drifted back eventually to Christchurch, New Zealand to work as a joiner and handyman.

My mother, Grace Smith by name, was a Fifer, born in the hamlet of Dunshalt just a mile from Auchtermuchty. That mile was a sore trial to my mother for she had to help at home with the younger children first, and then walk to school at Muchty (an accepted and helpful abbreviation) – or rather, she had to run. Knowing my mother, she would run. As she crossed the bridge over the railway line at Muchty she would look with horror at the station clock and realize how she had to keep on running. When Dr Beeching performed his miracle for British Railways he closed the station at Auchtermuchty, and that little railway line linking Ladybank on the main London–Aberdeen route, with Kinross on the mid-Scotland route, was no more. So the station fell into disrepair. Years later, when visiting my mother and sister who still lived in the old family home in Muchty, I felt it was not right that the station should be left so obviously derelict. The family of the eminent Scottish architect Reginald Fairlie owned Myres Castle, a large mansion overlooking the station, and had acquired the station name-board; and who shall blame them for wanting to hold such a piece of railway memorabilia. I felt that, as a rather junior product of the town, I would be quite content with the station clock which, now damaged and open to the weather, had caused my mother's consternation so long before. So it is now in our garage perpetually awaiting some sort of restoration. Both mother and my sister, realizing that they had to live locally after its disappearance, were really bothered about this and assured me I would be classed as a vandal. I think actually that put me in the same classification as Dr Beeching. During all the thirty something years since, I do not think anyone else has ever noticed the absence of the clock.

Mother's father was manager of the local brick and tile works, a busy little affair belonging to the Falkland Estate. To us children it was a place of apprehension and mystery because of the fierce flames of the brick kilns, the dangerous holes in the ground whence came the clay, and the old horse that towed the wagons around on the brick works' very own little railway line. In mother's childhood they had an even older horse. It was suspected eventually that if it lay down some night it would not arise in the morning, hence it had to be supported overnight by a belly-band attached to the stable ceiling. A familiar sound to her was the creaking of the rafters as it enjoyed its nocturnal swing-about.

In addition there was grandma. She was grandfather Smith's second wife whom, as a recent widower, he married fairly soon after my real grandmother died. Mother had started working in the local linen factory (there were several of these in the surrounding towns) on leaving school but at the age of eighteen had to stay at home when her mother died to look after her younger brothers and sister. She then had to cope with her stepmother who apparently did not take to the children – other than to Willie the youngest (he who quoted Kipling to me). So when mother's younger sister Maud departed to London to take up a job in the civil service she went with her and started nursing at St Pancras Hospital just at the start of World War I. We liked to hear her describe the arrival of the first Zeppelin airships over the city. She then moved back to Edinburgh and ended up as night sister at the famous Simpson Memorial Hospital. This was just one step below the level of matron. Max still has her trunk which held all her possessions. How a slip of a girl ever handled such an enormous piece of luggage I cannot imagine. Station porters must have been vital necessities to travellers. After various tribulations grandma ended up in Perth in what was at the time blatantly called an asylum. We were occasionally required to visit her, which was a great trial to us children. We sometimes had to wait in the extensive gardens while mother visited her alone, and we were terrified at the unusual people roaming around us.

While in London, mother formed a link with three other nurses which lasted for the lifetime of all of them, and figured also in our lives as the next generation. They had found they all shared the same Christian faith and beliefs and so supported one another in what was a very harsh regime by present-day standards. One was Eileen Hardy who later married Ernest Taylor, the chairman of Cow & Gate Dairies, later to become United Dairies. She remained extremely generous to us as a family and 'Mrs Taylor's Christmas parcel' was an annual highlight. Marion Hogg returned home to Canada at the end of the War. Jenny Blackwood remained to work in England and later retired to the Glasgow area. Surprisingly, not only did these four ladies keep in touch till they died, but their families did too. Max and his wife cared for Jenny Blackwood till she passed on at 100 years of age. Martha still writes to some of the Taylor family and to Marion Hogg's niece in Canada.

Of mother's little brood of brothers and sister, Robert the oldest boy departed in true Scottish tradition for the Melbourne area of Australia where he had relations. His fiancée soon joined him and they only made their first visit back to the homeland some forty years later in 1955. Sister Maud, who had gone to London with mother, soon married a shipbroker in the City. Andrew joined the army towards the end of World War I and was wounded in Flanders, but subsequently served in the occupying forces in Germany. I remember my mother asking him from time to time (he lived in Falkland only a few miles away) how his wound was behaving. He carried bits of ordnance in him for years afterwards. Gordon first joined the renowned and ancient weighing-machine makers, White & Sons in Auchtermuchty, then moved to Cumbria. The youngest, Willie the pet of the family, was a banker in Fife and then Perth.

Mother had met father at church during her visits to her old home at Dunshalt and they were married in 1922. The three of us arrived in due course and had to be reared in the difficult times of the 1930s depression. I can remember hearing father and mother discussing in serious tones the problems of having to be careful with the money, and I got the feeling even at that age that there was some uncertainty about the future. Family records show father's annual income in 1925, the year of my birth, as £243. In 1929 it was £190 plus £90 interest and in 1933 only £114 plus £100 interest. It was not a time when people's minds moved naturally to a luxury item like a headstone. And we had explained to us who the queue of men were that we passed in the morning on the way to school. They were 'on the dole' and we sensed some kind of stigma attached. Food was more basic in those days but I do not think we went short of anything, as far as I was aware. Children do not really notice anyway.

I have early recollections of trying to do school homework by gas-light. The 'mantle' which imparted the light was a fragile and highly sensitive item and the jet had to be continuously adjusted by a needle arrangement because the local gas pressure and quality were none too consistent. Then came electricity and the excitement that brought. Next, a new bedroom had to be built to accommodate the larger family. This was done by the builder from nearby Falkland, Craig by name. A good friend of father, he was very proud of his son Robert who was 'clever' – the highest accolade given to a Scottish offspring. Nearly fifty years later, on the evening of the day Prince Andrew was married to Sarah Ferguson, I was dining in the Caledonian Club in London and became aware of a large very confident Scottish gentleman with fancy sleeves and frilly breeches. Suspecting who he was, and that it was he who had been described in the *Telegraph* that morning as a son of a mason in Fife, I introduced myself as Marshall Meek of Auchtermuchty, son of another Fife mason. 'A great man,' said he immediately – meaning my father. The great man himself was, of course, Craig the builder's son who was relaxing after having shared in conducting Prince Andrew's wedding service as Moderator of the Church of Scotland that day. He proceeded to recall in detail all the contacts he had had with my family, including the memories of the brick works, after the passage of nearly sixty years. Also how, when his mother had died rather early in life, his father had acquired a very special piece of stone for the grave, and my father had carved thereon the inscription. I was impressed with his powers of recollection. He was indeed 'clever'.

Having mentioned the various uncles and aunts, all of whom except for Uncle Jim of New Zealand had families, I must admit the three of us children in my family did not mix easily with them. We were slightly apart, the reason being that our household belonged to Christian Brethren. Shortly after they were married my parents had become dissatisfied with the local church, and with the encouragement of some of father's relations, the Grays of St Andrews, they moved to a Brethren assembly which met at that time in nearby Falkland. Early recollections were of staring up at the ceiling in the main room of Falkland town hall where we met each Sunday, and tracing the intricate and symbolic plaster work. The outer emblem we likened to a bicycle tyre and it was then divided into segments, each having curious emblems within. I was to discover that it was like that because it was the meeting place of the local Freemasons. A more incongruous pair of tenants would be difficult to find. Around the hall were pictures of various Freemason groups and I soon learned from them that the senior members of our Royal Family figured largely in the movement. Brethren have no formal officiating officers, their meetings being conducted by their own members, which practice is based on a strict interpretation of the Apostles' teaching on the setting up of the churches as described in the New Testament. The informality and the earnestness of such assemblies appealed to those souls who were concerned, as my parents were, that the more formal churches, established or otherwise, did not satisfy their strong desire to worship strictly in accordance with the Scriptures.

These early days amongst Brethren greatly influenced my life, although my own family, as indeed also my parents, had eventually to leave them because their teaching became increasingly harsh and restrictive, and rifts and schisms followed. I look back in admiration at the dear old miners from the coal fields of South Fife who visited us – men with blue marks on their hands and faces from accidents and the coal dust, but who could expound the Scriptures and demonstrate Christian life in a way that has remained with me ever since. Looking back now it is clear that these years formed probably the last effective period enjoyed by such Brethren. They were eventually classed as 'Exclusives' by other more liberal (or more sensible) groups, and soon after World War II they fell under the malign influence of dogmatic and bigoted leaders such as James Taylor of US, and then his even more disastrous son J. Taylor Junior.

But at the time I was growing up the movement offered a sound, although by some standards somewhat restricted, family background. My wife Elfrida, whom I met in Ealing in West London in the early 1950s, was of similar persuasion and, although she grew up in Surrey, with a short wartime 'evacuation' experience in Bournemouth, there was remarkable uniformity of belief and practice between us even though our families were at opposite ends of the country. It meant too, that I had immediate contact with like-minded friends wherever I went in the country, and when I left home for Dundee there were kindly people and a place of worship assured. Which explains why my sister was being entertained by William and Hannah Bingham on the fateful occasion when it was suggested that Willie should have me in the shipyard drawing office. Willie was a leading light in the Dundee assembly. It was not long before he had me and others helping to pack what were termed 'unsolicited parcels' of food for sending to Hannah's relatives in the Ruhr area of Germany. Brethren generosity seemed to prevail even over recognized restrictions between warring nations.

CHAPTER 5

Maistly Muchty

THE LITTLE TOWN of Auchtermuchty has naturally achieved some sort of recognition because of its name. A favourite and oft quoted coupling of places expressive of Scotland's dialect is 'Auchtermuchty, Ecclefechan and Milngavie' (the latter place pronounced Milguy, and the others as best can). I have gone through US immigration procedures on occasions and had friendly questioning prompted by the name of my birthplace. It is a Royal Burgh of Scotland and we were taught that the name means 'field of the wild boar'. There are indications of Roman activities in all this area of Fife, with arguments still ongoing about the site of the definitive battle of Mons Graupius which was supposed to have been fought somewhere around. My grandfather, in his extraction of clay for his brick works at Dunshalt, found Roman artefacts which went to the Scottish Museum in Edinburgh. Rather later the area, and particularly nearby Falkland, figured largely in the time of the Stuart kings. Mary Queen of Scots used it as a suitable place for her leisure pursuits in the field. It was in his own palace of Falkland that James V died in 1542 at the age of thirty, and on his deathbed, having heard that Mary Queen of Scots, his daughter and royal successor, had been born at Linlithgow, made the oft quoted and dramatic remark – 'It cam wi' a lass and it'll gang wi' a lass.' He meant that the line (originally called Stewart) of Scottish royalty that had started with Marjory, daughter of Robert Bruce in 1371, would end with the new-born girl. To all intents it did, because this particular little girl, like some later ones, was not destined to become a 'regular royal'. Today Falkland Palace has been carefully and beautifully restored in part, and the magnificent gardens contain one of the very few original 'real tennis' courts in the country.

There is a cobbled central square in Falkland and around it are the church and the town hall, with the palace a few steps away. When I met Church of Scotland Moderator Craig at the Caledonian Club I told him of my recollection of hearing, from the town hall where we met on Sundays, the music from the church across the square where he was singing in the Sunday school. 'Aye,' said he, 'and we heard you too.' Close by the town hall is the birthplace of Richard Cameron, the Scottish Covenanter who was martyred in 1680. His followers eventually gave their name to the famous Scottish regiment, the Cameronians.

Neighbouring Auchtermuchty has fewer prestigious buildings than

Falkland but makes up for this by flaunting its historic decency and ordinariness. This is the feature that appealed to Sir John Junor, editor for years of the *Sunday Express*, when he made repeated references in his regular articles to the douce people, and respectable housewives in particular, of Auchtermuchty. I think he enjoyed cultivating the impression that he actually belonged to the place. But my sister, who had lived there all her life till she was seventy, was just one who mildly objected to any such inference since it was known that Sir John had hardly visited the place till relatively recently. One resident of many years and who inspired rather more affection was Jimmy Shand, the accordionist. His quiet dignity and his modest reaction to his popularity were greatly admired locally and everybody was delighted when the Queen knighted him not long before his death in 2000.

Then a few years ago the last episode of the TV series *Dr Finlay's Casebook* was enacted in Auchtermuchty (under the usual name of Tannochbrae) as a change from the earlier series based on Callander in Perthshire. Preparations for the filming were intense in the little town, with strong demand for the walk-on parts. And many TV aerials had to be removed for historical correctness and then, naturally, needed to be replaced with new ones. Not to mention the repainting of the various properties anywhere near the cameras. Muchty folk may be douce but they do not easily disprove the old adage – 'It takes a long spoon to sup with a Fifer.' There were many shots taken in the central market-square where the war memorial stands. I was intrigued because, although it was designed by Reginald Fairlie (he of the family who acquired the station name-board) it was built, and the names of the dead and the ornate regimental badges were carved, by my father. The most retiring of men, he would never have dreamt that his work would one day be admired across the nation.

As with many of these Scottish towns, the town hall stands amidships in the place with a good solid square silhouette and a sturdy bell tower. There is a story about the procuring of the Muchty town bell, when the town clerk went with his colleague from Falkland to bring back their respective bells – from Belgium I think, where they had been cast. On reaching home one was found to be cracked but the Muchty representative pointed out that the sound bell was his because, on receiving it at the foundry, he had inscribed his initials on it. He had, of course, put his initials on both. Whatever the truth of it, the bell has a fine tone and has rung for many years. In the early 1900s it was rung no less than three times every weekday including a wake-up peal and the bed-time curfew; and then no less than five times on Sunday. One town clerk who performed this task for thirty five years was a certain Andra Adam, and he must have had a very superior physique to cope with the stairs to the bell tower. However, by the time I was a small boy only the 8 p.m. curfew was rung, and it certainly implanted in my memory thoughts of sunset over the rich fields around our home and the call to get indoors.

Just across from the town hall was the home of the former master of the china-tea clipper *Cutty Sark*. Captain Moody was in command during the period of the great races against *Thermopylae* and other competitors. He was known as a hard driver of the ship, the most famous of a class of vessel that is generally recognized as the most lethal kind of vehicle ever invented. Long before I was to become acquainted with ships and the sea, I remember gazing with awe at the actual flag of the *Cutty Sark* which was flown from one of the windows of the house during those 'Savings Weeks' that were held during World War II, when we declared our patriotism, tipped in our pennies, and sawed down our railings to make into guns.

Then the shops. The 'Store', meaning the Co-op, was the main supplier of everyday food items, being the biggest shop in town. It provided for me the memory of a central cash desk to which and from which the customers' bills and money were transferred in a little brass canister along a wire from each counter. Each canister was sent on its way and then returned by a spring-loaded gun device that needed a good pull by the shop assistant to get it going. But all that disappeared before long. Mr Fawns was the smaller merchant my family seemed to prefer and I remember him lovingly counting the 'points' and 'coupons' we were allotted during World War II for nearly everything. Having dealt with the sugar and tea he would then announce 'and now your fats', meaning butter and margarine and the like. It was at that time I deliberately stopped having sugar in my tea and, instead, put the appropriate spoonfuls into a separate dish. In this way I accumulated both sugar to help with the jam making and a sense of smug satisfaction.

There was a little sweetie shop that ran a 'penny plate' where everything like liquorice straps or tubes of sherbert cost a penny each; and even a halfpenny plate, although there was seldom anything worth having there. Then the haberdasher and dress shop. We were allowed to operate the lever on the gadget, rather like a small fruit machine, dispensing reels of cotton whose range of colour used to appeal to us greatly. There was the ironmonger, where mostly everything you needed seemed to be just about 'expected to be in', and nearly everything you actually managed to purchase had to be taken back or exchanged. Also Valente, the ice-cream shop – evidence of the mysterious way that Italians must have moved into the country at some stage in the inter-war years. A boy used to come round with a tricycle that had a cool box above the front wheel, and ring his bell for attention. Ice cream was a very great treat – and perhaps because of that, for me still is. Next door to Valente was the Victoria Hall used mainly as a Saturday-night cinema, but we were not allowed to go to that.

Johnnie Forgan ran the shoe shop where we got shoes that invariably were hard and stiff and hurt our heels even when rubbed with castor oil – that is, the shoes were rubbed. As he fondled each item of footwear he would seek to encourage the sale by murmuring – 'Aye, a reliable shoe.' But Johnnie was a bit of a poet, as they would put it in these parts, and we had at home a slim volume called 'Maistly Muchty', where his little poems do, in a strange way, convey the emotions of Muchty people and their nostalgia for times and places past.

Gin I were a laddie in Muchty again
Wi' the heart o' a laddie carefree,
Could I live but again over the days o' langsyne,
That are noo fragrant memories tae me,
I'd gang doon by the Plains an' for goldies I'd fish
In yon deep minnen ditch I weel ken;
I'd smeek foggies' bikes in the holes o' the dykes
Gin I were a laddie again.

I wad play at the bools wi' my broon roughie taw,
Clap my peezers a' doon in the ring;
I'd bum my big peerie again at the jougs,
Gaither chestnuts, tae thread on a string,
And doon by the station lay preens on the rails,
Tae get them brizzed flat by the train,
Mak' a dragon sae braw, that wad outflee them a',
Gin I were a laddie again.

I will not try to translate, other than to explain that foggies are wasps, bumming your peerie is spinning your top, and bools are known in other circles as the game of marbles, with the roughie taw and peezers as constituent elements.

The reference to flattening pins or 'preens' below the wheels of the trains illustrates the closeness and affiliation between us boys and the local railway, where trains and engines were companionable rather than fearsome. The railway line ran just a field's breadth away from our house and we thought nothing of walking along the line rather than through the fields. There was usually only one, or at most, two short goods trains each day, and the passenger service ran two or three times a day at semi-recognized times. In my earliest days it was known as the 'steam-coach'. This was a curious single carriage and engine, all one unit, with the boiler and firebox at one end. The station (with its clock) was run by a combined signalman, porter and booking-clerk called Christie. I recall his delight the first time I asked for a ticket for London when I started to work there in the late 1940s. 'I'll gie' ye a ticket for London!' he exclaimed with immense satisfaction. He was not averse to bending the rules and popping over the rails from the platform to operate the signals by pulling hard on the signal wire, which in those days ran over a set of pulleys and connected signal box to signal. This saved him walking to the signal box itself. Because the levers in the box were heavily weighted he just had to heave hard enough to get them over the balance point.

The station was just over the wall from the cemetery. When father was working there, either erecting grave stones or carving inscriptions or whatever, Max and I sometimes accompanied him and by climbing on to the low retaining wall where the grass cuttings were held, we could see over the boundary wall and watch the manoeuvring of the goods engine as it shunted off the coal merchant's wagon or took aboard the output of Ferlie's foundry. The foundry was a well-respected local establishment – although a shade down-market compared with Whites Beam & Scale (i.e. weighing machine) establishment, which had a century and more of pedigree behind it. My brother Max and I had a little model railway – Hornby gauge 0, but frustratingly the engine was only clockwork driven and had to be wound up. Under full winding it tended to dash off and leave the rails. I remember the envy, verging on hatred, that I experienced when a school-fellow called Davidson, son of the local butcher, claimed he had an electric train set.

Like normal boys of those times we favoured one particular railway company or another. Whether our preference was determined by the livery of the engines or whether it was influenced by parents I know not, but we were LNER people with green engines. LMS of course were quite attractive too with red engines, but they served the midland route to London. We were East Coast people. As to effete electrically driven outfits like Southern, or weirdies like Great Western, those belonged elsewhere. They were in any case in England and so of less interest. A satisfactory venture was a visit by train by us three youngsters, quite on our own, to Strathmiglo. This was all of two miles away and we proudly bought our tickets by ourselves and journeyed alone to the destination. On the way we had to pass our home where fond parents waved to us as if we were bound for the antipodes. On detraining we bought strawberry tarts at the baker's shop in Strathmiglo, an inferior sort of township, and then walked home.

When father was doing warden duty during World War II, ready to sound the air raid siren, he enjoyed a cartoon on the operations room wall drawn by some talented local. It depicted Adolf Hitler in full war-cry heading down that same railway line in search of the ultimate goal of Auchtermuchty. At a small station he demanded whether this was indeed Auchtermuchty – to receive the laconic reply 'No, it's only Strath' – meaning Strathmiglo. The closest association Max and I had with the railway was when we were paddling and wading in the Barroway burn which flowed just one field further away than the railway. It ran under the railway at one point and we had a delicious feeling of bravery and novelty when we crept up the burn below the railway and with our heads between the bridge girders we heard, and felt, the train crossing the bridge just inches above us.

That field between Balgay Cottage and the railway is now the town's park with football pitch and play area. But during World War II it was still a field and was taken over by the military as a camp-site. It was first a headquarters for the searchlight and anti-aircraft gun units scattered round the area. The blimpish major in command was to be seen sitting on a little elevated platform observing the performance of his troops. Just what they were supposed to be protecting in the middle of the agricultural area of the county of Fife was not clear. One stick of bombs was dropped just the once across Muchty, in the middle of the night – presumably a chance off-loading as a Jerrie scuttled homewards. As we cowered in our beds, father set off to investigate and found neighbour Neil Keddie in his slippers, standing in one of the bomb craters. 'The ground's still warm,' he observed with wonderment. The only casualties were some of the hens (and the hen-house) owned by a local, And' Dick by name.

Before long, these valiant anti-aircraft warriors were displaced by Polish soldiers who had escaped after the first German onrush at the very beginning of the conflict. They were all of officer class and were obviously superior troops. One of them asked me to help him with his English, and together we used to read from H.E. Marshall's *Our Island Story*. After entertaining him to tea one afternoon he kissed my mother's hand in gratitude. She had obviously never experienced such pleasing treatment before. The memory of these men parading in the evening, lowering their simple red and white national flag and singing in fine manly tunefulness their plaintive national anthem, far from home and with future uncertain, remains with me.

Max and I spent a lot of time in the burn. In addition to the usual guddling for sticklebacks or minnows or even trout, a more serious exercise was to build dams, where with luck, a fair head of water could be built up before the whole thing collapsed and produced a rather frightening gush of water. On one occasion father arrived to check up on us as he sometimes felt he should, and found our approach to dam construction wanting. With his Royal Engineers' background he gave us a demonstration. Heavy stones first as anchor points, no matter if the water still ran through. Then boulders in smaller sizes as the height grew, and then block off the water with divots. So we had an early lesson in civil engineering – and an even more frightening rush of water. Needless to say we both ended up with engineering as a career.

We thought nothing of it at the time, I suppose, but while we watched father go about his sculptor's business, we were in fact learning the rudiments of engineering. While he manoeuvred the headstones in our backyard under the derrick crane (a later version than the one bought from Caledon shipyard in 1893), we were absorbing the rudiments of mechanics – the gears of the crane, and the effort needed to turn the handle, and the strain on the wire ropes. When he sharpened his chisels, heating and tempering and watching the changing colours of the metal as they cooled we were into metallurgy. When he was erecting headstones in the various graveyards and cemeteries we were taught the need to have proper foundations, and secure attachments of plinth to base and so on. When he was carving inscriptions on the memorials I began to appreciate the beauty of lettering. And all the time we were observing, I must admit with no particular enthusiasm, the various stone materials being worked. The silvery Aberdeen granites from the famous Rubislaw quarries, or the redder ones from Creetown in the West of Scotland, and the various marbles, some even from the fabled Italian quarries at Carrara.

There were various cemeteries that we visited with father, Falkland, Newburgh, Collessie, and even Strathmiglo, where the water needed for mixing the cement for securing the foundations had to be drawn in an old paint pot by rope from the neighbouring stream. My earliest memories were of sitting in the horse-drawn cart which father hired for transporting his headstones. Later came a rather primitive motor lorry from the local garage which we rather despised. Of special attraction were those occasions when the headstone was sufficiently heavy to need 'poles and tackle' in its erection. Normally the cemetery keeper was induced to help father and the lorry-driver in offloading from the cart and getting the headstone into position, using rollers and other basic mechanical devices. But the erecting of three pitch-pine poles into a tripod, and then mounting the blocks (with differential pulleys) and tackle to handle heavier items than two or even three men could manage, was a real engineering event for us. I can hear the lifting chain rattling over the blocks to this day.

For pottering between his places of work father ran a BSA 250cc motor bike. It used to have its single cylinder opened up occasionally and the piston rings scraped (so advancing our mechanical knowledge). This seemed to be a fireside job in winter months, with mother quite incensed at the sacrilege incurred within her domain. We were always a bit ashamed of that bike. It sounded like a Singer sewing machine rather than a proper manly bike like other fathers had, with a decent exhaust roar. If, when riding pillion, we reached something approaching 60 m.p.h., that was exceptional and verging on the risky, which was not in father's nature to be. Once a year in summertime the bike was carefully checked and father set off on a day trip on his own into the Scottish Highlands. I think this was a highlight of his summer, getting away from the family and seeing the old haunts of his bachelor climbing days. On his return it was all excitement to hear how far he had been and what he had seen. He occasionally bought an issue of the *Motor Cycle* magazine, I think mainly in June at the time of the Isle of Man TT races. It seemed only to be found by us in his workshop (perhaps mother was getting her own back about the piston ring scraping and banned it), and there Max and I would dip into it. I have not forgotten the thrill of the reporter's words on the Senior race, this being for machines of 500cc. 'There goes Harold Daniel, leading on his Norton, flat on the tank, steady as a rock and away to Sulby Bridge.' If I remember correctly it was a tremendous feat to attain an average of 60 m.p.h. for the whole race.

In our school days Max and I each had the privilege of running Muchty cemetery when the local cemetery keeper was on holiday for a week, or it may even have been a fortnight. Because we received a man's pay it was real money for us. My approach was to work full-out in the morning, mowing grass, cutting edges, raking paths, then lie in the sun and read in the afternoon. I remember absorbing the Frankenstein story for the first time because I found a copy in the gravedigger's shed where he ran a miniscule library on the top shelf above the lubricating oil and whetstone, no doubt kept for rainy days. Very occasionally the town clerk would call in to see that all was well and that we were fulfilling our duties. As in all cemeteries, the hinges of the heavy wrought iron gates were purposely never oiled. The noise on opening ensured that the cemetery 'superintendent', as he preferred to be called, would never be caught unawares with Frankenstein – or worse. Max was less fortunate than I was. He had to deal with a funeral. He needed father's help with digging the grave, but then he had to go through all the motions during the service – with father keeping a discreet watch from behind a headstone. I managed to escape any such duty and concentrate on my reading.

With our backgrounds thus biased towards engineering, Max and I went into different careers – Max to study mechanical engineering at Dundee where we shared digs for a time while I was at Caledon shipyard. Then he continued, being more academically inclined than I was and not tied to any company, to take his PhD at Glasgow's Royal College of Science and Technology (now Strathclyde University), the actual degree being awarded by Glasgow University. Before I describe in more detail my own university experiences I must take you back to my first schooldays – but it will already be obvious that Auchtermuchty was not exactly a natural breeding ground for naval architects.

CHAPTER 6

A Scottish education

THERE WAS NEVER any question about it. I and my brother and my sister would go to the local Auchtermuchty school like everyone else. It was something less than a mile away and the walk, unattended by any parents, was through the town. Such schools were known simply as public schools, in the real meaning of the word public, and they gave a sound start to everyone. Miss Ritchie was a formidable infant mistress who introduced us all to a simple fact of life, that like it or not, we just had to learn. We progressed through the years to age eleven, when we had to sit the Control Examination. I suppose its equivalent would be known nowadays as the Eleven Plus, when we were separated into those who would go on to secondary school, in our case to Bell-Baxter School at Cupar, Fife some nine miles away. Others who failed stayed on at Auchtermuchty and then had to find some other form of further education if they were so inclined. There was little by way of social activities and no formal assemblies such as are common today. There was indeed surprisingly little by way of religious education, the only snippet that remains with me was having to recite portions of the Scottish Shorter Catechism such as 'Thou shalt not steal' where we endeavoured to follow each other as rapidly as we could in a repetition devoid of all meaning. Mr Cormack's class was where we were groomed eventually for the Control Exam. He had also been my mother's teacher at the same school, and he exuded strong pipe-tobacco odours. He was not above fooling about with the girls (we were co-ed of course) in a way that, today, would have landed him in trouble.

We had to mix in with every kind of pupil, none from really wealthy homes, many from really quite poor homes, and almost exclusively all Protestant. The very occasional RC or indeed Episcopalian tended to be treated with a measure of suspicion. One boy called Robert comes to mind, his father being a farm hand from Dunshalt. There were few who were nearer poverty than such families at that time. Robert's under-drawers, presumably handed down, were longer than his shorts; he ponged a bit and for his midmorning 'piece' he had toasted bread that had long since gone soft, and also was curiously smelly. Boys can be cruel to one another and I now regret very much some of the disparaging comments that we made.

Fife farms had wonderful soil and the farmers themselves were recognized as being the better-off. But their wealth did not seem to filter down to the ploughman, cattleman or 'orra' hand. There was an annual fair when farm-hands were taken on or disposed of like chattels in a form of ruthless autocratic dealing that is now long past. I still have news of Dougie Milne of Demperston farm which was just a mile or two from us at home. The Milnes were naturally considered amongst the more comfortably off, but Dougie found it hard to accept my accusation when I last saw him, that he had nicked radishes from my plot in the school garden. In the last year at Muchty School we had the joy of attending gardening classes. At least you got out into the open air. But I am afraid Davy Bett the teacher, a most decent and well-respected horticulturist, was not fully in charge of his pupils since we regularly visited each others' plots for nefarious purposes. Radishes were obviously a crop that grew easily and so lent themselves to poaching.

I must mention the 'tattie' holidays. We had a three-week holiday when the potato crop was harvested, and it was accepted that it helped both farmers and youngsters (and their families) when the potato crop could be manually gathered with a hard-earned income as the result. If we volunteered ourselves, we approached the local farmer and we were each then allocated a 'bit' of so many yards carefully marked out. Each time the tractor towing the digger which unearthed the crop passed by we had to buckle down and gather the potatoes on our 'bit' into creels, before it came round again. The creels were then emptied into larger baskets which lay waiting for the horse and cart to collect. It was back-breaking, it was made harder if the farmer drove round more quickly, and it could be very cold work on a frosty morning. Gloves were useless for grubbing in the soil, but you could use mitts, and you could make a fair bit of money. The trouble was my parents were not sure that the company of the folk involved (adults from the district worked too) was suitable, and we children could not assume that we could always join in this relatively lucrative occupation.

One year when I did, Dougie Milne's older brother, who was the gaffer, decided that I appeared mature enough to be put in charge of one of the horses and carts that went round to empty the baskets and take the potatoes to the 'pits', where they were stored under straw and earth until despatched later to the wholesalers. I had never been near a horse, I had no idea how to control a horse, I had a fear of the whole proposition, yet it was a tacit and pleasing indication that I was strong and I could be trusted. That dear black one-ton shire horse, with a bony protruberance in its nose, was kindness and consideration itself. I had to do nothing other than hump the baskets. It knew the route, it knew when to stop and start at each basket and it knew the way home at the end of the day. It was an endearing animal, especially when it was back in the farmyard and stood so patiently while its colleagues were unhitched and made off to be watered. Having no idea how to unharness it, I had to leave it there till I found a hand willing to help.

I kept a spasmodic diary from the age of ten or so, and the intermittent entries make strange reading today.

March 9, 1935 Germans marched on the Rhine.
25 March, saw aeroplane with light.
4 June, *Queen Mary* failed to capture Blue Ribband of the Atlantic v *Normandie*.
5 June, stopped music lessons (to the joy of my teacher).
22 June, Mrs Hardy died (mother of Mrs Taylor of the Christmas parcels).
July, holiday in Gray's house at St Andrews.

For holidays we tended to borrow kind friends' houses, and St Andrews, all of eighteen miles away, was to us a fascinating little town that has occupied a special niche in the memory ever since. We went by bus and at a certain point just after passing Guardbridge, near the RAF Leuchars aerodrome, we caught a first sight of the sea – distant and mysterious, level and blue, and signifying sheer delight, sand, ice cream, bitter cold sea bathing and solemn parental lectures from the ancient gravestones in the cathedral burying-ground, with Samuel Rutherford figuring largely.

The diary did not become a regular feature until 1943, my first year away from home, but I have now sixty of them, more factual than contemplative or intellectual – and handy they are in family arguments as to dates. When Nigel Nicholson asked his father Harold why he was an inveterate diarist, he got the answer, eventually after much asking, that keeping a diary was a habit rather like cleaning your teeth. My teeth are thankfully in as good shape, and probably are better, than my diaries, but both are at least still 'doing away'.

So to Bell-Baxter School in Cupar, with a long history as Scottish secondary schools go, an unrelenting drive to educate, even if perhaps a little narrowly, and a set of standards of behaviour and performance that I can look back on with appreciation. We travelled the nine miles each day by bus and school hours were 9.00 a.m. till 4.00 p.m., rather longer than those of today. All the teachers wore gowns, and that Scottish weapon of retribution, the 'strap' or 'belt', was often retained in one of the sleeves. A three-foot length of stiff leather, the belt was used freely on the hand. 'Six of the best' was usually spread over both hands and certainly hurt for a good while and made writing difficult. Jimmy Downie (English and History) once chastised the whole class of nearly thirty because of failure to do well in one particular exam – although I think it was only 'three of the best' on that occasion, probably to conserve his strength. After that we had to re-sit the exam. Latin was important because you needed it to gain entry to any Scottish university. The senior Latin master was the walrus-like 'Tusker' McLeod, if not from Skye then certainly the Outer Isles. When he had his belt poised over his shoulder ready to thrash he would hesitate a moment to ask 'Have you the

Bell-Baxter School, Form 3, 1940: 'Tusker' McLeod's class, MM fourth from left, back row.

Gaelic?' – I think implying that was the only way one could justifiably escape the pain. A bit like the apostle Paul reminding his persecutors that on principle they could not lay stripes on a Roman citizen. 'Tusker' left to become Rector of Madras College at St Andrews. On the day he departed he cut his belt into several portions and gave us each a section. I still have mine, a nasty-looking six-inch by half-inch of by-now rock-hard black material. 'Bandy' Wood was his assistant, she who was so named because school-boys can be cruelly personal. She could of course be reciprocally nasty.

French had its own characteristic teachers – like Miss Ann Bachelor, formidable and dangerous in a feminine way, of whom we cited – 'Annie Bachie, toujours fâchée.' Tommy Muir, her colleague, was a dilettante who enjoyed conveying the impression he was indeed French, which was very far from the truth. 'Froggie' Forsyth, a nice sensible lady, taught German and French. German made more sense to me than French. Jimmy Downie's boss in English was Willie Lindsay, a gentleman by any standards, and hence I remember more of his teaching than the others. Mathemathics was administered to us in a fearsome manner by 'Doc' Inglis, who had various ways of making his point. I recall a poor little chap called Alan Wheatley from Falkland being dumped unceremoniously on top of the wardrobe where 'Doc' kept his gown, and there he sat in isolation, presumably being thereby helped to understand his algebra. 'Doc' had other dramatic moments such as feigning to swoon at some particularly alarming lack of comprehension by some struggling student. He would grasp, while falling, the door of the said wardrobe, groaning the while 'Hasten, hasten, fetch a basin.' Whereupon the much set-upon piece of furniture would start to topple over – thankfully without little 'Wheatles' on top. All this evidenced sound teaching psychology, I am sure.

'Daddy' Liddle taught art, also with endearing physical accompaniment. This time it was a sound slap on the head, as if that would instil some better appreciation of the nuances of light and shade or perspective. So much so, that some poor chaps automatically cringed when he came along behind us to examine our work, which led to 'Daddy' announcing 'So! You're expecting it' – thwack, for no reason at all that I or they could see. Whether farmer's son, Bob Bell, received one I do not remember, but he should have. We had been told never to use black paint in our work, but Bob leaned back and gazed admiringly on one occasion at his quite ghastly attempt at some formal design he had concocted. 'Fine,' he mused with a self-satisfied smirk, '– now I'll just add a spoonfae o' black.'

I had chosen to drop Physics and Chemistry after the third year of school presumably because I seemed more competent in English and Languages and Mathematics. In view of my subsequent career this was clearly a mistake, because it meant I had a lot of catching up to do in my first year as an engineering student. Not that the school was particularly active in supporting any aspect of engineering at that time, although it had improved in this respect by the time Max attended. The only teacher I recall who tried to impart any such helpful knowledge was 'Weary' Willie Wilson, a nice little man with a bit of a lisp. He had the highly commendable reputation of having worked in the John Brown Shipyard at Clydebank before taking up teaching, and had been responsible for the pipework design (a major shipbuilding item and not just plumber work) on HMS *Hood*, our biggest and most famous warship of the day – shortly to come to a frightful end in battle.

So then into the sixth form, with vague ideas of the civil service, a destiny much favoured by the school, except that wartime uncertainties made that avenue to progress less clear. Looking back I think my dissatisfaction at that stage which led to my departure and rapid entrée to shipbuilding was because of frustration at not having something definite to aim for. I played now and again in the rugger 1st XV, but apart from bicycle runs on Saturday there was probably not enough to occupy mind and body. My home background tended to restrict interests like boy scouts and such group activities with other young folk. But, in compensation, there were other blessings flowing from that protective home.

Taking a long-distance view from today of my schooling, I have no complaints about the form or content of the education and I do believe it was more effective than much that I see around me today. I am not sure, however, that the use of the belt or swipes to the head were essential. It did nothing to help self-esteem or self-confidence, which in some of us was lacking anyway at that stage. There were two other detrimental factors. Firstly and obviously, there was a war on for the last three years I was at school and this increasingly imposed restrictions on family finances, on physical movement and travel, and on career prospects. Secondly, the school was not geared up, in the way a school of today is, to cater for the social and cultural aspects that help broaden personalities and encourage those self-confident attitudes that can be so helpful to young people. I must say, however, that same school has long since changed from the semi-deprived regime I knew into a modern and progressive place. And Max reminds me that, even though he was only two years behind me, the school had initiated by then a debating society and a verse-speaking contest. I suppose I had the slight misfortune to be there just when wartime confidence was at its lowest.

I have explained how I arrived at university after nine months in the shipyard drawing office. If I had finished my sixth form at school I would still have started university in that autumn, but I do think the months in the drawing office were just as valuable in my case as completing the sixth form. If school days occupied minimum time with no frills, then most surely university did too. Had I studied naval architecture at Glasgow in normal times it would have been a four-year course with the 'sandwich' arrangement of spending the summer months in industry. I completed the same degree in only three years because the summer period in industry was deleted. I graduated in April 1946 before I had reached my twenty-first birthday. I have always felt, and still do, that I was too young and inexperienced to appreciate university life and make the most of it. I was simply there to fill out what was considered an essential part of my overall education and to acquire a degree that would help towards a future career.

In the same way that the nation being at war had a bearing on my later school life, so university days were adversely affected as well and particularly in my first year. Not only was I catching up on those subjects, higher natural philosophy and chemistry, that I had deliberately dropped at school, but we had to fit in overnight firewatching duties. In addition, we all had to join either the Air Training Corps, or what was earlier known as the Officers Training Corps (OTC) and then became the Senior Training Corps (STC). If anyone happened to see the earnest attempts by a few dedicated army regulars to turn an uninterested bunch of budding intellectuals into a warlike cadre of officer caste, it would soon become obvious why they changed the name to STC. Any satisfaction to be had from marching along Princes Street in

Edinburgh on the way to summer camp in the Borders, with the ribbons of our Glengarries flying, was ill matched to the motley group of gangly students whose rifles sloped at all sorts of angles and to whom the idea of keeping step was unwelcome, if not downright impossible.

There was only a handful of naval architecture students at Glasgow University when I joined after completing my first year at Dundee, a year which, in engineering, was common to all four Scottish universities. As to teaching staff, there was only the very newly appointed Professor Andrew McCance Robb, and one elderly assistant called Evans, in the naval architecture department. The marine industries were just too occupied with meeting wartime demand to think of sending people to university, and few students leaving school were inclined or were encouraged to start on higher education knowing military service would intervene at some point. This sorry state of affairs was to yield all too clear and malign consequences in due course, some of which I have referred to in my story on shipbuilding. One by one the few fellow-students with me dropped out, one or two like Philip Tanner who I thought was the brightest, to the armed forces; some just could not stay the course. I was the sole product from my year when I finished in April 1946, the only other at the graduation ceremony being Tom MacDuff, a John Brown man who had failed his exams the year before and had then been successful in the one re-sit allowed. Tom's path and mine were to cross many times over the years thereafter as he became head of the Bureau Veritas classification society office in London. When I joined British Shipbuilders in 1979, rather green as to the personnel of the Corporation, Tom provided me with a most helpful confidential summary giving pluses and minuses against all the senior staff. His judgement at that time proved right over the years.

To make matters worse Professor Robb, whose very first student I was, had not yet prepared his lectures fully. He had been with the Liverpool naval architecture consultancy Graham & Woolnough, right up to the year I entered. He was patently and admittedly preparing his lecture notes as he went along – not conducive to instilling confidence in a raw student. A very tall man, he had the disconcerting habit of rubbing very large chalk-covered hands together, and after postulating alternative scenarios in the presentation of his views, he invariably 'hazarded an opinion' that one or other was correct – again not the precise direction towards facts and knowledge that I would have been happier with. My final year represented the nadir of the naval architecture department's student numbers. From then on they increased and the year behind me included names that were to become famous in naval architecture and lifetime professional colleagues of mine. Roy Turner of Vickers Armstrongs at Barrow, who would eventually become chief naval architect there. David Moor, at that time with Denny's shipyard

The Meek family at Balgay Cottage, c.1953: Grace, MM, Martha, Max, Marshall Senior.

at Dumbarton, but who would become the superintendent of the Vickers experiment tank at St Albans. Together with Ian Yuille, who was to become instrumental in taking MOD ship design into the computer age, these men formed a self-confident and even arrogant triumvirate whose demeanour rankled somewhat with the few strugglers in my year.

There were lighter moments. The drawing office for the department was in the oldest part of the original university building on Gilmore Hill and it was just under the roof next to the tower. Bedellus (the Beadle) who passed our door to attend the clock and chimes high in the tower sometimes let us enter and climb to the top – a rare privilege. More often, we climbed out on to the little balcony outside the attic-style windows and dropped pieces of slate or plaster on the unsuspecting and inferior civil engineers who were busy with their theodolites and measuring chains in the university grounds below. I had joined the Engineering Students' Society, and we made visits here and there, one of which was to the John Brown Shipyard to see HMS *Vanguard*, the last great British battleship, just before she was delivered to the Royal Navy. We also visited a coal-mine in Auchenshuggle (*sic!*) just outside Glasgow. That was more traumatic because I am convinced we were sent down the lift shaft at the 'coal' speed and not the 'personnel' speed. The unhappy mental response and the 'g' forces on the stomach muscles were only equalled by the alarming sensation, on decelerating towards the bottom, that we were ascending again with equal acceleration. As we crouched in the 3-foot high seam awaiting a shot to be fired, our faces advisedly turned away from the coal-face, I noticed we all cringed momentarily at what we guessed was to be the moment of firing. Surprising how exhausting that was when it did not happen! It reminded me very much of small boys in 'Daddy' Liddle's art classes waiting for his swipe to the head from behind.

During these years in Glasgow I stayed in digs in three different places. Longest was a sojourn with the Harris family who belonged to the same kind of Brethren assembly. 'Pa' Harris was a crane designer who felt that I, as a very junior engineering student, needed to be probed with searching (and puerile) questions based on his own rather mundane drawing office experience. When I finally could stand them no more, I was rescued by the Dickson family, also Brethren, and stayed with them till I graduated. Their son George had become a close friend from almost the first day I arrived at the university and we remained so until he died a few years ago. George was studying for his PhD in chemistry when I first knew him and we used to walk the hills regularly behind Clydebank and on Loch Lomondside on Saturdays. We both found ourselves in London not long after, and shared digs together for some years. But I come to that shortly.

I should record that my parents and I had been successful in finding some help with finance. Almost automatically, Scottish students qualified for a Carnegie grant, thoughtfully provided years before by the great Scottish, but US-based, steel magnate – not large grants, but very helpful. I also succeeded in acquiring a rather more rare Caird scholarship. That was from the fortune of the well-known industrialist whose name means so much in Dundee, and was more of a coup. I suppose my Dundee connections helped. I felt slightly piqued when, in due course and having finished with a degree, my mother insisted I repay the Carnegie money. This was a suggestion that went with the grant when it was awarded.

As I came to my finals in naval architecture I was summoned before the Joint Recruiting Board, the wartime authority who exercised the ultimate decision on every student's destiny on finishing their courses. It really meant deciding which branch of the Armed Forces we should join. The formidable colonel who was in the chair studied my papers, and asked what my position was. I explained that although I had put the Royal Navy as my preferred option within the Forces, I had been employed by the Caledon shipyard and they would be expecting me back. 'But what do *you* want to do?' said he. I could only remember the considerate way the shipyard had not exactly sponsored me, but fitted in my studies with my apprenticeship, so I said I was fairly sure they were expecting me back, and I would be happy to go back. So it was that I reappeared in Dundee and in shipbuilding.

Part III

Research & Development

CHAPTER 7

BSRA

JUST AS I HAD two shipbuilding experiences separated by thirty years one from the other, so I had two spells in marine research and development, again separated by thirty years. It might help to set out my chronology: Shipbuilding 1942–9; R & D 1949–53; Shipowning 1953–78; Shipbuilding 1978–84; R & D 1984–6.

I have shown that the health of the shipbuilding industry was going downhill in a most disappointing way over those years and in the end the sickness was terminal. Even though the R & D that I now talk about was directly related to shipbuilding, especially in the early days, my span of involvement thankfully ended with the R & D business still in good standing, albeit somewhat transmogrified.

If I take a line of sight over these years and these industries 'I hazard the opinion,' as Professor Robb would say, that the decline in shipbuilding was mainly due to the ingrown culture of the ancient industry which no one was able to break out of; whereas in R & D the people were willing to press forward with innovation. When their original shipbuilding clients failed to appreciate and adopt their findings, they sought out new customers. Even as, by nature, R & D leaders are seeking to change and improve the way things are done, so the R & D companies themselves were willing to change their structure and operations over these same years, and they live on in very reasonable health to this day.

Towards the end of 1948, after I had enjoyed getting to grips with real ship design at Caledon shipyard, I answered an advertisement for a naval architect with the recently formed Aluminium Development Association. There had been an upsurge of interest in aluminium as a potential material to replace steel in shipbuilding following success with its use in aircraft and other vehicles during wartime. It was much lighter and so was very attractive, but it brought other problems like bi-metallic corrosion where it abutted steel material, and loss of strength in any sort of fire. All this I knew as I applied for the job. I was invited to the London offices for interview. I had only once been south of the border before this, when my brother Max had been doing a few weeks of work experience with the David Brown company in Huddersfield. My sister Martha and I made a pioneering trip to share his lodgings for a week and give him a little family support. So a long rail journey, Dundee to London, for this promising interview was a real event. I failed to get the job. It went to Dr (now Revd) Ewen Corlett who was to become another colleague of long standing.

But shortly afterwards there was another advertisement, this time extending an invitation to young naval architects to join the British Shipbuilding Research Association (BSRA). So another visit to London and my first acquaintance with the West End; for the Association had established itself in a rather splendid mid-Victorian house, the former home of the Earl of Donoughmore, at 5 Chesterfield Gardens, Curzon Street. This unlikely location came from the fact that BSRA was a product of the Shipbuilding Conference, the trade association for the industry, and it was based round the corner in Grosvenor Gardens. I was interviewed once in the morning, visited the Science Museum over lunchtime, and then was interviewed again in the afternoon, both times by the director Dr S.L. Smith and the chief naval architect Dr J.F.C. Conn. It only took a week after that for me to be offered the job and I agreed to start with them in early January 1949 for quite an attractive salary of £435 per annum.

For an industry which was to prove itself so backward over the coming years, the setting-up of a research body was really remarkable. The initiative came in 1945 from one or two progressive leaders and in particular, Sir Maurice Denny of William Denny of Dumbarton, and the Ayre brothers, Sir Amos and Sir Wilfred of the small Burntisland shipyard – the one in my native Fife that Jimmy Gardner had so clearly indicated I should have favoured. These men saw that, following the experiences of wartime, there must be a better understanding of the technology lying behind the design, building and operating of ships (although at that time the word 'technology' was a bit new-fangled). BSRA was growing rapidly when I joined, and programmes of research were being developed and expanded thick and fast. It was, for me, a very interesting and educational time, and not only from the professional and technical point of view but also because I was in London, and moreover in the West End, all a step-change from Auchtermuchty and Dundee. Moreover I became acquainted with the Cox family and the girl who was to become my wife.

I found at BSRA a group of naval architects who were to go on to make their mark in the profession and with whom I would have associations for all my working life thereafter. Peter Ayling became a long-serving executive secretary of the Royal Institution of Naval Architects and his tenure would cover a difficult time when it had to change its ways as the profession moved on; Bob Townsin later worked and lectured in naval architecture at Newcastle University and became professor; Neil Miller went on to become senior lecturer in naval architecture at Glasgow University; Bill Johnson, after years of leading research into vibration and structures, finished up in the hydrodynamic world at the renowned research establishment NMI –

where I too was to end up; Mike Parker stayed for his whole life at BSRA, and was largely responsible for the Association receiving the Queen's Award for Excellence in the application of computer studies; Harry Miller became lecturer at Robert Gordon's College in Aberdeen; John Canham became a leading hydrodynamacist at MOD's Haslar establishment; and Bob Clements also moved to NMI and became a senior figure there. Dr John Conn, the Association's chief naval architect, was my boss for the time I served with BSRA. He too advanced to become professor of naval architecture at Glasgow University. He was a most kind and considerate man, with a special flair for helping young people – especially those like myself who appreciated encouragement and needed a bit of confidence. I recall how, when I opened my very first bank account, he suggested using Williams Deacon's Bank because it was the Association's bank, so I would not incur bank charges; and then showed me how to write out a cheque properly. Harry Lackenby was his assistant. He was widely respected for his work in hydrodynamics, and stayed with BSRA till he retired after thirty-one years. He too was consistently helpful and considerate, always with a merry laugh. BSRA was a healthy breeding ground for ambitious naval architects.

Not only was there the pleasure of working alongside these colleagues, but because of the way BSRA operated, I got to know nearly all the significant people in the industry. BSRA's policy was not to invest large amounts of capital in experimental facilities but to get experimental work done by outside contractors. So BSRA itself became a sort of think-tank and a co-ordinating body for all that was going on. The various research projects were looked after by separate committees and these committees were formed from the leading shipbuilding personalities considered to be expert in that field. Each of us was appointed to act as secretary to one or more committees and in this way I got to know a very large proportion of the people who mattered. There is no doubt that at that time there was interest in and enthusiasm for research. There was a steady flow of reports being approved by the committees and being issued to the industry; and it was in the 1950s still a very large industry. That eagerness to advance knowledge waned over subsequent years – so much so that when I rejoined ship-building in 1979 BSRA was being treated as a sort of prestigious adjunct. It was nice to have and it lent an aura of progress, but it was not of great importance to the shipyards – although it was used quite extensively for trouble-shooting on particular problems. The shipyards were by then fighting a short-term battle against extinction. Research was too long-term, and after all, it needed financial support from the companies and their profit margins were always minimal.

What struck me very forcibly was the gentle pace of work at BSRA after the frenetic life of the shipyard design office. I felt guilty at not having some tangible output at the end of each day. Lengthy learned discussions occupied much of the time. We merely 'aimed' to be back from lunch at Lyons Corner House at Marble Arch by about 2.00 p.m. We played cricket in Hyde Park at lunchtime – a practice which would not be countenanced today. Jack Shave who ran the drawing office was a semi-professional bowler but he generally was gentle to the rest of us tyros. Neil Miller, who came from Wick and so rather far from the recognized seats of cricketing prowess, had only one stroke. It meant that if he connected, the ball became lost amongst the buses in Park Lane. When fielding, where I performed rather better than at batting or bowling, I managed to return a ball from far away which landed fair and square on the flat head of John Canham who was deep in thought at the time. To my very considerable relief he just shook his head and carried on contemplating.

Nevertheless, BSRA made very fair progress in helping the shipbuilding industry into a better technical position. I was more involved in hydrodynamic matters than structural, these two areas absorbing most of the Association's effort at that time. The need to determine more accurately the resistance to be overcome in propelling a ship through the water involved much thought, and the arcane business of converting the results from ship-model tests in the experiment tanks into the full-scale horsepower of the ships' engines led to endless argument, and often vitriolic disagreements between the pundits. The discussions on this subject recorded in the transactions of the Royal Institution of Naval Architects contain fascinating evidence of the bitterness of disputes between the likes of Professor Telfer of Trondheim and Dr Hughes of the Ship Division of the National Physical Laboratory.

All this led up to a classic research exercise where the *Lucy Ashton*, an old Clyde paddle-steamer on her way to the breakers' yard, was given a reprieve. She was used in a series of tests in 1950–1 that were really very important in the history of naval architecture. Although not a large ship, she did, for once, provide a full-scale test. It was easy to get accurate results from models. It was never easy to get full-scale results, and so there were always doubts about the accuracy of prediction from the model to the ship. There were other basic facts to sort out. Most people had a feeling that the smoother the hull the better as far as speed and fuel consumption was concerned, but nobody knew how much it mattered. Although the growth of weed and barnacles (and rust) was obvious on a hull that had been in the water for some time, nobody knew how much that mattered either in terms of fuel consumption. We learned a great deal about such things from these novel experiments with the *Lucy Ashton*. She was a paddle-steamer with a name taken from one of Sir Walter Scott's novels, and she had instilled much affection on the Clyde. She was launched in 1888, so was sixty-two years old when we did the tests. By a strange coincidence my maternal grandfather, he of the brick works in Dunshalt, had served as a marine engineer on the *Lucy Ashton* in his early days.

The problem was to replicate what happens in a ship-model tank where a hull of say, 10, or 12, or even 20 feet long is towed through the water by external means, namely, by the carriage spanning the tank. Obviously this is impossible with a full-size ship. It is no good trying to use the ship's own propulsion system whether it be the propeller or, as in *Lucy Ashton*, the paddles, because that introduces too many other complications. We would not be sure of the actual force needed to move the hull through the water because we would not know accurately the efficiency of the paddles (or propeller) in transmitting the engines' power to the hull; and in any case there are always interactions between the propeller and the hull. One solution is to provide a tow from another ship out in front, and this has been tried. But the wake and turbulence from the towing vessel make accurate measuring of the resistance of the towed ship very suspect. We adopted the novel idea of propelling the *Lucy Ashton* with externally mounted aero-jet engines. The ship was stripped of her own machinery, paddle wheels and deck-houses, and a gantry carrying four second-hand Rolls Royce Derwent V engines was mounted across the ship. I remind you that jet engines had not been around for very long in 1950. There were dire prognostications of the side effects on us intrepid experimenters who had to work close up to these noisy machines, the dropping out of our teeth being one, in addition to the expected terminal deafness.

None of these dire things happened of course, because we worked for most of the time in a sound-proofed cabin on the deck. Probably the most arduous duty, which I recollect very well, was having to operate the cine-theodolite camera out on the open deck. This was used to determine very accurately the timing of passing the measured-mile posts on the shore, from which the ship's speed was carefully determined. As the camera was forward of the jets and somewhat below their intakes, we had a slightly lesser noise to cope with, and we managed to avoid being sucked in; and we wore ear-muffs. The tests that we started in mid-summer of 1950 dragged on into winter. All this was done in the Gareloch, a supposedly sheltered sea loch off the Clyde Estuary, and we had a good many cold and uncomfortable hours to endure.

The accuracy of everything recorded had to be above suspicion in every respect. The thrust of over 5 tons from the engines was passed through hydraulic load-measuring capsules to the gantry and hence to the ship's structure, and this provided forward motion. These capsules had to be calibrated every evening. This was a particularly odious chore. It was achieved by humping a series of twelve 100 lb weights on to a sort of scale-pan and then taking them off again – for each engine. The test results from all these runs up and down the measured mile were corrected to a standard water temperature – the colder the water the higher the resistance (in principle just like being in treacle). The effect of any wind on the ship was first calculated and then compared with wind-tunnel tests on the ship's model. There was also a tide correction. In the end we were able to put figures to many of the things that had hitherto only been suspected, or guessed at. Yes, the smoothness of the hull did matter – a very great deal. This forced us to decide what the average smoothness of a ship might be as it came new from the shipyard, and so we established a bottom line for minimum resistance. Then we had to apply different kinds of marine paints and measure the differences in horsepower with each. Then we examined riveted joints versus welded joints, and faired seams of shell plating versus sharp seams to see what difference this made to horsepower. Even more serious was the effect of rusting and fouling, where we found the resistance might be adversely affected by up to 30 per cent. All this was to become vitally important during the critical years of the 1970s when oil price increased so very dramatically and fuel-saving was imperative.

We also compared the validity of the various methods of extrapolating model results to full-size ship results, a subject about which maximum heat has always been generated amongst the hydrodynamicist pundits. We tested various sizes of models in several different tanks, but mostly at the National Physical Laboratory (NPL – later to become NMI and the scene of my final labours). I am not sure that we satisfied every one of these experts, but they could all now argue from a more scientific basis. But in doing this extended series of model tests we found the longer models of 12 feet and upwards were suffering from a 'blockage effect' in the experimental tank. The models had just got too big for the tanks, and we had to develop a 'blockage formula' to correct the resistance for the fact that there wasn't room enough to let the water in the tank flow freely past the hull. And so research leads to further research. But in the end these *Lucy Ashton* tests were unanimously and internationally agreed to be of enormous benefit, and they were a landmark in the progress of naval architecture.

I went on many other ships' trials. They were usually conducted about the time of delivery of the ship to the owners and the most common purpose was to measure accurately the speed of the ship and the horsepower and the revolutions per minute of the main engines. As well as being contractual requirements which had to be satisfied, these values were in many cases compared with the results of specific model tests made on the particular ship. We were continually trying to improve this correlation of model predictions with ship results. There were also trials to study the vibration of the ship's structure, whether engine-induced or from the propeller.

Because ships were always being pushed to higher speeds with more horsepower, the phenomenon of propeller-excited vibration became very important. Its effect was to make the ship structure shake along its length, usually with maximum motion towards the ends. This could be either a nuisance, or downright uncomfortable, or even damaging to the structure especially at the stern, and so was very undesirable. But it was very hard to predict in the design stages just how bad it would be. Bill Johnson was our leading expert on vibration at BSRA in those days, and he together with Arthur Ridler, our ever-inventive laboratory engineer, developed a frightening device known as the BSRA 'vibrator'. It consisted of a series of adjustable one-ton weights mounted on a drive shaft, and these were made to rotate by an electric motor through a whole range of speeds. Usually mounted on the forecastle, it was meant to impart a known vibratory force to the ship's hull, against which the response of the structure could be scientifically measured. It was not used a great deal because few shipyards could, or would, find time and effort to install it. I suspect they felt their ship might be damaged in some way. It was agreed amongst us researchers that one of these days the whole thing would fly apart with almost certain lethal consequences.

It was to be many years before propeller-excited vibration was fully understood, and it needed the computer and the necessary programs to be developed before this troublesome problem could be dealt with at the design stage. In fact it was only when I was in Liverpool with Blue Funnel in 1974 that a major exercise was undertaken to solve this kind of vibration. By then it was an acute problem because of the large horsepowers being installed to give continually higher ship speeds. A three-year programme was set up jointly with BSRA, the General Council of British Shipping and the SMTRB, the Government funding body. I was asked to chair this rather remarkable union of interests, designated the PEV (propeller-excited vibration) Group, and it was really very satisfying because we knew we were leading world-wide in the field.

Then it became necessary to look at the effect of the hull in the proximity of the propeller and three more partners joined in – Lloyd's Register, British Shipbuilders and Stone Manganese the propeller manufacturers. The latter were naturally anxious to show it was not the propeller alone that was the problem. This was the PHIVE (propeller hull interaction vibration excited) Group. A further three years of work followed and again I was chairing. It was all a great experience because we eventually nailed down this difficult and elusive subject. Together with George Ward of BSRA and Hans Ritter of NMI, I presented the results at an RINA conference in 1979. I remember that conference particularly well because the Tara Hotel in West London where we were meeting went on fire during one of our discussion sessions. As we all stood on the pavement waiting for the firemen to put out the flames one of the conference stenographers could not resist saying to Elfrida (who was there as well) and not knowing who she was, 'look at all these odd men still discussing vibration while the place is burning down'. George Ward was a tower of strength at BSRA and had built up a great team including Pat Fitzsimmons and others. As so often in my story, however, the work done was really too late to benefit UK shipping. It was other countries who gained.

Many of the ship trials were with ships built on the North-East coast – from the Tyne, the Wear and the Tees, and the measured mile we used was at Newbiggin off the Northumberland coast north of Newcastle. That particular set of mile-posts was a prominent feature on the landscape because they were so tall. They had to be, because the water is relatively shallow there and the ships had to do their runs well out from land. In addition, they carried vertical columns of brilliant lights which meant we could continue the trials during the night. I little thought I would one day be living in the beautiful county beyond these posts.

We younger naval architects at BSRA in the 1950s were encouraged to get into writing technical papers and publishing our results in the transactions of the learned societies, chief of which was the Royal Institution of Naval Architects. The North East Coast Institution of Engineers and Shipbuilders was another well-respected body, as was the Institution of Engineers and Shipbuilders in Scotland. Our authorship was thoughtfully distributed over all three. I was immensely proud of my own first paper, although it was under joint authorship with Bill Johnson. Being my senior, he did most of the work. It was delivered to a good audience at the North East Coast Institution and described studies we did on a tanker (at 11,000 tons very small by today's standards), during its launch at the Bartram Shipyard in Hartlepool. There had been a suspicion amongst the shipyard management that during the actual launch process recent vessels had suffered undue stresses on the bottom structure as the ships passed over the end of the launch ways. So we calculated the likely stresses on this particular ship, whose name I cannot recall, and using some of Arthur Ridler's clever measuring devices we determined what actually happened. It has always been the case in these learned circles that the length, and hopefully, the depth of the discussion following the presentation of the paper demonstrates the success of the authors. I was well content with this my first effort as all the contributors were very kind and helpful, and more importantly, the shipyard management found the reassurance they sought. From that time onwards I have produced a gentle trickle of technical papers over the years to various institutions. Although it was many a time a real chore to write them, I always believed that I should try to pass on to others the fruits of my experience.

Because I was so heavily involved in the hydrodynamic programmes, I got to know the experiment tanks and their invariably idiosyncratic superintendents. All tanks had the same curious stillness that seems to come with stretches of placid water. There never seemed to be all that much activity, since one run of the carriage propelling the model along the tank seemed to generate a long period of analysis and calculation. There was always the curious all-pervading smell of hot paraffin wax because nearly all ship-models were made of wax, which was easy to form and cut to shape, and they could be melted down to use again. Willie Walker of Denny's tank at Dumbarton was a wonderful Scottish raconteur, much employed in public speaking, but a good and progressive superintendent. Munday of Vickers at St Albans was at the other extreme of loquacity and publicity. The arrival of my colleague of university days, David Moor, was shortly to alter that and make the place much more visible. Dickie Gawn of the Ministry of Defence Haslar tank was always bustling about, vocal and precise, until he tried to prove why dolphins had such an amazing hydrodynamic performance – and came up with nothing much. John Brown's tank at Clydebank was in the quiet and capable hands of J.M. Ferguson with whom I wrote my second technical paper for presentation at the Royal Institution of Naval Architects in 1954. It explained a 'methodical series' of tests on a particular hull where the various parameters – length, beam and displacement, were methodically varied so that design practitioners in the industry could readily acquire data.

The most active and best known tank was at the Ship Division of NPL at Teddington, later becoming the National Maritime Institute (NMI), with magnificent premises and facilities at Feltham. Little did I know in those days that I would eventually become managing director. Dr F.H. Todd headed it for a short time, followed by Dr J.F. Allan when Todd took up residence in the US. There were to be many famous names associated with NPL – Baker, Hughes, Kent, Silverleaf, Doust and lots of others, all of whom regularly published the results of their work and made a very real impact on the professional scene. The tragedy was that before long such research work became subject to commercial pressures. Establishments such as NPL were forced to be more cost-conscious and to take on more work commissioned by customers and hence confidential. The free dissemination of valuable information that we had enjoyed faded away.

Not only that, but the great names that were behind the setting up of BSRA and its promotion and expansion while I was there began to pass from the scene. The powerful shipbuilders such as the Ayre brothers of Burntisland, Dennys of Dumbarton, Stephens of Glasgow, Rebbecks of

Belfast left the stage. Those who succeeded must carry the reproach of increasingly failing to see the benefit of research, and eventually they caved in to the all-pervasive pressure to cut down first of all on research and development expenditure when the less profitable days for shipbuilding arrived.

It was during these years at BSRA that I found wider interests. For most of the time I shared lodgings in several parts of Ealing in West London with George Dickson the chemistry graduate I had become friendly with in Glasgow. George started his lifetime employment with Glaxo at their Greenford premises just before I moved down from Dundee, so it was natural that we should team up. Together we explored London as provincials tend to do, and did it probably more thoroughly than the indigenous Londoners would. I played tennis for the first time, and squash, and even my cricketing prowess, exhibited to such a dangerous extent in Hyde Park at lunchtimes, was recognized by my being included in the BSRA cricket team from time to time. I must admit that when we played the nobby upper classes at NPL at Teddington we were simply thrashed. Golf was only toyed with when we were away somewhere on ship trials and had a spare half-day to fill in. Then we had our bicycles. To anyone familiar with the roads to the West of London today, it must be inconceivable that we regularly cycled out on the Great West Road to Uxbridge, and then covered the hinterland of Iver, Burnham Beeches, Stoke Poges, Beaconsfield or up-river to Maidenhead or even Marlow, with a bit of rowing thrown in. These Saturdays were immensely satisfying – new countryside to us but with familiar names, good teashops, and a smooth glide through the evening coolness. With no more than persistent pedalling we covered eighty or ninety miles in the day. Then there was the photography craze, where both George and I dabbled. Not only did we fancy our abilities with picture composition, the use of single reflex lens cameras, filters and tripods, but we developed and printed our own films with generally very fair success.

We both went to one of the three Brethren assemblies in Ealing and there met a very good crowd of young folk. There was much interchange and entertaining in the various households, with us two Scottish boys being made somewhat a fuss of. Whether it was because we were semi-presentable bachelors or maybe just because of novelty value I am not sure, but one of the homes we were invited to was that of the Cox family. Mr Cox, a senior Board of Trade principal, had died in his forties leaving Mrs Cox and three sons and a daughter all just starting their career training. Because of the parents' strong religious beliefs there was no insurance cover when Mr Cox died, and so times were not easy for the family. Mrs Cox had to find work. Victor was articled and on his way to becoming a successful solicitor. Rob was the same age as I was and was training as an accountant; and likewise his younger brother Humphrey. Youngest was Elfrida who, on leaving school, also had to make her way and was working as a secretary. I spent a lot of time with them and Rob in particular, becoming proficient in matters of tennis and squash, and the top floor of their house was most useful for photography purposes. All these activities were enhanced and encouraged by the fact that Elfrida was there, rather shy and reserved, but as a younger sister to three older brothers, quite ready to defend her corner. It was to be another four years before we became engaged and then married in 1957, but the memory of those Ealing years carries a strange and permanently favourable aura. They came to a close at the end of 1953, a year that gave me the chance of witnessing the June Coronation of Queen Elizabeth. With a group of friends I took up station in the Mall at 4.00 a.m. in the rain and cold, but enjoyed the day greatly – because of course, Elfrida was there.

But I realized by now that I was not cut out to be a permanent researcher. I wanted to find something more active and where I could make things happen. In response to an advert, I applied for the position of assistant naval architect with the Blue Funnel Line of Liverpool. When I told Dr Conn I had been successful, he simply said in his decent way – 'it's a blue chip company, I'll support your move'. And so I departed London, sorry deep down to be leaving but glad to have a job in shipowning, always seen as the pinnacle of professional success.

CHAPTER 8

NMI

THIRTY YEARS AFTER leaving BSRA and the delights of Curzon Street, I found myself back in the same realms. I had done my twenty-five years in Liverpool and then five years with British Shipbuilders. As with my move out of Blue Funnel, again out of the blue I was invited to take an interest in a vacancy for the position of managing director of NMI Ltd. I could not refuse, having been very familiar with the establishment when it was known in my BSRA days as Ship Division NPL, and then all through my time in shipowning. I had met the senior staff of NPL-NMI regularly over these years, either on the council of the Royal Institution of Naval Architects or at the many meetings of that and other professional institutions, and as customers Blue Funnel had used the test facilities many times. I knew it to be one of the finest maritime technology establishments in the world. After various interviews with the head-hunters and then with Dr Jack Birks chairman of NMI, I was appointed from 1 August 1984. Headquarters had long since moved from NPL at Teddington to an impressive set-up in Feltham, where most of the offices, laboratories and test facilities were.

I did not find a very settled group of people compared with the Ship Division NPL that I had known earlier in my BSRA days. There had been too many changes, and proposals for change, to a long-established group of dedicated and far-above average people whose work depended on a higher degree of continuity than exists in other kinds of business. Yet we all had to accept that the environment around us was changing, and in ways that were bound to hurt. The decline in shipbuilding that I had experienced at British Shipbuilders meant a big reduction in model testing for new ships. There was increasing demand from the offshore oil and gas industries whose requirements were different. There was a tightening-up of Government financial support all round. There was heavy pressure from the Thatcher Government to push such Government-supported companies into the private enterprise domain; and Mrs Thatcher didn't like civil servants anyway. Above all, there was a growing move towards a merger with BSRA, the company I had worked for away back in the early 1950s.

Altogether there was much to grapple with. John Cammell, my predecessor as managing director, was returning after three years with NMI to the safe womb of the civil service. He had been seconded from the vehicle division of the Department of Industry and clearly felt it was a good time to depart the commercial scene. All this was at a time of life when I might have been thinking of a gentle approach to retirement. But I find much satisfaction in the fact that the now internationally recognized marine consultants BMT evolved out of my rather traumatic years at Feltham.

Ship Division NPL had a very long and proud history. The National Physical Laboratory itself was founded in 1899, and it was in 1901 that Alfred Yarrow, the well-known Glasgow shipbuilder, suggested that a new experiment tank was needed at a time when there was rapid expansion of shipbuilding. Hitherto there had only been available the privately owned Denny tank at Dumbarton and the Admiralty one at Haslar, Portsmouth. When Haslar turned down a request to accommodate the new tank, an approach was made to the recently instituted NPL at Bushy Park, Teddington. When Alfred Yarrow offered to the Institution of Naval Architects, who were acting as promoters of the project, the magnificent sum of £20,000 in 1908, the new tank became a reality, and it opened in 1910. Initially it was known as the William Froude Laboratory, although formally a part of NPL. Thereafter, under a series of eminent superintendents the first of whom was G.S. Baker, it went from strength to strength. Baker was from an Admiralty background, had worked at Haslar, was a powerful leader, and remained at NPL for thirty-one years. He was still producing reports, in manuscript, from his retirement when I was at BSRA in the 1950s. One in particular I remember because I had to process it. It concerned the behaviour and performance of ships in shallow water, and his handwriting was abysmal.

The history of NPL has been well written-up by David Bailey in his book *Ships in the Making*. He was a long-serving and very well-recognized and respected researcher there. It covers a long list of successes in every kind of maritime development, and especially so during both world wars. The projects examined, for example, during World War II included limpet mines; oil booms; amphibious army tanks; the bouncing bomb of Barnes Wallis' design; Pluto, the fuel pipe line across the Channel; and biggest of all, the massive floating structures that went to form the Mulberry harbours providing artificial breakwaters and port facilities on the French coast. Just after the end of World War II, the William Froude Laboratory was absorbed as a 'division' of NPL, and this was when Ship Division NPL became a recognized entity. All the staff were civil servants.

Baker was followed by Kent, and Kent by Allan, all famous names. When I was a young naval architect at BSRA in 1951, I remember being told very confidentially by my boss Dr Conn, that Alex Silverleaf of Denny's tank in Dumbarton had asked him for a reference. He was applying to NPL for a senior position, and as Conn himself had come from NPL, he was greatly interested. Silverleaf duly became superintendent, proving to be a dynamic leader with great skills in the presentation of NPL's case. It was over this period that Ship Division NPL made big advances and there developed a great feeling of confidence. The general policy and thrust of the NPL business was in the hands of a body known as the Froude Research Committee, and it decided on the allocation of funds. It was one of the earliest committees I served on as a shipowner's naval architect in the 1960s. James Lenaghan of Fairfield Shipbuilding was the chairman and was one of the better people at the top of the industry. Besides acquiring a close feel for what went on at NPL, I was again linking with people who mattered. I seem to have spent an undue proportion of my days since then on such committees.

It was during Silverleaf's very active term of office that the brand-new facilities at Feltham were built to cope with the increasing market. This became the headquarters of Ship Division NPL, opening in August 1962, although the older tanks at Teddington were retained and still used. By 1965 the staff had built up to 140 and all were quietly proud of the splendour of the facilities and equipment. The centre-piece was the new towing tank. At 400 metres long it enabled models to be run at speeds up to 15 metres per second and so cope with the very fastest ships. When one realizes that the carriage used for towing the model and supporting the gear was 40 tons in weight, the accelerating and decelerating forces can be imagined. The electric motors driving the carriage were of 1,200 horsepower. An interesting little fact illustrates the scientific accuracy lying behind the whole operation. A curvature had to be imparted to the carriage rails to correct the line-of-sight straightness to bring it to the curvature of the earth – otherwise the carriage would have been running uphill! Over the 400 metres of rail length the deviation to be corrected was 3 mm. Fortunately, the NPL's metrology division was at hand to check such fine dimensions.

Then there was the cavitation tunnel where propellers were tested, again everything geared to highest possible requirements. The cavitation tunnel was so-called because a propeller being pushed hard to absorb high power inevitably develops cavitation, and air bubbles are created on the low-pressure side of the propeller blade. This is always undesirable. It creates noise and vibration, and eventually wear on the material of the blade. As it was a closed tunnel with the water circulated at whatever speed was required, the decision was to build it as a huge vertical U-shape with the working section across the legs of the U. The hydrostatic pressure of the column of water would force the cavitation air bubbles back into the water solution, and the total pressure could be varied at will. To achieve this a height of 55 metres was required and the most practical way to do it was to build it mostly underground with the observation section at roughly ground level. When the covers were open for maintenance I used to look down that hole with trepidation. The tragedy to follow all too soon was that, shortly after I retired from NMI in 1986, the whole place – equipment, facilities, offices – were sold, dug up and scrapped. But I shall come back to that shortly.

As I had found during my Liverpool shipping days, that period in the 1960s covered the very apex of UK shipping activity, after which there was to be an irreversible decline. But during that time of exciting progress ever-larger super-tankers were appearing and containerships were being designed. At the other end of the size spectrum, trawlers were changing as fishing practices changed. Hovercraft were being introduced. Vibration and propeller design were being more closely examined. There was more intelligent interest in wave resistance and seakeeping. And there was the perennial pursuit of more accurate ship-model correlation. All this activity kept Ship Division NPL at the forefront of maritime development. The reporting of all these labours, other than strictly repayment work for clients, was freely available to industry, to other researchers and the universities. How very different from today when commercial secrecy prevails and results, if published at all, are only divulged at conferences of learned societies where you have to pay to attend. I have pointed this out publicly as best I can in recent times, reminding ourselves that a main objective of the Royal Institution of Naval Architects, to take just one example of a learned institution, is 'to promote the bringing together of the results of the practical and scientific experience of all those concerned with the design, construction and operation of ships and other marine artefacts; the value of these results being enhanced by the publication, examination and discussion by the Institution'. In actual fact bodies like this, my own learned Institution, depend a great deal on income from running conferences to discuss matters of research, and they must pay their way. It is not the way I was able to keep abreast of technical and scientific progress when I was a student, when almost everything was published and freely available in the many magazines and journals.

These glory days of Ship Division NPL were to fade as the climate surrounding industry, trade and Government became less benign. When James Paffett took over at the end of the 1970s it became clear that the work of Ship Division was altering and indeed its very constitution was being reconsidered. It was to need something like five years of discussions on various alternatives before a final decision was taken that Ship Division would remain within Government, but as a new establishment to be called the National Maritime Institute (NMI). The aim was to engender a real commercial attitude to its business. It was not easy for the staff. Some were slightly unworldly, as many good researchers tend to be. All were either long-serving members or hoped to be, yet they were surrounded by an air of impermanence. They saw themselves as civil servants, which had always implied a special sense of loyalty given in return for certain favourable conditions such as reasonable retirement arrangements. A lot more change was on the way. The real problem was that it cost more to run the expensive and magnificently equipped NMI than could be earned from its commercial work and research funding. This shortfall was to be the thorn in the flesh of NMI for all its days as the responsibility for NMI moved on from Paffett to Mallett, and then to Cammell in 1981. I was to succeed him in 1984 by which time the problems had in no way diminished. The number of ship investigations for shipyards could not be maintained, and the funding from central research funds were continually being cut back.

When I arrived the decision had been made to move towards full privatization, with a transfer of assets (valued at £14.8 million in March 1980) to the new company and an undertaking to slim down on staff and running expenses. NMI was now a company limited by guarantee, but thankfully, Government had accepted some responsibility for this wonderful national asset. They awarded transitional financial assistance over a five-year period, together with a capital investment grant of £10 million. Dr Jack Birks, who was chairman of Charterhouse Petroleum, was chairman of NMI Ltd when I became managing director, and my first fellow directors were Peter Cox, a prominent civil engineer; Alan Rudge who had developed a very successful electrical research company ERA; and Brian Smouha of Touche Ross. It was not the most auspicious background against which to serve out my declining years, especially as the staff were obviously torn between traditional loyalties on the one hand, and civil service union pressures to secure a best deal in the face of the enforced changes on the other. But I felt that here was a cadre of the best brains in the maritime research world, backed with a reasonable offer of Government help – and further moves in the offing of which I approved and will explain shortly.

The face-to-face meeting with staff was fascinating. At Liverpool up to the time I left the Blue Funnel shipping group in 1978, I was still addressed as 'Sir' quite commonly, and to my own staff I was 'Mr Meek'. Only when your first name was used by the main board directors was final acceptance in the hierarchy signalled. There was therefore a distinct shock to the system when I found myself at British Shipbuilders in Newcastle, and my secretary and all the staff from chairman downwards called me 'Marshall'. Not that I minded – it was a healthy indicator of how the old order was changing. But on arrival at Feltham my NMI staff almost took me back to Liverpool days. Here was a curious deference which left me wondering how my predecessors behaved. I had never been involved with civil servants before, and to hear some member of staff whom I was to interview identified helpfully in advance by my excellent secretary as 'a Grade 5' or whatever, was strange language. I could only assume that strict protocol had been the order of the day. It may be the staff had preferred it that way, but I felt very strongly that in the light of a changing commercial scene around them, and with the looming possibility of a merge with BSRA which was already being talked about, there should be a more open approach all round. So I went for lunch in the canteen when I was on the premises, and sat with whoever was there – although I must say it obviously caused a distinct unease with some. What my predecessors did for lunch I never really found out. Betty Gray my devoted secretary who guided me in these strange civil service realms, most loyally never touched on such intimate details.

I took to making the occasional unannounced tour round the offices, laboratories and workshops, and got the feeling that this too was rather unusual. It was obvious however, that this little bit of interest shown was really appreciated. I could enter into discussion on the work going on a bit more intelligently, I suppose, than they had recently been accustomed to under a professional civil servant. Where I caused maximum discomfiture was when I wanted to climb the water-tower which stood in the midst of the establishment and was a dominant feature amongst what were otherwise fairly nondescript buildings. The head of the building maintenance department who felt he had to accompany me was clearly more amazed than amused.

I could not presume to understand fully all the work going on. There were very bright people there who were internationally recognized specialists in their various fields, and a run through their names and specialisms will give an idea of the scope of NMI work. Ian Dand, an expert on ship manoeuvring and navigation matters; George Gadd likewise on the finer points of ship resistance; Neil Hogben, the ultimate authority on ocean waves; John English likewise on ship propulsion; Mike Gaster, into the higher realms of mathematical approaches to hydrodynamics, and shortly to achieve the award of FRS; Mel Davies on wind-tunnel research, but so versatile he could operate in many fields; David Bailey on the hydrodynamics of smaller craft; Tony Morrall on ship disaster investigations; Roger Standing and Steve Rowe who took us successfully into the offshore areas of research; and many, many more, all people to be proud of – if only we could find the income from the maritime market place to keep them employed.

I give one or two examples of things going on while I was managing director at NMI. The America's Cup was gripping everybody. Just the year before, the Australians with *Australia II* had defeated the Americans and so caused a major upset. Success was largely ascribed to the revolutionary wing-keels fitted to the hull. This opened up a whole new approach to yacht design and NMI were well-placed to join in the intense investigations, with their wind-tunnel capabilities to add to model-testing and theoretical studies. Herbert Pearcey was an NMI name closely allied to the harnessing of hydrodynamic expertise with aerodynamic know-how. A lot of work was done for the Royal Thames Yacht Club's challenger, again with special attention to the keel design. NMI were able to run models as big as one-third full scale and so make the examination of the keels in their many configurations more reliable. This was known as the Hollom craft after its designer. An alternative was the Howlett design with the testing mainly done at the Wolfson Unit. In the end their *White Crusader* was chosen because of enforced delays with sail problems on the Hollom design. Elfrida and I were invited to the naming ceremony of *White Crusader* at Hamble. Princess Diana did the naming and we were greatly impressed by the attractive way she performed the job and was happy to talk to everybody. The yacht was pretty much under wraps and strict secrecy was in order. Unfortunately *White Crusader* was knocked out in the elimination races. The obvious inference could be that the wrong design had been chosen.

Then there was the short-fat versus long-thin episode where the design of the conventional so-called 'long-thin' Royal Navy frigate was being challenged by a small independent company, Thornycroft Giles and Associates. The argument, which became acrimonious in the extreme between the various parties, lasted for years. I describe it in detail in a later chapter on 'Warships' because I was closely involved all the way through. But while I was at NMI, David Giles, who was the principal player on behalf of the short-fat proposal, commissioned us to investigate the mysterious hull design he was advocating which was supposed to offer superb qualities compared with the Royal Navy design. In the end the claims behind the whole proposition were disproved, but in the meantime Giles took such exception to NMI's results and performance that we ended up in legal arguments, and had to incur needless expenditure in legal fees.

The extraction of oil and gas from the sea bed had been going on for years, but in that critically important industry nothing stood still. It was the study of unmanned and remotely operated underwater vehicles (ROVs) that I became acquainted with first on joining NMI. These weird objects were powered by umbilicals from the mother-ship and a lot had to be learned about the behaviour of the ROV and its tether. We used our large towing tank for this, but also the useful piece of equipment called the circulating water tank. In it the model was kept fixed and it was the water that flowed past. I recall watching, together with Mel Davies, the powerful and sinister current of water sweeping through the working area, smooth as glass, and silently vanishing back into the propelling machinery, and I wondered what would happen if someone fell in. Because the performance of fixed jackets and other structures used in drilling operations was vitally important in storm conditions, we researched the wave forces on cylinder shapes representing the legs of the structures, and included the effect of marine fouling (– shades of *Lucy Ashton* tests at BSRA.) Then the results were compared with full-scale tests on similar shapes. These were done at our Christchurch Bay tower, an experimental structure sitting in the English Channel. It was because of this increasing offshore activity that we decided to enlarge the Number 4 Tank, our biggest stretch of water at Feltham. It was to be our last major capital investment, and it was to provide a squarish area of 1,500 square metres for use either in ship manoeuvring tests or offshore structure studies. Our pride and joy was a very special wave-maker that could produce a multi-directional wave spectrum very accurately. In the middle of the tank was a 6 metre deep pit to be used in testing very tall offshore structures.

From this short description the versatility and the sheer range of competencies available at NMI can be appreciated. One unfortunate aspect of NMI's Feltham location was that it was bang alongside the major runways of Heathrow airport. It was difficult sometimes not to let one's attention drift off and find oneself watching the endless and majestic procession of flights taking off and landing. In the summer and with the windows open it was very difficult to hear the person sitting at the other side of my desk, especially when Concorde was going over. It was all a far cry from my quiet home at Tranwell Woods near Morpeth in Northumberland to which I might by now have retired. I used to think of Admiral Collingwood, who was Nelson's second in command and had his home in Morpeth. Collingwood House still stands in the town centre. The plaque above the entrance tells us that as he spent the long months at sea chasing the French fleet prior to Trafalgar, he longed for the quiet woods and fields of Morpeth – and I did too.

It was just at this time I became president of the North East Coast Institution of Engineers and Shipbuilders. I had been a member for over thirty years and it was, as I said earlier, the institution where I read my very first technical paper, that on the stressing of a ship during its launch. My predecessor, Derek Kimber of Austin & Pickersgill, had just seen the Institution through its centenary celebrations in 1984. Derek, a man who loved acting under the spotlights, had actually asked me to delay taking over as president for a month or so until the celebrations were complete. I felt I could only accede, but I think the fact that the Duke of Edinburgh, an Honorary Fellow of long standing, was actively involved had much to do with Derek's rather unusual suggestion. It might have seemed a little odd that I became president just as I moved out of the North East area to NMI at Feltham, but I was about to be again closely involved with the area. BSRA had long been based on the Tyne, and I would be visiting regularly. But I was to be facing a contrary wind and tide. The run-down, not only in shipbuilding but in all the maritime industries, was increasingly having its adverse effect on every associated business and institution, and that included NMI.

As a family we had accepted that we had to move south when I was appointed to NMI. This really appealed to Elfrida who remains at heart a southerner, but had loyally accepted over nearly thirty years that the family had perforce to be in the North. Because we always had happy memories of starting our honeymoon in Winchester on our way to Jersey, our thoughts drifted to that area when we realized how the motorway system reached out from West London and Feltham. Winchester seemed just about as far as was practicable, so there we started looking for a home. Find one we did, a place just starting to be built at Kingsworthy. The only trouble was it needed quite some months before completion. I stayed at the Caledonian Club in the West End until it was ready, travelling home at weekends, usually by air to Newcastle. When we did move at the end of 1985 it was without family. Hazel was by now working in London and sharing a flat in the West End, before having her own in South Croydon. Ursula found a flat in Newcastle and was now contemplating marriage to Rob Wilson. Angela also found a flat in Gosforth, Newcastle. By the time we moved in at Kingsworthy we had begun to realize that, although the M3 motorway looked ideal for commuting between Winchester and Feltham, the reality was that motorways in the South at busy times just choked up. However, we got ourselves installed in what was really a beautiful Hampshire site only a mile or two from the heart of Winchester. We were trying meantime to sell our Tranwell Woods home at Morpeth, but failing. It hardly mattered, because NMI was about to enter its final metamorphosis, at the end of which I would be leaving anyway in a retirement somewhat delayed by my NMI appointment.

CHAPTER 9

BMT

EVEN BEFORE I left British Shipbuilders in 1984 to join NMI, there had been serious talk of a merger between NMI and BSRA. Their common problems and their similar-type businesses could only point to that conclusion. There were hurdles to be overcome of course, but in a curious way I found myself wholly familiar with both sides of this story. Each company was facing up to an excision from its parent body. NMI was being forced into becoming self-standing with minimum public-sector support. British Shipbuilders was intent on severing its direct link with what was originally its very own research body. BSRA had gone on steadily from the time I left for Blue Funnel in 1954. It moved from the unlikely environs of Curzon Street to more spacious offices on the Albert Embankment, where the staff could actually see ships, of a sort, on the Thames – but as Harry Lackenby would say, they could pull the blinds down when it worried them. The name had changed from the British Shipbuilding Research Association to the British Ship Research Association because it had to widen out its technological base in 1962.

It merged with PAMETRADA, the clumsily named, Wallsend-based, Parsons Marine Engineering Turbine Research and Development Association which had been instituted in 1944, roughly about the time BSRA itself was born. But again the UK capability in marine engineering and the need for turbine research was running down, and PAMETRADA went out of business in 1967. Thereafter BSRA moved from London to the Wallsend site, causing a major upset to the staff and organization, but at least it was a bit nearer real maritime activities. At that time Dr Bob Hurst was appointed director of research. He was a New Zealander, a chemist, and had worked on bomb disposal during World War II, for which he was awarded the George Medal. He was the man for the job because he was not hampered with traditional UK shipbuilding attitudes. A modest individual (I met him once on leaving the Athenaeum, and he claimed he had been reduced to feeling like a sort of plumber), he pushed the Association forward during a critical time.

All through my years in Liverpool and also while at British Shipbuilders, I had served on BSRA research committees. I could see that British shipbuilding companies were no longer really interested in research and development. Much of BSRA's output and advice was falling on unresponsive ears.

Lacking industry support and interest the research activities began to lose their way. I agree with George Ward who suggests that BSRA may have been too dominant for the good of the shipyards, and it might have been better if the companies had shown more initiative in their research, with BSRA acting in a supportive role. Here again if people had looked overseas, they would have seen that European and Far East shipbuilders were more self-reliant in their R & D. Perhaps the most progressive section at BSRA was that looking at ship production and manufacturing where David Goodrich, originally from Bartram's shipyard in Sunderland, and then with the Royal Corps of Naval Constructors, did good work. It was not used. There seemed to be a death-wish in the shipyards. A comment at the time was: 'They seemed to be happy to sink giggling into the sea.'

David Goodrich was shortly to become director of BSRA at a time when British Shipbuilders were paying BSRA a direct grant. This was to replace the previous arrangement where individual shipyard companies were member firms of BSRA and contributed to the cost of running it. British Shipbuilders then decided in 1984 to deal commercially with BSRA at arm's length, thereby removing a subsidy which had met half the annual budget. BSRA staff were now faced with the same problems as their opposite numbers at NMI.

If I have been critical of UK shipbuilding companies, I have to admit that UK shipowners were not much better. They too were about to tread a path to oblivion just a few years later, and I use the example of 'The Efficient Ship' project to illustrate why their performance was little more commendable than the shipbuilders' in the end. The psychology of the shipowning community has always intrigued me. I shall describe my own years with one of the greatest UK companies in the next section, but I think they (and UK shipowners always were a homogeneous group) really did consider themselves superior to many other industries, and certainly superior to UK shipbuilders. Any idea of tying up with shipbuilders was anathema. Yet both industries were well into decline when I was at BMT in 1984–5. The Government had been more helpful financially to shipbuilding than shipowning, but on the other hand UK shipowners had always preferred to be independent.

It may well have been rather too late, but the Department of Trade and Industry promoted a feasibility study into what was called 'The Efficient Ship' in 1984. Other countries, Japan, Norway and West Germany had all trodden this route. The intention was to halt the decline in UK shipping, even at that late stage when the number of ships in the UK fleet had dropped from 1,600 in 1975 to 500, by producing a ship design which would incorporate the latest technological developments. I mentioned some of these when I described my shipbuilding experiences at British Shipbuilders where we spelled out what could be done to reduce fuel consumption, to reduce manning levels, introduce full automation, and adopt modern communication methods. BSRA did most of the work on the study for DTI, who also used NMI's Ship Support Unit for project management. Underlying all was the need for close collaboration between individual shipowners and equipment manufacturers, and shipbuilders. There was a bold suggestion that a trial ship should be built incorporating all these modern technologies.

The DTI were enthusiastic and clearly treated this exercise as a final throw to help the marine industries to help themselves. On completion of the project I was asked by DTI and all the parties involved to present the proposals to industry and the public. This I did at a massively attended meeting in July 1985 at the Sedgwick Centre in the City. I always felt it was one of the more important addresses I have given. The audience, which included representation from virtually every shipowning company, seemed to be enthralled as I explained the various features we had examined, and the improvements that could be made. BSRA's Ted Harding had helped devotedly in the preparation, and handled the visual presentation with absolute precision. David Bailey's record of the event in his *Ships in the Making* describes my rallying cry thus: 'If all sections of the UK shipbuilding and marine industries commit themselves wholeheartedly and without delay to a national effort, the country can stay among the leaders. But if DTI's proposals are ignored there will be no second chance and UK shipping, merchant shipbuilding and associated equipment manufacturers will drift further into decline.' There was a lot of press comment and I had to give interviews to the BBC and others. People clearly felt that a momentous stage had been reached in our maritime industries – but absolutely nothing happened! I was particularly disappointed in one comment by John Newton, director of OCL, at the time the world's leading containership company and whose ships I had designed: 'No, they wouldn't be joining in any such venture.' The reason given did not make sense to me. His company has now gone. The haughty shipowners were little better than the shipbuilders. So it was to be downhill all the way for these major industries and it was no wonder that the Government thereafter lost all interest in them.

Knowing both BSRA and NMI so well, I had always considered a merger to be in the best interest of both. In this David Goodrich and I were in complete agreement. Eventually the two bodies were to merge and became British Maritime Technology (BMT). I spent a lot of time negotiating with the Department of Trade and Industry in order to establish NMI's position in the proposed merger. Brian Smouha with his well-recognized authority in the finance area was a great help. The final settlement as to funding was, in the end, really quite beneficial and was to cover the first five years. The total funding was £18 million of which more than half was for Government research projects. It included £2 million which BSRA had in reserve, and £1.5 million for staff payments.

BMT now owned all the facilities and the land, most importantly at NMI but also at BSRA. BMT was inaugurated at a combined celebration at NMI on 1 April 1985 marking the start of the new company and also the opening of the extended Number 4 tank. Norman Lamont as Secretary of State for Industry was guest of honour. We met up in the heads just before the ceremony and he asked me how much his department had put into NMI over recent years. I had, naturally, been primed by my people for any such obvious question. When he came to refer in his speech to the assistance we had enjoyed at NMI the figure somehow got about doubled. I served for eighteen months as executive deputy chairman, with Jack Birks still chairman, and David Goodrich as managing director. During our early discussions together before I firmed up on my appointment as managing director of NMI, David had urged me to accept, saying that 'I was the only person who could see it through', meaning the merger between the two companies. But now David seemed to forget his earnest plea, or considered my job done, and soon made it fairly plain that he considered he could run the new company better on his own. Then I did retire in September 1986 to start probably the best and most satisfying part of my life.

Before that happened my final months at BMT were largely taken up with resolving merger problems, the principal questions always being – where would the money come from to run the new company in the longer term; and how to reconcile the terms and conditions of the two sets of staff. The effect of the merger on the NMI civil servant staff was difficult to handle. I had to offer them the choice of joining the new BMT and giving up civil servant status, or letting them stay in the service and leave BMT – an unhappy experience for me and for them. That was when I learned how favoured civil servants were as regards matters of redundancy payments and pensions, compared with their colleagues in BSRA and in industry generally. I was quite surprised to find, in my simplicity, that there was no such thing as a pension fund specifically for the NMI staff. Every member's pension funding and benefits on leaving the civil service and joining BMT had to be individually calculated from scratch. Losing all those for whom we could not guarantee a job, even though they were going back into the civil service pool, gave no joy at all. It was yet another of the repeated knocks these loyal people had suffered. The effect on the BSRA staff was not so severe and we managed to find, in the end, an all-round agreement on the conditions of employment for both.

The new board of BMT faced from the start the realization that it was costing £10 million a year to run the company, and the marine market was in a poorer state than it had ever been. As deputy chairman my fellow directors were now non-executive deputy chairman Geoff Fuller, who had been chairman of council of BSRA; Stewart Tennant of Harland & Wolff, my old apprentice colleague at Caledon shipyard in the 1940s (how the names keep recurring); and Willie Ferguson, a British Shipbuilders colleague from the Scott-Lithgow shipyard. Alan Rudge and Brian Smouha, already on the NMI board, continued with BMT. After I had retired in September 1986, and well before the end of the first five years of funding, the board realized that drastic measures would need to be taken. By this time I was not sorry that I had retired leaving David Goodrich as managing director. There would be few who could do what he did when the position became dire. I could not, I think, have done it. Because Paul Channon, Secretary of State by this time, was quite impervious to pleas for subsidy, the BMT board was faced with a very hard decision. To save about three-quarters of a million pounds a year, the Feltham facilities would be closed. Further, just twenty months after the launch of BMT and the inauguration of the remarkable new Number 4 Tank, the whole site was sold for development. The repercussions on the entire maritime research community can be imagined. The bulldozers moved in, and within a few months everything I knew as NMI had disappeared.

The value of the site ran into many millions of pounds and chairman Jack Birks rightly decreed that the funds so acquired must only be used as a cushion against times of adversity or for acquisitions, and not for operational assistance. From that start BMT has gone on to great strength but in rather different directions from the original BSRA and NMI businesses. It will always be an open question whether it was right to dispense with such valuable national assets. I do not think the Government in position at that time had much to be proud of. Nations such as Denmark, Holland and others with similar facilities have kept theirs. Since then I have often listened to consultants in the maritime businesses complain that BMT can quote lower competitive prices in the market place because of that generous and fortuitous start they had. Thinking of my own role in the setting up of BMT, I cannot say much.

As to the whole technological scene that prevailed over these years it was a sorry picture. I described it in a paper to the RINA in 1984 called 'Taking Stock – Marine Technology and UK Maritime Performance', and showed that in the UK we knew all about technical progress. Ships were vastly more efficient in carrying cargo, by an order of ten or so; and in saving fuel by at least 50 per cent. Structural savings were achieved; and cargo deadweight carried per crew member had increased ten-fold. Yet our seaborne trade was steadily moving into the holds of other nations' ships, our fleets were shrinking, our shipyards could no longer hold their very modest share of world tonnage, and marine engineering was reaching the point of extinction. Everybody accepted the picture I painted, but nobody could come up with a solution to the unhappy paradox of knowing what needed to be done, but being unable to do it. There was no combined front to be formed; third world countries took over; unfair shipping competition prevailed; and in the UK economics, industrial relations and above all the attitude of Government sealed the fate of our maritime industries.

As to myself and family, we had never been able to sell Redstacks at Tranwell Woods. We had struggled to keep it and its large garden in reasonable trim over the time we had been in Winchester. But when our own personal decision time came as to whether, on retirement, we continue to try to sell Redstacks and live on in Winchester, or revert to the North, it did not take long to resolve. We were able to sell the Winchester property before there was any need even to print a sales brochure. When the same Pickfords removal man discovered he was heading back to the same house he had helped us move out of so shortly before, he could not resist asking respectfully 'What's going on?' We fully intending rearranging our belongings around the house to break with the earlier traditions, but sure enough, everything just settled back as it had been before we left for the South. Two years earlier for my sixtieth birthday Elfrida had given me a box of oil paints and the appropriate gear – whether a recognition of some latent artistic talent, or a strong indication I should give up ships, I am not sure. When we left Redstacks for Winchester we had taken down a large wall-mirror leaving unfortunate holes in the beautiful bathroom tiling. A little polyfilla and a little of my sepia oils made perfect camouflage. When we returned to Redstacks we put the mirror back up again in the same holes – the only (futile) use of my oil paints so far.

Everything did not necessarily stop on retirement from BMT. In fact, nothing much changed as to the things that occupied me, except I lived on a pension instead of a salary. I would like to tell you about that in due course. Meantime I must move on to my shipowning experiences.

PART IV

Shipowning

CHAPTER 10

Blue Funnel

MY TIME AS A naval architect with the Blue Funnel Line of Liverpool is like the central layer of marzipan in the simnel cake Elfrida makes at Easter time – the best bit. The layers above and below – shipbuilding, and research and development – give a necessary body to the whole, but those twenty-five years with a famous shipowning company between 1953 and 1978 were, for me, the most satisfying.

There is a problem, however – which name to use for this company I joined when I left BSRA. Should I use Alfred Holt and Company, or the Blue Funnel Line, or Ocean Steam Ship Company? A little history is called for and here I draw heavily from *Blue Funnel* by F.E. Hyde which admirably describes these early days. Alfred Holt registered his company in 1865 as the Ocean Steam Ship Company. The Holt family were enterprising Liverpool merchants and were into cotton, banks and insurance companies. Alfred showed a very distinct bent towards engineering and was able to combine his natural talent in that direction with the enterprise and capital of his entrepreneurial family. He became involved in ships only after serving an apprenticeship with the Liverpool & Manchester Railway. He was a railway buff and spent all his spare time on the locomotives, but failing to find employment as a railway engineer he joined the shipping firm Lamport & Holt as a clerk. Sailing ships were giving place gradually to small steamships and it was amongst these latter that Alfred Holt, the engineer, now found his interest. He set up in business as a consulting engineer with help from his father, in No. 1 India Buildings. So started an association between the Holts and India Buildings which was to last well over one hundred years.

Alfred Holt continued to develop his ideas of marine engineering and ship design and in 1853 bought, jointly with his father, a small steamer called *Dumbarton Youth*. This was the first ship to carry the famous blue funnel. Then a second ship was laid down, the *Cleator*. This was to be the vessel that encouraged Holt to look away from the immediate shipping circle he was in, to what might happen if proper ambitious thought could be given to real long-distance routes. The existing trades to the West Indies and, indeed, according to Alfred and his brother Philip's judgement, all those this side of the Cape of Good Hope and Cape Horn were already pretty well occupied. Other ship operators did not believe the steamship could be made economic over new routes to the Pacific or India Ocean. Alfred and Philip did. Based on their experience with the little *Cleator*, the two brothers moved on to bigger things. They ordered the building of *Agamemnon*, *Ajax* and *Achilles* at Scott and Company, Greenock. It was with this working capital that the Ocean Steam Ship Company was created. On 19 April 1866 Captain Middleton, the first-choice master for all Holt's leading ships, sailed for China in the *Agamemnon*, and British shipping was about to enter the modern era. I do not need to describe in detail the astonishing developments thereafter. They are all described fully by F.E. Hyde. More recently, with just the right amount of detail and with great lucidity Malcolm Falkus has given us *The Blue Funnel Legend* which brings the history almost up to our own day. Again I have used it extensively. But what I wanted to explain was that here we have a company called the Ocean Steam Ship Company, which was to keep that name up to the 1960s, yet was far more commonly known as the Blue Funnel Line. It is by that name I find people most easily recognize the old company still. But in addition, it was actually managed by Alfred Holt & Company. The house-flag flown by the ships showed the letters AH (in a childish sort of logo). It is not surprising that the company was equally well known as Alfred Holt, or just Holts. And just to add variety, the local Merseyside dockside people referred to the ships as the 'China' boats even in my day, because of their many services to the Far East. The Ocean Steam Ship Company was to suffer a name change to Ocean Transport & Trading in the late 1960s, as the nature of the company changed and non-marine businesses were added. It was so named at the time I left. Latterly, it became the Ocean Group plc, to accommodate the even greater variety of businesses embraced, until sadly, the great name of Ocean finally disappeared on the recent merger with the National Freight Corporation. The new and mundane-sounding company, Exel, emerged. So it is difficult, in describing my part in these great affairs, to decide which of the evocative and illustrious titles to use. I settle in these chapters on my shipowning experiences for 'Blue Funnel', as did the authors Hyde and Falkus.

If I tried to identify some features that marked out the company I found on joining, I would say there was a remarkable sense of 'belonging' amongst the employees; loyalty to the company, even though the management must have been rather distant to some and especially the seafarers; respect for the flag and the company motto '*Certum pete finem*' – even though there seems to be no accepted translation of it. Reputedly derived from a passage in Horace's Epistles and interpreted by some pundits as 'seek a certain end', it just conveyed to us a sense of 'keep right on to the end of the road – but see you do your best on the way'. There was definitely a paternalistic attitude. There was even more definitely a demand for the highest standards of conduct – both business and personal. The lady superintendent Miss Milroy forbade mini-skirts and sleeveless blouses for years up to the 1960s, at the more personal level. At the business level the masters of the ships had to put down a deposit of several hundred pounds on taking up their command. They lost it if they incurred some casualty.

The line of leadership of the company had passed from Alfred Holt and his brother Philip to their nephews, Richard and Lawrence Holt. Richard had died in 1941, but Lawrence had retired just before I joined at the end of 1953. He called in to the naval architect's department occasionally. He seemed to have an affinity with the naval architect, Harry Flett, who was my boss. Few others shared any similar affinity. The first time I met this great 'Mr Lawrence' was when Flett brought him out of his private office to meet this new recruit – moreover one with Caledon shipyard connections. This registered with the old man who had a disconcerting tic in one eye which made me want to wink back. After commanding me to keep at all times my eyes on the horizon, with the flag flying at the top of the mast, he told me of some visit he made to Scotland in earlier days, I think to the Abernethy region. He had managed to absent himself from his tiresome family, and was found lying asleep in the pig-pen with his arms round one of the porkers. The point of the story was rather lost on me, but I could not help noticing his trousers which were exceptionally baggy at the knees, and his collar wings were doubled up under his tie. On future such occasions I was addressed as 'his Dundee boy', each time with exhortations re horizons and flags.

But that same figure had proved himself a remarkable leader, particularly during the war years, when he took a direct and personal interest in the welfare of his seafarers in the horrendous experiences when so many ships and men were lost or suffered severely. Typical of his resourcefulness and care was his suggestion to the naval staff in 1940 that merchant ships such as his should be armed with anti-aircraft weapons and that these be manned by a complement of trained men additional to the ships' crew. The idea was adopted and there grew an organization eventually having a peak strength of 13,000 men by 1944. This was a crucial element of support to the beleaguered seamen. Lawrence Holt was continually writing to and commending his officers and crews as they went through specific episodes of hardship and bravery and was enormously instrumental in maintaining morale. Perhaps today he is best remembered as one of the principal founders, together with Kurt Hahn of Gordonstoun School, of the Outward Bound Sea School at Aberdovey. Lawrence had been so affected by the incredible lifeboat voyages which had perforce to be endured after sinkings, that he resolved that there should be more formalized training of seagoing people. He had already set up his own company lifeboat training school in Birkenhead. As I myself had found, he unfortunately became a little unreal at the end. According to Falkus his parting instruction to Lindsay Alexander, one of the ascendant younger managers at the time of his retirement who later became chairman, was in the form 'Remember Britannia, and look after my flock.'

Sir John Hobhouse, a cousin of Lawrence, was senior partner in 1953. The company still used the title 'managers' for what others would call directors. One hundred years after Alfred Holt's initiatives and ventures, there were still similarities with the past. The Far East trades were still the main area of operations. The company was still not publicly quoted and had a tightly controlled list of shareholders. The managers of this empire numbered only seven. They sat in an open-plan arrangement on the seventh floor of the new India Buildings which had been built to succeed the earlier building in the inter-war years. It was a sort of elevated sanctuary called the 'quarter deck' and you mounted a completely unnecessary step to enter it. This instilled the appropriate reverence. The great men sat in pairs with their desks facing each other. The idea, I gather, was that the understudy would back up the senior at all times. It was to be some years before I even trod foot there, and a little longer before it was extended in due course to accommodate us directors of the subsidiary companies.

Sir John Hobhouse, a lofty and distant type compared with Lawrence, was seldom seen around, at least in the technical departments. I once had to take him round one of our new cargo liners in the Birkenhead docks. It was a brand-new ship just delivered from Caledon shipyard, and as an assistant naval architect, proud of the little part I had played in its design and building, I endeavoured to point out the novel features. Sir John was little interested. His eyes kept straying to the sheds and the cargoes they contained and what that represented in earnings. The last of the Holt name to hold a position at this level was George, a bachelor nephew of Lawrence, a kindly man, diffident and thoughtful, but not having the same authority as Sir John Nicholson who followed Hobhouse as senior partner in 1957. When Sir John Nicholson took over, we members of the staff, and the shipping world in general, knew that this was a man born to command. I have more to say of him later.

On leaving BSRA in London at the end of 1953 I yet again found friendship, and a place to live on Merseyside, because of my Brethren connections. A nice old chap in Ealing called Frank Devenish was manager of the Waitrose grocery store. He introduced George Dickson and me to Rose's lime juice and Carnation evaporated milk when such delights began to appear after wartime deprivations. He put me in touch with his nephew David Devenish in Birkenhead, and there I stayed for the first few months. David was a director of the Royal Insurance Company with whom Blue Funnel always had close links. There was invariably at least one Blue Funnel manager who was on the board of the 'Royal'. The unfortunate Devenish family had never known any one with such an amount of baggage as I had, especially books, plus a bicycle. Jack Shave, the drawing office boss at BSRA (also the demon bowler in our Hyde Park lunchtime frolics) was kind enough to loan me his car, an ancient Vauxhall, to get my stuff up to Merseyside, and Elfrida's brother Rob came with me. I had only recently passed my driving test and as yet did not own a car. We found the vehicle consumed as many fan-belts as gallons of petrol, and we spent a fair percentage of the time on our backs trying to replace these. When we arrived in Birkenhead I asked for directions from a young fellow in the street for the area of Tranmere Rovers' football ground, given to us as a landmark. His eyes lit up. 'Are you coming to join them?' said he eagerly. I have retained a slight affection for that outfit, struggling in the shadow of the great Merseyside teams.

I crossed the river to work each day on the Mersey ferry, where everybody walked round the top deck all the way across, rain or shine, always in the anti-clockwise direction. The river was full of ships, and the docks lining nine miles of riverfront were always busy. The passenger liners, Canadian Pacific *Empresses* and Cunard *Caronia* and the like, lay in the river alongside the landing stage. Nothing could equal the Blue Funnel cargo liners which seemed to dominate and convey an impression of quietly superior class. Everybody knew the overhead railway, an elevated light railway system which traversed the whole length of the docks from the Gladstone system at Seaforth in the north to Dingle in the south. Much used by the local dock labour, it gave a marvellously close-up view of marine ongoings since it ran close by the head of all the docks. Almost every dock was home to its own shipping line – Elder Dempster, Lamport & Holt, Booth, Furness Withy, Canadian Pacific – and all the rest. Blue Funnel, naturally, was based at the modern Gladstone Dock for cargo discharge, and across the river at Birkenhead for loading. Liverpool was just about at its peak of industrial activity. At the end of the quarter century that I worked there that bustling port had died and gloom had descended. I shall explain why, as we go along.

The new India Buildings, replacing the original where the company started, were opened in 1932, and with its Portland stone exterior and generous use of marble inside it was quite a notable Liverpool feature. The architect was Herbert J. Rowse, who had also designed the Mersey tunnel, the Liverpool Philharmonic Hall and Martin's Bank building. A lofty central arcade ran end-to-end on the ground floor. Blue Funnel were mainly concentrated on floors six, seven and eight. The seventh was where the managers sat with various supporting departments close by, such as the steamship department. This was really the operations side of the fleet's management – scheduling, routing, and so on. At the other end of the quarterdeck were the freight departments dealing with both inward cargoes and outward. Centrally placed on the seventh floor was the board room and outside stood the *Agamemnon*'s bell of 1866. The bell was struck once at noon by our sergeant from the Corps of Commissionaires to summon managers and heads of departments to the midday operations meeting. Here everyone had to stand and not sit, to signify that it was to be short and very business-like and all should return to their desks as quickly as possible. Various support services were on the sixth floor – personnel, accountants; and on the eighth floor where I was, there were the technical departments and the seagoing personnel department. This was all on one half of the building, the other corresponding half was occupied by the Elder Dempster shipping company with whom Blue Funnel had close links. The whole building had been severely damaged and largely burned out due to bombing in the 1941 blitz. Operations had to be moved to the home of Richard Holt during this emergency. But one mezzanine floor of India Buildings was first re-occupied, and eventually headquarters staff arrived back in the building in 1946. When I joined in 1953 the building was almost complete but it was not till 1958 that it was fully restored.

Blue Funnel always had strong technical departments. Alfred Holt was an engineer with great confidence in his abilities and took a very real interest in the technical aspects of his ships and their operation. It was reported of him that, not long before his death, he had said that when he died he would be able to say to his Maker 'These are my ships.' He appointed H.B. Wortley as his naval architect and, against the normal practice of the company where only close associates or family were favoured, he was later appointed a manager. Alfred Holt and Wortley were a progressive pair and they ensured that it was indeed possible for steamships to rival, and then take over the long-distance Far East trades from the sailing ships. There was one other naval architect who was only there a short time until Harry Flett, a dour and cautious Aberdonian, became naval architect. He was still in that position when I joined.

On applying for the assistant naval architect's job I was interviewed by Flett and William Dickie. The latter was a thrusting and ambitious North East Coast ship-repair manager who had caught the eye of Lawrence Holt during the intense post-war replacement programme. Dickie became a full manager – again an outsider entering the inner priesthood of the company. Falkus describes him thus: 'He held no university degree, spoke with a North East accent, and had served no time as assistant manager – and he had neither the training nor experience to hold much sway with Flett and the naval architects.' Flett himself had been there through the inter-war years and Falkus rightly labels him as 'ultra conservative'. I assume it was my background with Caledon shipyard that helped to get me the job. It certainly was not the fact that I had been at BSRA. These two cronies could not in any way understand or appreciate the work of a research association, both being practitioners of the most rudimentary sort and far removed from the researcher's world.

Dickie and Flett were a fearsome pair. They tended to operate together, Dickie leading, Flett backing up, and they terrorized the shipyards and ship-repair companies working for us – quite needlessly so. I had not actually confronted them in my Caledon days, but I certainly had heard of them. Not long after that, Dickie died and this left Flett exposed, fragile and edgy. He was sixty-three years old when I joined Blue Funnel. The company retiring age was sixty. Not long before that he had absented himself with a minimum of notice one Saturday morning. We still worked on Saturday. He was being married, after a life of bachelordom. What with his age and his lack of academic background, the loss of Dickie as his principal prop, and confronted by two supposedly well-qualified and ambitious young naval architects by the names of Wilson and Meek, he was cagey and suspicious. I was glad I had this naval architect colleague of my own age, Jim Wilson, who had joined a little before me. He too was a Glasgow graduate, and was from the Fairfield shipyard on the Clyde. Jim was a great companion, always ready to help or commiserate, and together we endured a few disheartening years. In spite of his age Harry would not on any account consider a successor, even though prompted by an over-respectful management to do so. Obviously Jim Wilson and I were in the running, but we knew we were being categorized by Flett as young, inexperienced and altogether unready for such an important position as naval architect to Alfred Holt & Company.

Ever since the days of Wortley, the naval architect of the company had been a very respected figure, more so than in other shipping companies. It was obvious from the way Lawrence Holt deferred to Flett that the respect was still there, but there did not seem to be any similar rapport between Flett and the current senior partner Sir John Hobhouse. However, Dickie was succeeded by Stewart MacTier (later Sir Stewart). His arrival in 1955 marked a turning point. He was distantly related to the Holt family, his mother being a Hobhouse, had been educated at Eton, and read mechanical sciences at Magdalene College, Cambridge. He had served initially with the Blue Funnel associated companies in Singapore, then with our London-based Glen Line. I remember very well my first meeting with him when he became manager in Liverpool with responsibilities for the technical departments. Enormously tall, he conveyed a friendly and understanding presence, totally at odds with all we had been accustomed to. He was to be sorely tried by Flett over the next years, but once I had taken over as chief naval architect, I enjoyed a happy and, I think, fruitful partnership with him until he retired in 1967.

The naval architects' department shared the negative atmosphere within the company at the time. We took a photograph of Harry Flett enjoying his daily after-lunch sleep and we used it in the creation of a spoof technical paper as if presented to a learned society, entitled 'Thrusting Ahead'. He sallied out from his inner sanctum perhaps once or twice a day to stand alongside Albert Redman, a senior draughtsman, for ten minutes at a time without saying a word. He caught Albert with an illicit ice cream in his hand on one occasion and it dripped away behind Albert's back for rather longer than the customary ten minutes that time. Albert was cussedness personified, and was never happy unless he was making things difficult for everybody. I remember him decreeing, with a malevolent smirk, that 'we shouldn't make it too easy for these blighters'. This was *à propos* of not adding extra and, as he judged, unnecessary access steps and footholds at the mast-tops where seamen had to climb to service the derrick blocks. These men's convenience and indeed their safety were of little account to Albert.

I thought of this as I re-read an article recently written by a seaman who had sailed on *Memnon* at about that time. In the magazine *Sea Breezes* he recalled how on one of his earliest voyages he graduated from 'peggy', the most menial drudge in the seaman's ranking, to junior ordinary seaman. The time came on the outward voyage when he had got over his days of seasickness and was able to help in the overhaul of the running gear. He records: 'This I thought, was the real thing, proper sailor's work and a vast improvement on washing dishes and scrubbing decks. It was, however, hard and dirty work with every mast-head block twice as heavy as needful and every hand-hold lug just out of reach or tucked away behind something.' Albert was clearly not minded to help him. He used to take a walk through the city in the afternoon when he felt like it. Jim Wilson maintained he was infatuated with the Mersey Tunnel and was to be seen visiting the entrance regularly, eating Fox's glacier mints as he went. There were one or two ladies in the department who did the drawing and tracing and any artistic design work. Chief was the long-serving Ida Kewish who employed dramatic actions and flowery phraseology. Except her swoon was real when, while playing idly with a stapling machine she accidentally sent one into her thumb. She obviously thought it had clenched into the closed condition, till Jim Wilson manfully flicked it out with his penknife.

In the 1950s the endless succession of Holts '*A*' class ships was being ground out. Falkus tells us that Sir John Nicholson called them 'work horses wrapped round the maximum single shaft diesel power obtainable in the later 40s and early 50s – we built so many not because of their excellence but to make up for war losses'. I shall describe the Blue Funnel ships in the next chapter, but that state of affairs suited Harry Flett just fine. With a management quite content to see a string of similar ships steadily entering the fleet, it meant he didn't need to change anything much at all, no nasty decisions to make, plenty of ship trials to attend where he was fêted as an eminence. 'Keep these young chaps in the office – they'd get out and about some day soon enough. If I need help on any modifications I'll get the shipyards to do the work. They'll be so desperate to keep us as customers they won't ask for payment.' Such was Harry's thinking. We were building at Caledon, Vickers Walker, Harland & Wolff and Cammell Laird, so any one of the yards was only too happy to help Harry make any decisions without the Holt management knowing, and then he could claim them as his own.

If I sound rather embittered it was because we could sense that the company had become stuck in a sort of atrophied rut. Flett was so scared in his old age, and the managers were so timorous of him, that anyone could see something had to change. That was why the arrival of Stewart MacTier was so important. Yet even he was apprehensive about offending his naval architect. We could see him call to see Flett about some matter, perhaps after lunch. Flett's doors to his sanctuary were unique in the building. Although glazed in the upper half, they were opaque up to a cunningly calculated height which prevented ordinary mortals seeing in. Stewart MacTier could, from his elevation, see over this line. When he discerned Flett asleep in his post-lunch pose, he, being a gentleman, could only shuffle his feet in the (vain) hope that the old boy would come to. We even saw MacTier arrive to discuss something or other uncomfortably close to the critical hour of 5.30 p.m. To our amazement, and also no doubt to MacTier's, Harry, after giving a few moments of his valuable time, would reach into his wardrobe, don his brown trilby, click the door shut and nod to his boss on the way out. He was not to be detained from his evening tryst at the bar on Exchange Street station before he joined his train to the eclectic dormitory town of Southport, there to fall into the arms of his new-found wife. When he eventually died on 2 July 1961 I had to take a few of his personal possessions out to his widow in Southport, whom of course I had never met. She turned out to be the nicest, most comfortable soul you could imagine.

The development of our ships had ossified. Other companies like P&O, Furness Withy, Union Castle and New Zealand Shipping were moving on. Even more crucially, so too was Ben Line of Edinburgh, our Scottish competitors on the East Coast berths of the UK. We had a virtual monopoly of the West Coast ports. And the Japanese NYK, Mitsui and OSK lines were forging ahead. While we should have been studying new methods of cargo handling and ways to cut down the time spent on the berth loading or discharging, Flett and Redman were discussing at great length, together with the head of the stewards and victualling department, the shape of the working tops in the galley, whether they should be square-edged or rounded to prevent plates sliding off when the ship rolled.

We knew that Flett's retirement and therefore the question of his succession was being discussed even in 1954, yet he was to hold on till 1961 when he died on his seventy-first birthday. As can be imagined these were trying years, and not just for Stewart MacTier. As some sort of consolation my notes show that I received a £50 rise in my salary to £825 in April 1954.

Stewart MacTier's colleagues in the management at that time need a mention, or at least the ones I had most dealings with. Under Sir John Nicholson as senior partner there were two managers more or less running equal in the line of succession. Such were dubbed 'crown princes', and these two had been introduced in 1953 with every expectancy of advancement. Lindsay Alexander had a brilliant academic career behind him, was sharp and concise and over the years I had great respect for him. He served in the Royal Engineers during World War II but was captured in North Africa and taken to Italy. At the Italian capitulation in 1943 he escaped and made his way through the Apennines to rejoin the Allies at Anzio. Outstanding success at Brasenose College, Oxford followed, and so into Blue Funnel as a picked specimen. He was not quite so fearsome as Sir John whom he succeeded as senior partner and chairman in due course.

Ronnie Swayne was different. He was a charming and friendly man but much less precise than Alexander. In fact he was known for his ingenuous and rather comic failings. Falkus tells us the stationmaster at Lime Street station kept a £10 note handy for those occasions when he arrived for his train to London breathless and penniless. I liked best the little story retold recently by Eric Proffit, a raconteur of standing, in the old boys' monthly newsletter, the *Nestorian*. Ronnie Swayne was in Japan and due to arrive by train, in Yokohama I think it was. The local Japanese agent was poised on the platform to welcome him having first drilled several of his staff to board immediately on arrival and make sure that brief-case, baggage, umbrella, overcoat and all personal gear had accompanied its owner off the train. Once the great man had disembarked and the doors closed the agent bowed low in welcome – to be confronted by the visitor's stockinged feet. The shoes had gone off with the train.

But Ronnie had been a commando during World War II. The official record of the daring raid on St Nazaire tells us how he distinguished himself during that epic in which the *Campbeltown*, loaded with explosives, was successfully crashed on to the great dry-dock gate. This dock was used as the Western base for the German capital warships. It was put out of action for the rest of the war. Ronnie, in charge of a commando unit, was on one of the supporting gun-boats but had been unable to reach the port and disembark because of the fierceness of the opposition that had by that time been generated. His own men and the RN personnel were so disappointed that, when forced to withdraw and finding themselves near a very much larger German warship in mist outside the port, they took it on. A fierce gun battle followed against hopeless odds. Eventually, with all his effective force, soldiers and sailors dead or wounded, Ronnie drew alongside and shouted up to the German captain what must be a classic declaration under such circumstances – 'I'm sorry, we can't go on'. He and all the remaining men were taken prisoner. After the war Ronnie kept in amicable touch with that German naval captain – which shows just what Ronnie was like. When I was building the large LNG ships *Nestor* and *Gastor* in the 1970s at Chantiers d'Atlantique at St Nazaire we used to visit the war memorial to the UK forces killed in the raid and note especially the name of one of Ronnie's men, Sgt Durrant, the first VC ever awarded to the army in a naval engagement.

In my day one or other of the managers was detailed to make the 'milk-run' to Oxford and Cambridge with a view to selecting likely candidates as future company managers. In this way two new names appeared, those of Kerry St Johnston and Julian Taylor, both to become full managers in due course and later, managing directors when the business became a publicly quoted company. I must say when these hand-picked products actually arrived in the company they were a source of curiosity and mild concern. No particular attempt was made to tell the staff who they were or why they were there. If Stewart MacTier had a fault it was a somewhat patronizing Eton and Magdalene air at times. In making passing reference to Kerry St Johnston's arrival he described him to me as being 'from a police family'. Kerry's uncle had been Chief of the Lancashire Constabulary. St Johnston found his role on the commercial side, and interestingly, both he and Sir Ronnie Swayne ended their careers as chairman of OCL, a company I shall be describing.

Julian Taylor, although holding no engineering qualification, was directed towards the technical side. He was to follow MacTier in due course. I first heard of him in 1957 when he was discovered by Bill Smith, one of my superintendents, on one particular ship being built in Vickers Walker shipyard on the Tyne. We had not been apprised of his arrival. The story was that he was found in one of the lower holds with his head in a bilge well. This was a precursor to a later occasion that features in Blue Funnel annals. Julian was making the formal and final inspection before hand-over of our first containership *Encounter Bay* in Hamburg. He came to the manhole leading to the highly inaccessible duct keel below the main holds. Naturally he decided to enter, to the considerable discomfiture of the whole retinue of both shipyard and owners' staff. There in the bowels of the bottom structure he faced an inscription erected by the German workmen – 'welcome to Mr Julian Taylor'. Julian always wanted to probe everything. I shall make more reference to him as we go along.

The other main technical department on the eighth floor of India

Buildings was marine engineering, quite large and incorporating many ex seagoing people. Because of the regressive nature of the naval architects during the post-war period, the engineering department tended to be regarded, and rightly, as more progressive. They certainly saw themselves as such and, because I was determined to move the naval architects on, there tended to be a bit of competition – and even, perhaps, a touch of the adversarial at times. Both when in shipbuilding and when in my research and development episode, I had become accustomed to the naval architect being the leader. He designs the ship and the marine engineers assist in their own area. In a shipping company where ship operation is involved, the engineers' role becomes more visible. A certain Commander Baker RN was chief superintendent engineer when I joined. He was something of an aberration in the long line of home-grown superintendents, and conveyed a laid-back 'senior service' attitude, different from the normal competent hustling kind of senior people usually found in the department. Under Baker, who did not occupy the position for very long, there were colleagues such as 'Tubby' Arnold, Willie Falconer, Bob Stevens and Bill Maguire with whom I would be collaborating for years to come. Further along the passage there was the technical estimating department where John Sullivan held sway, looking after the expenditure on repairs and maintenance. John was a handsome and keen sportsman and took his turn at umpiring at Wimbledon.

Chapter 11

The ships I found

BLUE FUNNEL ships were cargo liners. By this I mean they were not tramps, nor were they passenger ships although many, indeed most, did carry some passengers. In 1953 world-wide air travel had still to come and people used ships – either the major passenger liners or the combined cargo/passenger ships such as Blue Funnel, to get around the world. Many preferred the latter for the feeling of closeness to the sea and the mariners, and to avoid the mass passenger regimes of the great liners. The cargo liners offered frequent sailings and the scheduling of the cargo liner meant an assured arrival date. It was this scheduling that marked out the cargo liners – sailing on a carefully predicted date on a predetermined route, whether the ship was fully loaded or not. For years and years any one of the crack '*P*' class ships sailing to Japan, for example, would fulfil its three-month round trip with complete regularity. The masters tended to stay with one ship for a long time, and I remember Captain Desmond Stewart saying he looked forward to a break in his routine. He had not enjoyed a Christmas at home for many years, nor Easter, nor had he seen the daffodils and spring flowers in bloom. His ship's rigid schedule did not allow it.

Most of the cargo liners carried twelve passengers and the bigger '*P*' and '*H*' classes trading to Japan and Australia carried thirty-five. The mysterious limit of twelve was related to the requirement for a passenger ship to have a doctor on board if passengers exceeded that number. The limit of thirty-five was related to certain arcane regulations and expensive safety requirements that became mandatory above that number. In referring to ship's doctors I divert for a moment to speak from my present time of writing. I have just become reacquainted with 'The Blue Funnel Club'. This club was founded by a Professor E. Farquar Murray in 1927 in the North East of England, with its base in Newcastle upon Tyne, to bring and keep together the many doctors who had sailed in Blue Funnel ships. His words were: 'The memories, the good fellowship, the sense of the greatness of things enjoyed and appreciated by all those who had the good fortune to make trips as surgeons in the Blue Funnel Line made the formation of the club inevitable.' Although an honorary member of the club I had not been in touch with them for many years until, having met their secretary at the Alnwick Probus club, I was invited to attend the Annual Dinner in 2002 in Gateshead. It was a strange feeling. The ships have now all gone and the

Blue Funnel Line has gone. Yet here we were with a large model of an actual blue funnel on the table, flanked by ships' port and starboard sidelights, Alfred Holt flags everywhere, and a bell struck by the club chairman at each of his announcements. There are very few doctors now who have any experience or links with the former company, but the still flourishing club seems to provide a welcome meeting point for medical people in the North East, most of whom have at least an appreciation of the sea.

Tramp ships, as distinct from cargo liners, are an inferior breed. They are chartered, and having no regular route, must sail to whatever port is decreed. They are wanderers. They are usually less sophisticated as to machinery, equipment and accommodation and so are cheaper and simpler, often carrying just one kind of cargo. The cargo liner is expensive because it is able to handle many cargoes, whether bulk, liquids, heavy lifts or refrigerated, and its crew believe they are superior. In saying all this however, we are all aware that there are very few cargo liners sailing today. They have been superseded by the containership and I shall be describing how that happened shortly.

I remember a heated dialogue between Harry Flett and our nautical adviser Captain Elder, who was the senior master brought ashore to head office to act as adviser to the management. Unfortunately, Captain Elder had in his earlier days sailed on tramp ships. The subject under discussion was how to get one of our ships deep enough in the water to make a repositioning voyage safely in a ballasted condition. Ships do not steer properly or hold a course in a seaway if they do not have enough grip of the water. It was unusual for one of our ships to do a ballast voyage like this, because the closely scheduled voyage patterns invariably meant never being completely empty for any length of time. Although the door between Flett's sanctuary and our outer office was slammed shut, we could hear very well as everything was said at top decibels. Captain Elder was suggesting filling the aftermost hold with sea-water ballast up to the height of the propeller shaft tunnel and so get enough draught to cover the propeller. Unfortunately he avowed that was what he used to do quite safely in his tramp days. Flett went into overdrive. 'The only place for sea-water,' bawled Harry, 'is outside the ship'. Then the clincher – 'And we are not tramps!' Silently, we agreed with him – for once.

The story goes that the blue of the funnels was a piece of serendipity. The *Dumbarton Youth*, Alfred Holt's first ship, had some blue paint lying in the forecastle store. It was applied to the funnel during refit, and for almost 150 years thereafter that light blue funnel with a black top was to generate familiarity and respect. It is strange that because ships need a funnel for discharge of exhaust gases, the funnel has become a feature, almost *the* feature of the ship. A ship without a funnel would be immediately noticeable for its peculiarity. I have been quoted as saying a ship without a funnel is not a ship. It would be very odd if a motor car used its exhaust as its most noteworthy feature – although there is apparently now some kudos to be gained from having twin exhausts rather than just one, especially if the tips are chrome-plated.

Blue Funnel ships were famed not just for the colour but also the shape of the funnel. Until I committed the heresy of changing to a more modern streamlined shape on the *Priam* class in the 1960s, they were always tall, cylindrical if not round, and raked aft just a shade, an eighth of an inch per foot, to avoid the appearance of toppling forward. Jim Wilson and I supported, tentatively and fearfully, the suggestion that Harry Flett might make the change in the earlier class, the *Glenlyons*, but Harry was not going to risk his reputation. He would change nothing, so the ultimate sacrilege had to wait till he had gone. The *Nestor*, one of the famous oldies of the fleet, built in 1913 at Workman Clark in Belfast, boasted for many years the world's largest funnel. She was in fact also the longest ship ever built for Blue Funnel. The nearest to being a true passenger ship, she carried 350 first class passengers when she was built, although that was reduced by half by the 1930s.

One Blue Funnel ship actually lost her funnel. Falkus refers us to the *Phemius*, built in 1921, which was caught in a very severe hurricane in 1932 in the Caribbean Sea. He quotes the detailed log of the event describing the extreme conditions the ship had to face. The damage makes grim reading. On the first day of the hurricane, which lasted five days from 5 November, the funnel went overboard without anyone noticing, so bad were the conditions, and thereafter all power was lost. She was then caught in the hurricane centre where of course, there was a complete lull. What depressed everybody was the sheer weight of birds and insects swept into the eye of the storm that then overwhelmed the ship. It was impossible to avoid trampling on them. Once the expected hurricane force winds from the opposite direction had then passed over, the ship struggled clear completely helpless, and was towed eventually into Kingston Jamaica. In spite of the fact that Captain Evans had saved his ship by the strenuous efforts of every man on board and was roundly applauded for his courage, he was reprimanded by the company for having run his vessel into a hurricane. Lawrence Holt decreed that he forfeit his £200 deposit on the grounds that he failed to exercise due forethought and prudence, thereby bringing his ship into manifest hazard. Such was the Blue Funnel company I was finding my feet in.

Blue Funnel ships were built strong and were built to last. Just as examples of our ships' longevity, I take the two I have just mentioned. *Nestor* built in 1913, broken up at Faslane on the Clyde 1950. *Phemius* built 1921, sunk by U-boat in 1943. One was thirty-seven years old on scrapping, the other twenty-two before she was sunk. *Ulysses*, the sister ship of *Nestor*, was twenty-nine years old before she too was sunk by a U-boat. Alfred Holt's pride in the integrity and strength of his ships was retained by succeeding generations. Most ships, if properly built to do their job, will last about twenty years, and this is often accepted as the norm. Blue Funnel ships on average had much longer lives, but the problem then becomes one of ensuring that the commercial life in terms of required speed and cargo handling and maintenance costs equates to the physical life of the ship. I have been asked many times if it is possible to design ships for a shorter life so that they do not outlive their commercial life. It is not really possible. If the ship is to meet the forces of the sea it will, of necessity, be built to last something like twenty years.

So I cannot claim that every long-lived Blue Funnel ship was always the most economically successful. The sad fact is, and I shall come back to the subject later, the company had no particular method of measuring the success of individual ships. The simple approach used was to measure the freight earnings of each voyage and compare them with the outgoings. No attempt was made to take into account the wider picture and include the value of the ship, or indeed its terminal scrap value. Any idea of comparing the economics of one of our own company-designed ships against one bought second-hand from another company was never countenanced as far as I know. The extra margins of strength in our ships were commonly known as Holts' extras. Every incident that happened to a ship in service was carefully recorded and produced the appropriate modification not only to that ship but to all the following ones. For each new ship the Holt 'Specification,' a document notorious in the shipyards for its size and elaborate detail, was amended to incorporate every improvement; so much so, that in my day it was an awesome document many inches thick.

Structural steel was increased in thickness in strategic areas to reduce stress in the material, and to cater for corrosion over the ship's lifetime. More expensive hydraulic riveting, rather than pneumatic, was demanded at critical points such as the join of the centrecastle deck-house with the main hull. All fittings and fastenings on deck had to be extra secure. The maintenance procedures, chipping, painting, greasing, lubricating were rigidly enforced. The ships had to be navigated with utmost care. It was nice to think that all these requirements made the ships safer and last longer and they certainly instilled a pride throughout the fleet and the company. Whether they were economically justified no one ever knew.

Even though Alfred Holt had left the scene over forty years before I joined, it was obvious that his philosophy of self-reliance, both in technical and commercial affairs, still prevailed. Throughout all the departments there was an ingrained assumption that we were better than other shipping companies and that we should keep it that way. How much of this was derived from the knowledge that the fleet was not insured on the open market I would not guess, but I am sure it had a very real effect. Even though the operation of ships must always involve potentially higher risk than is found in many other industries, and even more so in the early days of the company, the decision had been taken away back in 1874 to move to self-insurance. This was a momentous resolution and clearly implied that every practice, whether in design, operation or maintenance, must be of a highest standard.

The masters and the officers were chosen from the best; the managers were punctilious in setting and checking standards whether in personnel or on the ships; the ships were built to a higher standard than Lloyd's A1. Having come to Liverpool with my experience of shipyards where the classification societies, and Lloyd's Register of Shipping in particular, are held in greatest esteem, I was amazed to find Blue Funnel had almost total disregard for Lloyd's Register. Not only did they scorn the prestigious 'A1 Class', but they employed the smaller society, the British Corporation, and that only for the statutory requirement of assigning freeboard and establishing the load line – that is, determining the maximum permissible loading of the ship and applying the Plimsoll line to the hull. When the British Corporation was absorbed into Lloyd's Register in the 1950s, our company took a jaundiced view of the merger.

You will therefore hardly be surprised if I say Alfred Holt himself was not in favour of Mr Plimsoll MP and his 'line'. He opposed the Merchant Shipping Acts of 1875–6 as a matter of principle. In the same way that he strenuously argued for freedom of conscience in his religious (Unitarian) beliefs, and in his political (Liberal) views, so he objected to being told how safely he should run his ships. *He* would decide. He referred to the 1875 legislation as a 'hasty and most arbitrary bill, drawn up and forced through Parliament to appease an outcry for *some* legislation!' The reason he objected so strongly was because the Acts were approving a *lower* margin of safety than he would allow for his own ships. Assuming, wrongly, that his fellow shipowners were as anxious as he was to have higher standards, he saw Plimsoll's activity as political humbug. We know very well now just how necessary the legislation was; and I have observed the very same scenarios enacted many times since, where some shipowners will always be prepared to cut corners for financial profit if they can get away with it.

There was a considered balance of cost to Alfred Holt in running his in-house insurance even though he had no very sophisticated approach to his figures. He became convinced that it was better to run safer and more expensive ships, and avoid accident and loss, than pay out insurance premiums. But it also meant the company had to build up large reserves and even go carefully in distributing dividends. It was a feature of the company nearly all through my own years with them, that they liked the assurance of having money in their pocket. That policy originally adopted by Alfred Holt was to cause much heart-searching when the times of high inflation came in the post-World War II years, and the sums of money held were huge. In 1961 the decision was made to abandon self-insurance, but it will be quite obvious that the original policy embodied the tradition of pride and perfection. On the other hand the permeation of the minimum risk philosophy through the staff could lead to a stultifying of new ideas, and an undue reluctance to take any risks at all. In the case of Harry Flett, this is exactly what happened to him and the naval architect's department.

It is difficult to say how many ships were in the fleet when I joined in 1953. With sixty or more on the books, with new ones steadily joining, sometimes several in a year, and with others being phased out, it would need too much effort now to establish the numbers at any one moment. Between 1947 and 1957 there were at least two ships delivered every year; in 1949 and 1950 eight new ships entered the Blue Funnel fleet. Between 1945 and 1950 the size of the fleet almost doubled (to 540,111 in gross tonnage terms) as the replacement programme gained impetus after the end of the war. It was possible to have five Blue Funnel ships lying stem to stern in Singapore, which was the hub of our Far East routes. It was a problem for me to learn the names, although the fact that the ships fell into classes did help. There was the very large '*A*' class I have already referred to – the 'work-horses', and there were various 'marks' of these. There were the four '*P*' class, the crack Far East ships; and the four '*H*' class on the Australian trade. There were the remaining Victory ships, wartime US-built, but doing excellent work; and the three *Ulysses* class purchased while being built for Silver Line. Not to mention my old friends from my Caledon apprenticeship days, *Telemachus*, *Rhexenor* and *Stentor*; and a little later *Nestor* and *Neleus*. But the same rigorous standards applied to them all whatever the origin, whatever the age.

It would be wrong to say all company-designed Blue Funnel cargo liners were the same, but they certainly followed a pattern – a conservative one. If I describe some of their features, it will help to explain the heavily entrenched opinions I came up against on joining. Alfred Holt and his naval architect Henry Bell Wortley, appointed in 1895, were instigators of progress, but after they went things gradually got stuck. Holt delivered a paper to the Institution of Civil Engineers in 1877, 'Review of the Progress of Steam Shipping during the Last Quarter of a Century'. It was a remarkable event because the paper itself occupies only ten pages of the Institution's transactions, yet the discussion takes 123 pages and ran over three separate evenings – such was the interest in ship developments at that time. He dealt with three main topics – screw propellers, the use of iron in shipbuilding in lieu of wood, and the development of the compound steam engine. I suppose Holt spoke to the Institution of Civil Engineers rather than to the Institution of Naval Architects, which had been founded in 1860, because of his civil engineering background. Wortley put that right in 1900 when he presented 'The Practical Results of Some Innovations in Modern Shipbuilding' to the INA. He too covered three main progressive steps – the spacing of ship side frames 3 feet apart, rather than the standard 25 to 27 inches, to economize on weight and cost; the use of widely spaced pillars to support the deck girders at something like 30 feet apart, instead of the customary forest of close-spaced pillars which severely impeded the stowage of the cargo; and the adoption of a cut-away stern frame instead of the usual forging or casting which completely framed the propeller, to create better propeller efficiency.

The average length of the ships at that time was passing through the 350–390 feet mark to 400–420 feet; the gross tonnage increasing from 5,000 to 7,000; the speed increasing from 11.5 to 12.5 knots; and the power moving up to 4,000 hp. Until 1892 the ships had a flush main deck with open rails, and the crew and passengers were in deck-houses. Thereafter, and with the arrival of the triple expansion steam engine replacing Holt's own version of the compound engine, the hull design incorporated the 'three islands' – a poop and a forecastle for crew, the centrecastle for passengers and special cargo. This was to be the configuration of the ships up to the time I was involved in the late 1950s – meaning nothing much else happened as to the layout of the hull, the holds and tween decks, or the cargo working gear. There were natural increases in size during that period. The '*P*' class and '*H*' class of the late 1940s, immediately post-World War II, were our 'big' ships, but their layout was just as conventional. The main difference was in their speed where there was a jump from 15.5 or 16 knots to 18, and this demonstrated that there had been more progress in the engine room than in the hull design. The big question by that time was whether to use steam or diesel machinery, a choice that involved long calculation of differences in weight of machinery and in the space required; also in differences of fuel consumption and cost, and in maintenance. My earliest such calculations were based on a fuel cost of five pounds per ton, an unbelievable figure seen from today's viewpoint, and it remained at that level till the early 1970s.

From my earliest acquaintance with ships I had learned how harshly seagoing people were treated. I suppose there is a historic British attitude to seafaring where the men (and only men) were expected to be hard and tough and inured to discomfort. But I did not expect to find on Blue Funnel ships that the seamen in an average cargo liner would each have only one half of a double cabin measuring 7.43 square metres (a space 10 ft x 8 ft) in size; or that they would have to share one hot-water tap between all the seamen; or that the doctor taking me round the top-of-the range '*P*' class ship in 1955 would admit that if he wanted to kill a man he would put him in the hospital. It was on the poop deck where vibration from the propeller was at its worst.

One of my successes was to achieve much better accommodation for both officers and crew. Together with Neville Ward, an interior designer and a most delightful colleague in the Faculty of Royal Designers for Industry (I shall describe my link with him later), I wrote a paper for the Royal Institution of Naval Architects in 1974. It described the new Blue Funnel approach to better accommodation. By that time we had transformed shipboard conditions and a crew member had almost five times as much space, in a single cabin, and it included a private bathroom. Shipping companies had largely removed crew spaces out of the forecastle by the time of World War II. They had moved crew out of the poop area by the 1960s (away from the propeller vibration), and concentrated both officers and crew somewhere either aft or amidships, but usually above wherever the engine room was sited. This was just one example of how we managed to break out of the ultra-conventional state of affairs I had found on joining Blue Funnel in 1953.

In those days our cargo liners were all of the same layout, with the goods stowed in traditional manner in large open holds. Dunnage, chocks and lashings were required to keep the stow safe in a seaway. Two tween decks provided 'platform space' for the lighter or smaller packages, again all chocked, tommed off and lashed against damage at sea. Cargo deep tanks were roughly amidships and adjacent to the engine room because of their weight when carrying palm oil, latex or other liquids. Cargo gear consisted of conventional electric winches and derricks, some at the masts, some on posts between hatch ends. The company recognized the value of efficient cargo handling and provided more gear than other lines did. All this complex stuffing of cargo into the ship and the securing of it was to disappear when we moved over to containerships in the 1960s. And none too soon, for the time a ship spent in port loading and discharging was becoming ridiculous. It was about half of the ship's year. Blue Funnel ships were somewhat better than others, but even they were more a kind of floating warehouse than efficient transportation vehicles. Something had to change to make shipping more profitable, but it was to be another ten years or more before it happened and I was to be closely involved. The container revolution was to break on the shipping scene like a wave, and wash away all the traditional practices. And there was to be a totally different kind of ship.

Chapter 12

The end of the old order

THE REST OF THE 1950s completed the wartime replacement programme. I have been critical of the lack of progress in ship design, but I have to admit that the primary requirement at that time was to procure enough ships to keep the company viable and growing. The cost of these ships is interesting. Falkus shows that the *'A'* class ships like *Agapenor* (1947) cost £675,000, rising to £1,247,000 for the *Lycaon* (1954). The next class of six were a kind of amended *'A'* class, sometimes called Mark VI. The *Diomed* (1956) cost £1,350,000. These figures do not mean much to us today such has been the change in the value of money, but at the time they were expensive ships of the highest quality. Much later, when I was discussing the possible building of LNG carriers with Vickers at Barrow, Len Redshaw the managing director showed me the combined profits made by Vickers on building all the Blue Funnel ships that had come from their Walker shipyard on the Tyne. The margin was almost nil over twenty years. It looked as if the shipyards were taking the orders for our ships just for the honour of building them, and to keep the workers employed. I think they would have confessed too that they were often over-optimistic and misguided at the time they took the orders, and in spite of the voluminous specifications we issued to them, they failed to appreciate the high standard that was being demanded by our company.

Mark VI of the *'A'* class were just a little longer than the previous ships, illustrating Flett's very careful incremental approach to any change. They were also a little faster at 16.5 knots compared with the 16 knots of the earlier *'A'* class. We were seeing here a trend in ship design that was to prevail right through to the 1970s, each successive class being faster and larger than the previous one. The trend was not limited to cargo liners, but was found in bulk carriers and tankers as well, although the increases with them were more in size than speed. 'The economies of size' was a catch-phrase of the time. Such trends all came to a rather brutal stop with the extreme world-wide rises in oil price in the 1970s.

What Flett had not realized was that by retaining the same beam as the earlier ships he was allowing the stability to get less. As ship after ship is repeated there is always a rise in the centre of gravity. The amount of cargo gear goes up with each successive design; there is better accommodation; there is more navigation equipment; the wheelhouse on the Mark VI was made of steel rather than teak. All these items are high up in the ships and above the centre of gravity. *Demodocus*, the first of the Mark VIs, 'fell over' when one of the cargo-oil deep tanks was being emptied. Not right over, of course, but enough to bring the ship's side up against the wharf. This is not at all desirable, and it provided a lesson. The sensible way to improve stability is to increase the beam, but Flett had a fixed idea that increasing the beam made the ship slower, and so he stuck to the same beam. The second paper I had published back in my days at BSRA and been so proud of was on this very subject, and disproved this theory. But young naval architects under Harry Flett had not much chance of being listened to.

The rolling delivery of ships moved on, always in multiple purchases. It was a feature of Blue Funnel that they preferred to purchase a class of ships rather than acquire units in ones or twos as others like Ben Line did. Next came the six '*M*' class with *Maron* costing £1,879,000 in 1960. The '*M*'s were a little longer, a little wider (Flett had by this time learned the lesson about beam) and had a little more cargo deadweight. A big decision in Flett's terms was to move the engine room a little further aft to give four holds forward of the engine room and two aft. This was to give extra cargo deep-tank space amidships.

I was despatched to the Caledon shipyard for a few weeks to oversee these structural changes. This was a pleasant experience on several counts. I stayed at my old home in Auchtermuchty where my mother and sister still lived and travelled over to Dundee each day. It was the first time I had been back to the shipyard where I had served my apprenticeship, and most of the old colleagues were still there. But now I was that most revered of all visitors, a shipowner's representative, and Blue Funnel at that. I qualified to have lunch in the directors' dining room. This was the ultimate recognition of status. Jimmy Gardner who had been so artificially rude about my starting there on my first day was now quietly attentive, to the point of being obsequious.

As to my domestic affairs during this time, after a few months staying with the Devenish family on arrival on Merseyside, I lived for the next four years in lodgings in the Aigburth area of Liverpool. My landladies were two unmarried sisters called Ada and Ethel Taylor who took in occasional tenants, and now gave me the run of the third-floor flat in their house. They belonged to the Brethren, attending one of the three assemblies in Liverpool at that time. As I might have expected they took an overly close interest in my doings. Ada, the older of the two, was crippled with sclerosis and had a curious apparatus hanging on her bedroom door which clattered every time the door was opened. It was some form of exercise frame. A doctor friend who stayed a short time with me pointed out that it was mounted upside down. Ethel was lame in one foot but was the more active. In addition she was deaf. Ada used sleeping pills. Things became a little difficult at times if I was late getting back at night and they had forgotten to leave the door unlatched. But they were kind-hearted souls and there were lots of young folk in the assemblies. This helped to ease the first few frustrating years of working for Harry Flett. Then I bought my first motor car, a second-hand fawn-coloured Ford Consul which gave a new dimension to my activities. The Miss Taylors shared in the experience, expecting to be taken around rather more than I would have wanted.

The company still worked on Saturday mornings but we were allowed to dress more casually on that day. On a December Saturday morning in 1955 I had a call from my sister in Auchtermuchty to ask me to get home quickly as father was very ill. He had been diagnosed as having stomach cancer some weeks before, and had suffered much over the previous months. In those days people did not run to the doctor so readily as we do now, and I think his cancer had been allowed to go on for too long. The fact that he had no pension other than the old-age state provision and a lifetime's saving meant he felt he had to continue to work on, though ill. He died on the Sunday at the age of seventy-one, his strong Christian faith demonstrably sustaining him to the end. His final words 'what a beautiful place', form the most effective evangelical sermon I know. The first such loss in a family always makes a mark. Father had been greatly respected in the town and everybody was very kind to us, starting with Jimmy Braid, the same cemetery keeper whom Max and I had relieved at holiday time and who had often assisted father. His words of comfort as he started to fill in the grave were typically terse but expressive – 'aye, that's your dad'. Mother continued on in the old home together with my sister who has always been the one who keeps together, not only her immediate family, but cousins and those even less close. Her letter-writing is immaculate and continuous, although she has conceded more recently that use of the telephone is sometimes easier.

My father had hoped to see his grandchildren before he died, but it was not to be. Max was enjoying a bachelor life in Glasgow; Martha showed no signs of matrimony; and I had only recently started to see Elfrida again. To avoid the attentions of my meddlesome landladies and other busybodies I used to drive to Ealing in West London on a Saturday afternoon after work, spend the evening with her there and return home thereafter. That was when it was essential that the Miss Taylors did not deadlock the door. We decided to get married in the autumn of 1956, but in a perverse way, the company had decided just then that both Jim Wilson and I should be sent abroad on specific trips in an effort to groom us for possibly succeeding Flett. Jim was given the US as his educational area, and I was given the Far East, and in addition, a run round our main European ports. We had actually fixed a wedding day but Elfrida was very clear in her reaction. She would not give up her job in London, move to the strange new world of Birkenhead where we had just bought a house, and where she would know nobody, and then be on her own for some months. So, to the consternation of Stewart MacTier and his manager colleagues who thought they were doing me proud, we postponed the wedding until March 1957. There was, at that time, some income tax advantage in choosing the end of the financial year, which soothed the turmoil a little.

My educational trip started in London in November 1956 and everywhere I went in the next few months, whether visiting technical or marine department superintendents, ship's officers, or directors of those great companies in the East who were our agents, I received a most gracious and helpful reception. Indeed, such was the novelty of having a visit from a slightly naïve naval architect from headquarters that it presented a welcome opportunity not only to educate, but also to vent some more general views regarding head office. It was altogether a very valuable experience. First, I was in London as the guest of Glen Line. This was our sister company based in the city, but having the customary presence and premises on the King George V Dock. Because they operated our ships from the East Coast ports (actually with red Glen funnels) and had more opposition from the likes of Ben Line of Edinburgh than Blue Funnel did on the West Coast, they were rather more interested in making the ships cargo-friendly than we were in Liverpool. They had more ideas about better protection of the cargo from the structure of the holds and tween decks, about easier and quicker ways of loading and discharging, and were more keenly aware of the attraction of ships with higher speed. All these features would soon be made real because Glen were to be the operators of the next class of cargo liners to be designed. In the middle of that visit George Smith, a very gentlemanly director of Glen Line, took Elfrida and me out to a rather special dinner in Soho. I think it was on the instructions of India Buildings, to make up for busting up our wedding arrangements.

Next stop was Amsterdam and I made my first aeroplane flight. I was in the care of our Dutch sister company, NSMO, who made sure I had fullest access to their offices and to the ships, to certain ships of other friendly shipowners, and to the major shipbuilding companies. These latter, NDSM at Amsterdam, Rotterdam Drydock and Wilton Fijenoord, were large companies and I had a feeling they were rather better run and more capable than I had seen in the UK. I was to learn a lot more about shipbuilding world-wide in the next few years. One rather special visit was to the national ship-testing establishment at Wageningen run by Professor Koning. I had read about it in the professional magazines and institution transactions, and had studied their work. It was the equivalent of NMI in UK which I have described earlier. Mr Rahusen, the boss of NSMO, decided he too would like to see it although he himself was not in any way a technically minded person. We had a very interesting time and were greatly impressed. On the way home to Amsterdam afterwards Mr Rahusen was ruminating on all he had seen and came up with his unsolicited and considered judgement: 'What we need in Blue Funnel,' he suggested, 'is not so much all of that high technology, but something a bit more practical, perhaps something lying between Wageningen – and Mr Flett.'

Next stop was Hamburg. I found it quite strange being here. It was only ten years since the end of World War II yet everything seemed quite normal. Nobody ever referred to wartime, and it was to be the same over all the years that I had dealings with German colleagues up to the late 1970s. I have no doubt we secretly wondered what each had been doing during the war and how much each had been involved, but no words were ever exchanged on the subject, no criticism, no blame or denunciation at any level – just a feeling that we were glad to be doing normal business. Again I had a chance to see other companies' ships. Our agents and superintendents clearly wanted me to understand that the rest of shipping was moving on and Blue Funnel had much to learn about modern ships. I remember in particular being taken over the *Lichtenfels* of Hansa Line, a vessel with heavy lift gear, and hearing all its novel features explained both by our own local superintendents as well as by the German officers.

Then back to London at the beginning of December to get ready for the Far East. It had always been the intention that I would sail out on one of our ships and rectify the greatest weakness in any naval architect's education namely, training and experience at sea. Naval architects just do not get to sea enough to find out what happens to their ships. The reason is quite simple. The designer of a motor car or any road vehicle, or of any aircraft or railway train only needs to spend a few hours, or a few days at most, seeing his product in use. But for any kind of deep-sea ship it is going to need at least several days of sailing between ports, or more likely weeks, in order to do the job properly. Few individuals or companies are prepared to accept that cost. However, it was indeed intended that I should have the experience of a long voyage, at least to Singapore, and probably further. It was not to be. Gamal Abdel Nasser, president of Egypt, decided to expropriate the Suez Canal in the autumn of 1956. Such was the ensuing state of tension that our ships had to be redirected round the Cape and it was decided that it would then take too long for me to go by sea. So it was to be a flight, and another opportunity for a naval architect to gain sea experience was lost.

I travelled first class in a BOAC Constellation, sitting right at the rear in a reclining leather-covered full-length seat rather like the backward-tilting one my dentist uses today. It was a beautiful propeller-driven aeroplane with flowing curves to its fuselage, four distinctive-sounding engines and triple rudders. There were only twenty-four passengers at take-off. Compared with today's jet travel, progress was leisurely. First stop Dusseldorf, then Istanbul, Basra and arrival at Karachi by the next afternoon. There we had a refresher stop at the BOAC Speedbird Hotel, then off to Delhi, Calcutta and Rangoon, with a final long hop to Hong Kong, arriving midday on the second day out. Kai Tak airport at Hong Kong was famed for its dangerous approach to landing. I had looked through the plane window as we descended and observed at much too close quarters the lines of washing strung from the windows of the enormous blocks of flats as we passed. A better airport was built shortly after with the runway extended out to sea, but it was still notorious for the difficult approach path from the landward side. The enormous, new and much safer airport only opened about the time of the hand-over of Hong Kong to the Chinese Government. At the time of my initial visit in 1956 there was occasional reference to that faraway date of 1997, when the colony would revert to China. Now it has happened, and Blue Funnel has long since gone.

I was met by our engineer superintendent Mat Gordon, a Fife man like myself. In years to come he would send me post-cards of Auchtermuchty and St Andrews from the most unlikely places. He kept a stock of them handy. Hong Kong was a very important base for Blue Funnel and Glen. We employed many Chinese seamen and they were recruited locally. These were Cantonese men and they had their own ships. We also employed Shanghai seamen. As there were ethnic differences between the two, they always sailed on different ships. Mat Gordon enjoyed going round the recruiting offices on Holt's Wharf which was the base for our empire in Kowloon, when the seamen's families came to draw their allotments – the contribution from the men's pay that was passed direct to the dependants. There Mat would tickle the chins of the little babies and have a word with everybody. Prior to the war in the Far East we had large holdings in Shanghai with wharves and godowns and other properties, but these were all lost to us and Hong Kong became our base. Mat had just taken delivery of a new locally built company launch called *Ares*, acquired for his own personal use in visiting ships as they lay in the harbour, or in crossing from Kowloon to Hong Kong Island. As a little formality we conducted a ship trial on *Ares* just to make sure it could do all it should, and that the 'Holt specification' had been met. Looking back to those days I admire the precociousness we exhibited in staying in the top hotels. I would be hesitant at using them nowadays, but then business visitors from UK, even beginners like myself, happily stayed at the Peninsula in Kowloon, or at Raffles in Singapore, or Four Seasons in Hamburg – and travelled first class in aeroplanes. Tighter budgeting and a steadily sinking exchange rate have fixed all that.

I kept a log of all my visits and travels so that I could do a report on return to UK. There was a lot going on in Hong Kong. I visited Taikoo Dockyard and some small shipyards and repair yards, and marvelled at the places where they built quite large junks with no plans at all. Lloyd's Register had to be visited and the Government surveyor's offices, as well as the offices of Jardine Mathieson, the powerful company who acted as agents for our Glen Line ships, and Butterfield and Swire who looked after Blue Funnel. And all the time our own ships were coming and going. I had to listen to a lot of advice and criticism when I went round them.

Some of the ships were getting on a bit. *Medon* was a Harland & Wolff ship built in 1942 to the order of the Ministry of War Transport, and so was a non-Blue Funnel designed ship. But although plain and ordinary she had some good features, like a low fuel consumption because of her unusual machinery. *Myrmidon*, which seemed to follow my eastern journeyings and was shortly to provide hospitality for my Christmas dinner in Kobe, was a wartime US-built Victory Ship and lasted until 1971. *Breconshire* was a Glen Line ship, one of a class that because of their speed and solid construction were much used in the more arduous wartime duties. Churchill referred to them with particular acclaim for their part in the Malta relief convoys. *Breconshire* had actually been converted into an escort aircraft carrier on her launch from Caledon shipyard in 1942, and reverted to us in 1946. *Gleniffer* was a 1943 US-built Liberty Ship. All these passed through Hong Kong in the few days I was there and I accompanied our superintendents as they organized and supervised an enormous amount of repair and maintenance work. Labour was cheap in Hong Kong and men *and* women were prepared to undertake harsh tasks like cargo deep-tank cleaning in the foulest conditions of darkness, heat and dust without demur.

Now I was off to Tokyo on Air India for my first look of many at Japan. Again I could not help thinking how short a time it had been since the war in the Far East ended. Although everybody was friendly, two features struck me. First, the inscrutability of the average Japanese compared with the European – you could not detect their real thinking. And secondly, the strange, unexpected enthusiasm for speaking about the atom bombs and their effect on the nation. There was a universal acceptance and affirmation that there must be no more war because of what had happened. But when I got to Nagasaki I was shown in greatest detail where the epicentre of the bomb-burst had been (incidentally, it missed the industrial and shipbuilding area) and they were really proud of the museum by now erected at the site. All the horrors of burned limbs, melted bottles and boiled concrete pavements were on display. On a later visit to Japan I saw Hiroshima, where the first atom bomb had been dropped, Nagasaki being the second, and everything was repeated there.

As far as our company and our ship operations were concerned, there was just a clear intent to do business, expand trade and develop good relations with Blue Funnel. So I was royally entertained on arrival at Yokohama by Mitsubishi Shipyard, Osano repair yard and Lloyd's Register. Next morning I was wakened by the shaking of the hotel, my first experience of an earth tremor. Then on to Kobe by train where I caught up with *Myrmidon* again and did the round of visits to our ships – *Maron*, *Glengarry* and the Japanese OSK Line's *Panama Maru*. These were busy days, full of interest, with everything new including the geisha parties, the sake, the silly games and the warmth of the charcoal fire under the table. On Christmas Eve I was taken to the Mitsui Shipyard club-house at Tamano and treated to a Christmas party in my honour. Although the festival meant nothing to the Japanese, they had very kindly laid on a Christmas tree of sorts, and a beautiful iced cake (it was made of sponge), not to mention the geishas. At the start they proposed I might like to 'speak to God like in England', so I said grace in a most unusual setting. And we ended by singing 'Auld Lang Syne'.

Back at Kobe for the evening of Christmas day I was right royally entertained to dinner on *Myrmidon* as she lay in the harbour – a typical jolly shipboard occasion. She was due to leave early on the morning of Boxing Day so I had to go ashore eventually for the night. As I left I was assured by Captain Duncan Mackintosh and his happy fellow officers that I need not worry, the ship would sail on time. I must have looked doubtful, but sure enough it had long gone by the time I looked out of my hotel window in the morning. As I enjoyed all this shipboard hospitality I did not know that I, a naval architect, would one day be responsible for the food and drink and for all the catering staff for all the ships in the fleet. That came with the wider responsibilities thrust upon me some time later as a director of Ocean Fleets.

By train and plane I arrived at Nagasaki far in the south. It was to be the first of many visits because this was the homeland of the mighty Mitsubishi shipbuilding company who would be the first builders in the Far East of Blue Funnel ships. Mixed in with visiting the shipyard, the ship experiment tank and the research centre, I toured the city, the atom bomb museum, the early Christian churches (Christianity first arrived in Japan in the Nagasaki area) and the home of Madame Butterfly. From nearby Shimonoseki (more Mitsubishi shipyards), I sailed on our *Eumaeus* back to Kobe through the Inland Sea, a trip of great beauty, and then flew back to Yokohama. For New Year, which did mean something in Japan compared with Christmas, I took myself off alone by train to the Nikko national park north of Tokyo. This was pioneering, with very few other non-Japanese about and not much English spoken in this rugged and beautiful area. Yet, on a walk to the local Keggin waterfalls three young Japanese men joined me of their own volition, speaking no English but apparently just wanting to be friendly. On the train back to Yokohama I was quietly passed from the seat behind a couple of the ubiquitous satsumas that most passengers were eating rather noisily, just another spontaneous gesture of friendship.

From Yokohama I sailed back to Hong Kong on *Perseus*, one of the four '*P*' class, the large ships carrying thirty-five passengers. We had two Captain Wilkes in the company, one was 'gentleman Wilkes', the other 'bastard Wilkes'. The former was master of *Perseus* and before we left Yokohama he helped me to buy a pair of very good binoculars for five pounds and I still have them. We called at Nagoya and then Kobe. Such short voyage legs and frequent ports illustrated to me how hectic the officers' job was at this stage. Cargo working was continuous the moment the ship arrived; the cargo gear had to be prepared before arrival and then stowed on sailing; hatches were continually being opened and closed; there were cargo and passenger agents to see to; ship stability to be checked; cargo stowage in the holds needing continuous supervision; repairs to be organized – and this was happening all the way outward from Malaysia to Hong Kong and Japan and then back again on the homeward voyage. It was no wonder that everybody was glad to depart homeward-bound from Penang, usually the last port of call, with only the open ocean and home before them.

I did the rounds on these voyages. I accompanied the master on his routine but rigorous inspections, which were a feature of Blue Funnel ships; I stood alongside the chief officer on the forecastle as we cast off to leave port; I accompanied the carpenter as he sounded round the tanks and bilges; I inspected the galley and store rooms with the chief steward; I listened to the doctor complain about his dispensary and the vibration in the hospital on the poop; I spent hours on the bridge talking with the officer of the watch; I did the rounds of the engine room with the engineer officers. It was excellent experience for a naval architect and I was very privileged. Back in Hong Kong after quite a stormy (and seasick) voyage, it was again a round of ship visiting, plus a two-day visit to the Portuguese colony of Macau where the most important feature by far was the casino. Then I flew Cathay Pacific to Singapore via Bangkok.

A first visit to Singapore must always be memorable – the heat and the smells of rubber and spice, and a feeling that this was *the* port in the East where Blue Funnel and Mansfields their agents were at their most visible. I did more ship visits, always on the receiving end of criticism or helpful suggestion. I sailed up the coast on *Agapenor* to Port Swettenham where we lay shackled to a buoy while working cargo, and I visited *Orestes*, one of the older vessels that generated rather more than the usual ironic comments from the ship's people. Then I examined the latex and palm-oil plants in the port. We carried regular and highly profitable quantities of these cargoes. A visit to nearby Kuala Lumpur was followed by a flight back to Singapore, and still more calls to *Glengyle* and *Charon*. It will be obvious by now that Blue Funnel ships were found throughout every port and sea lane of the Far East.

I sailed from Singapore to Fremantle, in West Australia, on *Charon*. This was one part of my expedition that was of more immediate interest because the company considered that *Charon* and her sister ship *Gorgon* needed to be replaced because of their age. These two Caledon-built ships ran a regular service between Fremantle and Singapore calling at ports in North West Australia. Their service was unusual because in addition to carrying cargo, they took passengers in both directions and also sheep on the northbound passage to Singapore. In season, on the southbound leg they carried cattle from ports in North West Australia to Fremantle. The proposal was to replace the two sisters, and it was hoped the trade could be handled by just one new ship.

I was asked to have a good look at these old stagers and their particular design while I was in the East. It was quite obvious that they had seen their best days. The conditions in the sheep and cattle decks were miserable for the animals, and the passenger accommodation was none too grand – although some cynical observers thought it good enough for Aussies. The sheep were carried in two tiers with those in the lower tier suffering most, and the ship structure in way of the urine-saturated pens was undoubtedly suspect. At the same time the Australian Government regulations for animal transport were being tightened up. There were two other unusual features about this service. At the North West Australian ports such as Broome and Derby where the cattle were loaded, the tidal range was very large. At low tide the ship actually sat on the sea bed while the cattle were rushed aboard – not a normal or desirable practice for any ship.

Charon did not call in there on my trip for she was fulfilling the other unusual service. At the beginning and end of the Australian Christmas school holidays the ship was taken over by school children. There were many Europeans in Singapore and Malaysia. They were usually quite wealthy, and West Australia, at almost 3,000 miles away, was the nearest country where there was schooling to the standard they sought. So when I sailed from Singapore at the end of the Christmas holiday in January 1957 I found myself accompanied by 140 self-confident, rumbustious and adventurous boarding-school youngsters going back to school. These particular voyages were just another aspect of this service that the imperturbable officers took in their stride. A book called *Schoolship Kids* by Juliet Ludbrook, who was one of these kids in the 1950s, describes in detail the kind of children who sailed and what went on. What I did not realize till I had looked at her book was that these youngsters were not to see their parents again for a whole year. The Christmas holiday was their long summer holiday and there was no question of an intermediate break.

There is an oft-repeated tale of one boy who was so anxious to make a clandestine visit to a certain cabin on the deck above that he climbed from his cabin porthole via the outside of the ship to enter the one on the higher deck. During an early morning walk round the deck I found two small boys busy with matches. They were carefully lighting them and trying to insert them into the vent pipes of the fuel oil tanks, no doubt hoping to see some spectacular fireworks. All that excitement has gone because now everybody flies, and indeed my particular experience of a 'school voyage' was getting near the end of that little bit of Blue Funnel history. It was all memorable for me, the trim little vessel with its officers in their summer whites, the dark blue of the ocean, flying fish ahead of the ship, Krakatoa Island and then Christmas Island in the distance, and eventually the beautiful golden beaches of the great continent. I stayed in Perth on arrival and had the usual few days looking around.

I was really rather spoiled, because not only did our agents in all these ports go out of their way to entertain and educate me, but in both Singapore and Perth I was able to make contact with Brethren of the same ilk as those at home. I was invited to their homes and I suppose it was not all that surprising to find links with people in UK. Indeed, a lady called Isla Abraham in Birkenhead who was to become one of Elfrida's closest friends on her arrival on Merseyside had her family in Perth and their home was just one I visited.

But I was soon flying back to Singapore for a final session – more ships, more shore installations, more discussions about the replacement for *Gorgon* and *Charon*, and a trip to Penang and the little shipyard at Butterworth. That was where I met our engineer superintendent Simms. He had been an officer on the *Phemius* when she lost her funnel in the hurricane. He had also been the first man across the causeway into Singapore after the Japanese surrendered in 1946, and on entering the former Mansfield's offices found his old clerk still sitting there as he had done when Simms was forced to leave four years earlier. Then in the middle of February 1957 I flew home, again on a Constellation, and at the captain's invitation sat in the co-pilot's seat while we crossed India. I had made four voyages; visited twenty-four Blue Funnel ships and twenty ships of other companies; also nineteen shipyards and various ports, installations and facilities – not a bad grounding for an aspiring practising naval architect. I was gratified that my report on my findings and recommendations was read by the four Blue Funnel managers most involved in new ships and they annotated it here and there. It even carried a favourable comment by Sir John Nicholson himself. I still have it.

The withdrawal symptoms that might have emerged on returning to work under Harry Flett after three months of interest and excitement were masked by the two weeks of preparation for our wedding which was now actually to happen. We had to get our house that we had already bought in Birkenhead in order. On 2 March 1957 Elfrida and I were married in Ealing at the registry office. Brethren did not have premises certified for weddings so our photos were taken in rather mundane surroundings. However, this was followed by a wedding breakfast at which there was naturally a conjunction of Scottish and Southern English friends. Then we had what would nowadays be termed a dedication service in the local school assembly hall. My brother Max was my best man. As a start to our honeymoon we spent two nights in Winchester, which led to a decision some twenty-seven years later to find a house there when I became managing director of the National Maritime Institute at Feltham. Then we flew from Eastleigh Airport to Jersey for a fortnight's stay. But what has always been a sadness to me was that we did not feel we could invite my mother and sister to the wedding. They had very sensibly severed with that brand of brethrenism a few years before because of the increasingly extremist and non-scriptural teachings that were being enforced, and so were effectively outlawed. I suppose Elfrida and I were reasonably content to carry on, having so many friends around us, but I think we would have confessed to doubts about the whole thing even at that stage.

It was, however, not to be too long before we too decided we had had enough of exclusive brethren. Their concept of 'separation from evil' led them to make impossible demands on families. Their condemnation of insurance of all types and eventually their imposition of a ban on belonging to professional bodies and institutions was too much and we bade farewell. It was not a happy time as we had to sever links with many good friends, but I think we would have done well had we quit earlier. For some years we attended a sort of residual assembly in Liverpool that was formed from quite a number of people in the same position as ourselves. Gradually however it too suffered losses due to folk getting old and others moving jobs until we closed down and joined Park Hall, a long-standing 'open' Brethren assembly in Birkenhead. This we attended until the move to the North East of England in 1979.

Our first home was a nice little detached house at Prenton on the outskirts of Birkenhead with the very pleasant Wirral countryside just beyond. Because we had to buy it and furnish it from our own resources we felt we should sell my much loved Ford Consul motor car and so economize. It seems strange now that until our daughter Hazel was born in 1960 we did without a car, a deprivation that is difficult to imagine today.

There were stirrings in Blue Funnel when Sir John Nicholson, now senior manager, Sir Stewart MacTier and other new blood began to work through the system. In 1957 it was still not a strong enough influence to unseat Harry Flett, but he was forced to face up to some proposals which were rather unwelcome to him. We were asked to study the purchase of a large passenger ship (one moreover with two funnels and so a novelty for the fleet). Our company had been engaged for many years in the pilgrim trade, carrying Muslim worshippers from Indonesia and South East Asia to Jeddah, the port serving Mecca. Between 1949 and the late 1960s one particular ship *Tyndareus* took over this duty from a number of smaller cargo liners which had been adapted to carry pilgrims. The trade really started about 1870 when the early Alfred Holt ships started to use the Suez Canal. Because they necessarily sailed past Jeddah on the Saudi Arabian coast, they were able to pick up this revenue-bearing live cargo to and from Malaysia and Indonesia. The pilgrims' accommodation needs were minimal since they were happy to travel in the bare tween decks. Up to 1,000 or more could be found space in a typical Blue Funnel vessel. Over any one year before World War I the total shipped might be about 5,000 plus 500 children. Although the fare might have been low by any normal standard, it represented a lifetime of saving for many of the pilgrims. It was only in the 1920s that permanent wash-places and lavatories were provided, as well as rice boilers. So the trade continued with ups and downs in the numbers carried and always with pressure from the authorities to improve the pilgrims' lot. In 1949 the company decided to use only *Tyndareus* as a full-time pilgrim carrier. She was a big ship in Holt terms and initially carried almost 2,000 souls. This was reduced gradually over the years as better conditions were demanded.

When it was suspected that the ageing *Tyndareus* might not easily get through her regulatory 1961 survey, there was a search for a replacement; and so the *Gunung Djati* was found although that was not her name at the time. I was despatched to see this ship along with Jim Wilson and a representative from each of the engineering, electrical, victualling and shipwright departments in 1958. She was lying off Tigh-na-Bruaich, a village on the Kyles of Bute in the West of Scotland. Her name was *Empire Orwell*, and she was a ship with a history. Built in Hamburg in 1936 as the passenger ship *Pretoria* for the Deutsche Ost Afrika Linie, she had spent the war as an accommodation ship at Hamburg. She had been taken as a war prize by the UK Government in 1945 and served as a troop carrier under the name *Empire Doon*. Boiler troubles soon emerged and she was laid up until she could be re-boilered in 1949. She then became *Empire Orwell* and sailed under the Orient Line for the Ministry of Transport. She had actually been chartered to carry pilgrims from Karachi when troop-carrying fell away, but never did so. Our party gave her a close examination because with a history like that, she was far removed from our type of ship. It was an eerie sensation to tread the echoing tween decks with their rows of close-spaced beds used by the troops and the vast empty kitchens. We each had ourselves locked in the padded cell in turn, just for the rather awful sensation.

Our conclusion was that with some expense she could be made into a dedicated pilgrim-carrier. So she was bought by Blue Funnel as she lay in these Scottish waters. Pilgrim requirements for comfort were still fairly minimal, so this made our job easier as to actual fitting out. But no ship, especially one so unusual at this, could simply merge into the Blue Funnel fleet. Her characteristics had to be examined in detail and her stability against flooding after damage was especially critical. Barclay Curle in Glasgow undertook the necessary conversion work and made her capable of carrying 2,000 pilgrims and 106 first class passengers. A notable feature was the mosque built into the accommodation spaces where a movable arrow was fitted to point in the direction of Mecca as the voyage progressed. I am not sure the officers were always as conscientious as they should have been in keeping the direction right. Naturally, a classic Blue Funnel name had been intended, that of *Dardanus*, but the company were persuaded by our Far East agents to switch to something more appealing to the travellers, and so the ship became the *Gunung Djati*, after a Javanese Islamic missionary. A painting of his tomb was hung in the first class saloon. Blue Funnel lost interest in this pilgrim trade after a few years and in 1962 after doing two voyages each year, *Gunung Djati* was sold to the Indonesian Government, still as a pilgrim ship.

Glen Line of London had been a wholly owned subsidiary of the Ocean Steamship Company since 1935, operating to and from the UK's East Coast ports. But whereas Blue Funnel carried something like 90 per cent of all cargoes on the West Coast, Glen Line carried only a quarter of East Coast cargoes. The whole question of new ships was becoming acute in the late 1950s with the end of the *'A'* class and *'M'* class deliveries. Glen Line were pressing hard for more modern ships in order to face up to their competitors. So we naval architects were challenged with producing a truly modern design to cover our Far East trades. It was to be called the *Troilus* class. Right away we had to undertake the customary comparison between steam machinery and diesel, and one of the vexatious unknowns was how much power to design into the reversing turbine of the steam version. In a diesel you reverse the engine rotation to go astern. You cannot do this with a steam turbine so you have to build on to the main turbines a reversing turbine, and that costs money depending on its size.

Nobody really knew how much reversing power, and so how big a reversing turbine, a steamship should have to make it stop in a reasonable time or distance. So the company made a bold decision to carry out trials to find out. I was put in charge of this project and sailed from Liverpool on *Helenus* in July 1957. She was in a loaded condition and en route for

Australia so it was a very serious decision to hold her up for a day. We did six long runs off Great Ormes Head on the North Wales coast using the Decca navigation system to measure the ship's position at any moment – one series at constant top speed and varying the reversing power, and a second series at constant reversing power but varying the ship's ahead speed. I was able to show that it was ahead speed that really mattered. At 19 knots it took nearly a mile to stop and took five minutes. At 16 knots it was just over half a mile. The actual reversing power did not matter very much at all; even doubling it meant only a few hundred feet less in distance to stop. The reason was simply that a ship propeller designed for efficient forward motion is of little effectiveness when going astern, however much power is put into it. We never needed to use these results because when we were well along the line with the design, a series of alarming political and military developments in Malaysia, Singapore and Indonesia caused a serious rethink. It was decided not to proceed with building even though we had taken options on shipbuilding berths and machinery items.

However, Glen Line persisted in arguments for new ships and Sir Herbert McDavid their chairman was consistently pushing for higher speed vessels. It was satisfying to us that by 1959 we were looking at 20 knot ships of at least 11,500 grt, and they were to be diesel-engined. The terms of reference given to us included the following:– speed to be sufficiently above the *Glenearn* class to make it possible for four ships to maintain a monthly schedule to the East instead of five existing ships, while providing the same cargo-carrying capacity; the design not to be circumscribed by too rigid an adherence to the company's past design practice; and the insurance of the ships, in common with all others in the fleet, was to be carried by the company. This was strong meat for Harry Flett, especially the reference to parting with previous practice. Nevertheless with Jim Wilson's and my carefully modulated encouragement, and a management anxious to see progressive movement, we did get some innovation – not yet leading the field, but at least catching up on what our competitors had been doing.

The advances included all-welded construction for the first time. Up till now Blue Funnel never quite trusted welded structures and insisted on a great deal of riveting. So much so, that at the join of the centrecastle to the main hull the pattern of riveting was recognized throughout the industry as beautiful and impressive, and a bit ridiculous. It had to be hydraulic riveting, since the normal pneumatic rivet hammers were not powerful enough for the size of the rivets. Shipyards were no longer willing to do this. We also got rid of the three-island 'poop-centrecastle-forecastle' design at long last, being greatly helped in arriving at a flush-deck design because from an early stage we were dealing with two shipyards in Holland, Van der Giessen of Krimpen an der Ijssel near Rotterdam, and NDSM in Amsterdam. They

Centaur – *MM's first ship takes to the water, 1962.*

were quite forceful in proposing the change from the traditional Blue Funnel three-island layout – much more so than the Fairfield Shipyard where we placed orders for the other two of the four ships in this *Glenlyon* class, as it was known. Harry Flett used to get us to prepare arguments for retaining the centrecastle, and we had to include his view that it provided greater structural strength; and that it provided better compartmentation in the event of fire, none of which was in the least convincing. So it was an achievement to arrive at the normal flush-deck configuration. In any case it gave us greater freeboard, and this was beneficial for these ships which were now, at 20 knots, much the fastest we had ever operated.

The placing of these two orders with Dutch shipyards was brave, because we knew rather little about European shipbuilding at that time, and at the back of the corporate Blue Funnel mind was the recollection of one of the few ships we had ever built overseas. That was a previous Glen ship, the *Glengarry*. She was being finished at the Burmeister and Wain Shipyard in Copenhagen when World War II started. In spite of frantic efforts to sail her at the last moment before Denmark was over-run, she was captured by the Germans and became a commerce raider called first *Meersberg* and later

Hansa. We managed to retrieve and recommission her in 1947 as *Glengarry*. That episode made the company demand war-risk insurance cover from the continental shipbuilders, and that naturally put them at some financial disadvantage against UK shipyards. I observed the astonishment of Peter van der Giessen, managing director of the shipyard, on being presented with this demand. He put it to Stewart MacTier, 'Do you really think there will be war again during this contract?' Nevertheless, it was a pleasure to be dealing with these two Dutch shipyards as they were always helpful and constructive, more so than Fairfields. Yet it was Fairfields, under the competent leadership of James Lenaghan, that produced the *Glenogle*, the first of the four to sail. That was just before the disappointing slide of that shipyard and so many others in UK into eventual oblivion. I suspect they made little or no profit from our two ships, but at least they avoided paying the late delivery penalties that became a regular source of irritation and argument with so many later UK-built ships.

Just before I became involved with these *Glenlyon* ships, Jim Wilson and I had gone through a particularly dismal period when in a sort of desperation we started to apply for jobs elsewhere. It looked as if Flett, now nearing seventy, was eternal. After one or two attempts elsewhere, we both applied for the technical manager's position at the Barclay Curle shipyard on the Clyde, which was advertised in the press. We both had interviews, but I withdrew at that stage because Stewart MacTier indicated just then that I should consider myself in the line of succession to Flett. It was not a wholly satisfying assurance at that stage and I am not sure whether MacTier knew about the Barclay Curle proposition or not, but Jim Wilson took the job and left Blue Funnel. However, in August 1960 I was indeed appointed deputy naval architect at a salary of £2,400, shortly to be increased by £150. On the strength of this Elfrida and I felt the moment had come when we should get back into car ownership and I bought a new Ford Consul, white with a green roof, for £841. In writing down these figures I do a little comparison on the lines – house purchase £4,000; salary £2,550; car £841. Just over forty years later, and using the equivalents of today, salaries and car prices have increased by about sixteen times, almost exactly the same for both. House prices have gone up by at least thirty times, or double that of cars or salaries.

That year, 1960, was eventful for us in yet another way because to our great joy our first of three daughters, Hazel, was born in July. We had had to wait a while for Hazel, but then these rather lonely days for Elfrida were immediately transformed. Thinking of those quiet long days, especially when I was beginning to go on business travels, there was one particular trial Elfrida and to a lesser extent I had, and it illustrates how maritime customs and practices were ingrained into people in Liverpool and the Merseyside area. About two miles away, at Dingle Jetty on the other side of the Mersey there was a fog-horn that was exceedingly tiresome to us. In foggy weather it sounded a double blast every nine seconds which was of course intended to warn and give direction to any shipping that might be around. Sometimes it sounded over many hours, day or night, and it was especially infuriating if the fog had already lifted where we were. Late one night I was so exasperated I managed to trace and ring up the operator who was actually in charge of the device and explained to him how trying it was, especially as the fog seemed to have lifted where I was in Prenton. He was helpful and explained how he was instructed to keep it switched on as long as the jetty nearby was obscured to him; but yes, it did look as if the fog was lifting and he would go out and take a proper look. Sure enough it was then switched off, but I could not help thinking what a casual approach this was to something that touched probably several hundred thousand people's lives. I suspect most days or nights that it was operating there was no shipping movement at all, or if there was, the ships would be perfectly able to navigate by radar.

By now Harry Flett was becoming really difficult. He absented himself frequently and if he told Stewart MacTier where he was going, he never told me. He was not keen on dealing with Dutchmen (or any other foreigner I suspect), so I ended up doing the negotiations with them, which I enjoyed. He let it be known that he would not be travelling anywhere by air. We had reached the stage of the general planning of the accommodation on the four ships and a visitation was made to us by both the Dutch shipyards and also Fairfields to discuss the layout. It was considered that Flett's proposal for the space allocated for crew cabins would not be enough to accommodate the length required for the beds. When Mr Groeneveld of NDSM asked how he proposed to reconcile the problem, Harry bellowed at him, 'Cut their legs off!' Groeneveld, a retiring gentleman, was naturally speechless, and Johnson the Fairfield representative started to gibber. But old Speksnejder of van der Giessen, a wily operator who had been around long enough to know shipowners' peculiarities, leaned forward and tapped Flett's knee. He clenched his other fist in front of Flett's face and confided in a low voice, 'Mr Flett, you are like my favver, strong!' Harry's face glowed with satisfaction at the compliment, and the crisis passed.

Now that I was the recognized deputy, Harry felt he should at least speak occasionally but there was never a normal sort of professional discussion. In the middle of 1961 he began to disappear for ever longer periods until I had a call from him, unusually, to say he was unwell. Two days later he rang again but was quite incoherent, and in another two days, on a Saturday, I was told by Stewart MacTier, that he had died that morning of septicaemia – on his seventy-first birthday. I have often wondered why the management kept him in the post for so long, but then I tell myself had he gone eleven years earlier at sixty like everyone else, I would certainly never have succeeded him. On the following Monday I was interviewed by Sir John Nicholson and Stewart MacTier and formally appointed as chief naval architect of Alfred Holt and Company. I had 'arrived', and with words from Sir John that remain with me, 'No naval architect of this company need ever doubt the confidence of the management placed in him.' Exactly thirty years later I met Sir John, long retired and now quite old, at the memorial service for Sir Ronnie Swayne. I confirmed, in answer to his query, that I was indeed now president of the Royal Institution of Naval Architects. He sniffed an aristocratic nose and announced to all around: 'I knew it.'

Chapter 13

Naval architect

To be a naval architect in a shipowning company was the plum professional job. Most major shipowners in the UK had technical staffs, but in the lesser ranks of shipping there would only be engineer superintendents and not naval architects. Such companies (including many 'tramp' companies) were content to order ships from the shipyards and let them control design with only a minimum of interference. Other companies would take more active interest, with the owners themselves becoming involved both in the initial design and with the building process. These often employed a naval architect, probably with a small staff. With all the weight of tradition and history behind Blue Funnel, their chief naval architect had a larger staff than most others and the company took intense interest in the design of its ships. This interest began long before the orders were placed so that by the time the shipbuilders were invited to tender for the new ships, they were presented with a fully worked-up design embodying all the features that had been tested and developed over the years. Hence the voluminous 'specification' that was dumped on the shipbuilders when they were asked to quote. The shipbuilder, however, still held the ultimate responsibility for structural integrity and for performance characteristics such as the speed, horsepower, stability and the like. He had to verify Blue Funnel's design.

The shipowner's naval architect had the responsibility, along with engineering colleagues, of ensuring that the company got the ships they wanted. Large sums of money were involved. The first ship I was wholly responsible for, *Centaur*, which was the outcome of my observations and discussions on my trip to Western Australia, cost just under £3 million and I was immensely proud that I was virtually handed that sum (probably equivalent to about £60 million today) and told to produce a ship. I shall be describing that ship shortly. Meantime I had to see the four *Glenlyon* class ships finished and into service.

It was so much easier now that I was in charge. I wrote a paper on the design and operation of these ships for the RINA in 1964 and reading it more recently again I see how reducing the stevedoring costs was predominant in our thinking, and was to become even more so in the next class of cargo liners, the *Priams*. Between 1950 and 1962, the year the *Glenlyons* entered service, costs of cargo handling on our ships had roughly doubled,

Flintshire, *one of the* Glenlyon *class, at Rotterdam, 1962: Elfrida, MM and George Smith of Glen Line lead out the launch party.*

and so too did the costs of crewing and victualling. The cost of fuel over that same period had actually gone down to the point where, even for these high-speed ships, fuel was half the cost of stevedoring, or even down to one-third in some ships. That state of affairs is difficult to comprehend from today's standpoint because the repercussions of the 1970s, when the world-wide cost of oil went up ten times over, were still to come; and they have remained with us ever since.

It was on these *Glenlyon* class ships that we introduced the heresy that heavy-loaded cargo-oil deep tanks might not be best placed in the middle of the ship. Convention said that the bending effect on the ship due to such concentrated loadings must be minimized for arriving at the most economic structure and so the tanks were normally situated in the middle of the ship. We felt that the need to reduce cargo handling costs meant that the best square spaces nearer amidships should be devoted to ordinary break-bulk cargoes, and not to tankage. Even though pushing the cargo-oil deep tanks, which were always more easily filled and emptied, towards the ends of the ship meant heavier ships' structure, we believed it was beneficial to the overall economics. This raised a lot of argument amongst technically minded friends; and we were to press this theory even further on the next class of ship by arranging the heavily concentrated oil tanks right at both ends of the ships.

Building the four *Glenlyons* at Glasgow, Krimpen an der Ijssel near Rotterdam, and Amsterdam meant incessant travel. We had our own superintendents in each yard but in ships of such novel design there were always things that needed to be discussed. Liverpool was not too well served by airlines so I had to use British Rail sleeping cars a lot for London and Glasgow. There was a minor air service running from Liverpool to both London and Glasgow called Starways, which was sometimes useful. At the London end it operated from a desk below the stairs of Heathrow Terminal 1. Its aircraft were the wartime DC3s, twin-engined with propellers, and a little tail wheel which meant that on boarding it was a climb up to the front seats from the rear door. On these flights in winter you scraped the ice off the windows to see out, and if the wind was contrary it wasn't much quicker than the train; but they were reputed to be very safe and strong aeroplanes. Soon we were to have another complicated ship in Glasgow, the *Centaur* at John Brown's shipyard, whose building overlapped the *Glenlyons* – but at least it was on the same river as Fairfields shipyard.

I began to build up my staff after the loss of Jim Wilson and the retirement of the obtuse Albert Redman. We were no longer dealing with Caledon shipyard at Dundee. Our ships were now too big for their berths. We had also finished meantime with Vickers Naval Yard at Walker and so we had to exercise much more control for we could no longer rely on companies familiar with our practices and demands. Ray Adams had joined in 1958 and comfortably took up the principal assistant naval architect's role. He has been a close friend ever since, moving to Newcastle to join me at British Shipbuilders when I left Blue Funnel twenty years later, then becoming my treasurer when I became president of the Royal Institution of Naval Architects. Other young men like Harry Goodwin and Bob Brown joined mainly from the shipyards. We did not train young people straight from school or university, a fact that was sometimes adversely commented on by the shipyards when we acquired their trained people.

Nearly all stayed with us for many years, such was the nature of the company where most staff expected to join for life, and I think also there was attraction in the naval architect's department itself where things were changing for the better. I must mention some of the girls too. Marie Quest, Pat Haynes, Irene Murphy, Phyllis Bowyer and others were in the department for years on end. They were all exceptionally loyal to the company and to my department, and incredibly versatile in their talents – drawing and printing up plans, keeping the records, researching facts and producing illustrations for our technical papers and publicity. Pat was a sailing girl and moved to our nautical adviser's department where charts and dividers became her tools. When Blue Funnel folded, Irene left to train and then take up a senior position in the social services. One who did not stay so long was a jolly girl called Jean Nugent who was, I suppose, a typical product of the early 1960s. She used to go to some subterranean dance hall, unfamiliar to me, in her lunchtime and come back bearing slight odours of disinfectant. The Beatles were not quite recognized world-wide at that time but it was the Cavern in its earliest days that Jean was frequenting.

I started to give occasional lectures on ship design, the first being to the Liverpool Port Employers. The discussion which followed was, I clearly remember, rumbustious and exciting. The Liverpool docker was enjoying his heyday in the driving seat of the port's activity – or rather inactivity, and a naval architect was fair game. So my days were crammed full and even more so when our second daughter Ursula arrived early in 1962. She surprised us with her bright red hair, apparently inherited from my father. By this time we had found many friends around us who helped Elfrida while I was away so much, and Grandma Cox was always ready to come up from Purley to lend a hand. As our work-load grew and we became involved in ever more modern ships I kept on increasing the staff until over the years they became a tight-knit and proud group of highly qualified technical people. In April 2001 I managed to locate eighteen of them and invited them to a nostalgic reunion dinner in London at the Caledonian Club. Everyone attended except for two who were abroad at the time. Some I had known for over forty years, and most had not seen each other for twenty years. It was a wonderful and memorable evening and reflected the spirit of Blue Funnel as we knew it. We repeat it now each year.

Glenogle from Fairfields, the first of the *Glenlyon* class, was delivered at the end of 1962 and was more or less on schedule – something that would prove rare in our later experiences with UK shipyards. We ran sea trials off the Arran measured mile in the Clyde and recorded a speed of 22.4 knots, away above that of any similar ship, albeit she was in the light ballast condition as is usual on shipbuilders' trials. She sailed on her maiden coastal voyage from the Clyde to Hamburg to start her first loading and that short voyage was the first occasion where I had my responsibilities tested in service. I had admired the way the Chinese crew, most of whom only came aboard the day before, quietly went round the ship, checking, securing, tightening everything. It was just as well, for we went north-about through the Pentland Firth and from the moment of exit from the Clyde we ran into very heavy weather. Because the ship was in ballast condition her movements were quite violent, rolling heavily up through the Minches, and pitching and heaving in the Pentland Firth in the teeth of an easterly gale. Speed had to be reduced drastically and at 6 knots we more or less drifted through the Firth on the tide.

What struck me was the motion of the ship when, on cresting each wave, she performed her head-down plunge in a series of springy or bouncy steps

Centaur at sea (reproduced by courtesy of John and Marion Clarkson).

each lasting a couple of seconds or so until she crashed into the wave trough and everything disappeared in the spray. The ship was actually 'springing', or 'whipping' as some call it, as the waves passed under her, something I never experienced again until we sailed our new containerships in 1969. Crossing the Australian Bight on the first voyage of the *Encounter Bay* I found the same effect, but there it was more understandable because the whole structure of the ship was different and much more flexible. Under these severe conditions on *Glenogle*, where my relatively inexperienced mind was prone to imagining all sorts of stresses and strains, I was comforted by the quiet and reassuring presence of Captain Bill Moore – a typical highly competent Blue Funnel master who wrote occasional articles on maritime affairs for the *Daily Telegraph* – except he did tell me much later that he himself was glad that Captain Elder our nautical adviser had also been aboard that night. It was on such occasions that one appreciated the steadfast talent of Blue Funnel engineers down below, keeping brand-new machinery running perfectly, knowing that if anything went wrong we would be in real trouble. By the time we reached the German coast all was calm and there was immense satisfaction in standing on the bridge while this fairly conventional-looking cargo liner wanted to, and did, overtake everything on the way up the Elbe to Hamburg.

Three of the ships were completed in 1962 and the fourth, *Glenfalloch*, early in 1964. We used the results from their trials, and then from their first voyages to provide information on horsepower and speed such as was lacking in current practice in naval architecture. I mentioned that in my years in research there was great interest in the prediction of ship speed and power from model tests, and this was still true because of the new ship forms we were producing. The hull form of these *Glenlyon* ships had been tested extensively at the Vickers St Albans experiment tank where my old friend from student days, David Moor was supremo. He was justifiably proud of the performance of these ships on their trials, but we needed data on what happened to speed and power after the ships entered service. So, following my personal determination always to make what we learned available to a wider public, we set about providing such information. Ray Adams enthusiastically ran a research project on the ships' performance, and the ships' people co-operated very helpfully. We published our results in my paper to the RINA. It showed for example that wind and weather at force 5 from ahead reduced the speed from 20.6 knots to 19.7. It may seem strange to us now that in the 1960s such elementary facts were unknown. We also found that on one early voyage of *Glenfalloch* paint failure on the underwater hull caused a drop in speed of almost 1 knot, which is a lot in shipping terms.

Centaur, the new ship that replaced the two sisters *Charon* and *Gorgon* on the Malaysia–Western Australian run has always been my pride. I was given the go-ahead to design it just after Harry Flett departed and I have often thought that if I had been asked to do this at a later stage in my career I would have hesitated because of the conflicting demands that had to be met. As it was, I started on it with all the confidence of a new boy, right in the middle of completing the four *Glenlyon* ships. The new ship's length was strictly limited by the berth space in the ports, as was the draught. There was no question of just doubling the size of the two existing ships which were being replaced, so we were pressed for space from the start. The requirement for 180–200 passengers at the same time as 5,000 sheep meant a sort of segregation was needed and so the passengers were placed aft and the animals in the tween decks forward. There were holds for cargo and some of it required refrigeration; and there had to be the ever-present deep tanks.

I went to Australia with Stewart MacTier to discuss the port arrangements and navigation at Fremantle and to call on Deputy Prime Minister (later Prime Minister) of Western Australia, Charles Court, at Perth. His daughter-in-law Margaret will still be a recognized name in tennis circles. He was taking a particular interest in the project because Western Australians regarded this Malaysian service as a very important commercial link between their relatively undeveloped part of Australia and the outer world. Mrs Court was to launch the ship eventually. As a geographical link Fremantle is

The RINA Annual Dinner, 1970: (left of table) Bob Brown, Jack Chapman, MM, Chengi Kuo, Jack Kershaw, (right of table) unknown, Ray Adams, Howard Wilson, Neville Ward.

closer to Singapore than to Sydney. Just how quiet and secluded Western Australia was at that time could be judged by the size of the telephone directory lying by my bed in the hotel. It was slimmer than the Liverpool directory but covered an area bigger than Europe. However, the West Australian economy was soon to take off, starting with the colossal iron ore project exporting from Mount Tom King to Japan. We also discussed the Government requirements, which were always evolving, for the carriage of animals. At the Melbourne offices of the Department of Agriculture we found that much more space per animal was being demanded than we expected and this made it difficult to accommodate enough of them to make the project economic. In addition they were firm in their requirements for water and feed. At every step we could see we were being faced with searching questions that affected our project's viability.

We had flown out to Australia on a Boeing 707, the very newest aeroplane, and one that was to become so familiar around the world. It still needed almost as many stops as I had on my way to Hong Kong in the Constellation. Coming back from Sydney we were in one of the first Comets to have been modified after the fatal disasters with these planes when metal fatigue caused three of them to break up in the air. MacTier was not one to use effusive language. As we took off for Heathrow on the last leg from Zurich the captain had announced 'we have few passengers, we have minimum fuel and the air is cold, so our take-off will be a little steeper than usual'. As we were tilted back forcefully, with the curtain dividing the cabin from the cockpit floating horizontally past our heads, he merely said 'Dear me, dear me!'

At home our own Ministry of Transport was being exceedingly tiresome. Passenger ships have always received special attention from the safety point of view and just at that time our great P&O, Cunard and Canadian Pacific liners were going out of fashion as air travel took over. The Ministry staff were clearly short of suitable ships on which to lavish their attentions, and our little 200-passenger ship became the target of almost obsessive examination. Much of the discussion centred on the stability of the ship if it were to be damaged in a collision, and some of the solutions adopted to satisfy the demanding scenarios were rather ridiculous – like demanding that a certain weight of animal fodder would be sited in a certain area of the tween decks for a certain duration of the voyage. There seemed to be the implication that if the cattle were hungrier than usual the ship would capsize.

I mention cattle, for we had to make the two-tiered sheep pens used on the northbound passage also suitable for 700 beasts carried southward from Derby or Broome in North Western Australia to Fremantle. The upper platforms in the sheep pens were made movable and were stowed under the deckhead when the cattle arrived. These animals had been driven down from the Kimberley Mountain areas and they were then corralled in a large pen a fair way from the quay until, when the ship arrived, they were induced into a race which led on to the quay. My vivid recollection is that the race was 2ft 9 in wide, just wide enough to take the largest animals but also small enough to prevent them, having once started to run, from turning round. That dimension applied to the passageways within the ship as well. The animals had seldom seen human beings before, and the time for loading them was rigidly fixed by the period that the tide was out and the ship was lying aground. It was an exciting exercise, hard on the ship, the men and the animals.

In addition to the sheep, which were past wool-bearing and were therefore bound for Malaysia and the curry pot, we often carried dairy cows. These were destined for the herds of wealthy landowners and demanded special treatment. The patient, accommodating and versatile Malay seamen milked them, and we had to design a dairy equipped with butter-making machinery to utilize the product. The menagerie was frequently augmented by a handful of racehorses, carried in stalls on deck, on their way to yet more wealthy Singaporeans. Not surprisingly, there was concern about the proximity of so many animals to the cruise passengers. We solved this by building large ventilation fans in the underdeck areas and leading the effluent to the top of the two masts, which were made specially large for the purpose. We carried out wind tunnel tests at NPL at Teddington to make sure it all worked. Some people said it didn't matter much anyway with Aussies as passengers.

The passenger cabins could not be as roomy as I would have liked because of overall space limitations, and this was where I valued greatly the expertise of Neville Ward of the interior designers Ward & Austen. Neville not only had a knack of getting maximum usage out of constrained spaces, but he had a remarkable ability to get the shipyards to co-operate with him. Normally, shipyards have a nicely developed contempt for interior designers whom they see as effeminate and troublesome, always failing to comprehend that the structure of the ship must have precedence over pretty interiors. Neville was invariably successful in showing that a well-designed dining room or crew cabin was perfectly compatible with a sound ship structure. A first in the building of cargo ships of that time was to persuade the shipyards to build one or two sample cabins as prototypes. This idea was wholly beneficial as it enabled us to iron out problems before full manufacture started. Ronnie Swayne, the manager in charge of the Australian trade, insisted that we incorporate the works of contemporary artists in the décor. One such was Sidney Nolan, somewhat before he became a recognized celebrity in the art world. It was unanimously agreed that the end result with *Centaur* was highly commendable operationally, aesthetically and financially.

Centaur was just a little late on her delivery date and sailed under Captain Glyn Williams from the John Brown shipyard at Clydebank to her home port of Liverpool in December 1963. Because she was one of the very few passenger ships around and because she was rather unique, a large troupe of journalists from both UK and Australia was on board for that overnight trip, and the carefully designed long bar in the lounge was heavily used. Late in the night it was found that one of the Australian hacks had disappeared. After frantic search by his colleagues and amid growing fears that the worst had happened, a faint tapping was heard in his empty cabin. Because of the tightness of space throughout the accommodation we had arranged that the bed folded back during the day to form a settee. On throwing himself on to the bed our semi-stupified reporter had failed to ensure that it was locked into position, and it had immediately tipped up to deposit him down the back of the settee seat into 'a bourn from which no traveller returns'. The furniture had to be smashed up to release him and thereafter the cabin stewards were put in sole charge of bedmaking.

I had come to know Captain Glyn Williams well because he was appointed early in *Centaur*'s building period and we collaborated closely over these two years. I had accompanied him to Derby to see where the ship would actually lie aground during the cattle-loading, and could not fail to be impressed by the wild and lonely North West coast of Australia. Nowadays both Derby and its sister port Broome are tourist resorts, the latter being much favoured by honeymooners. *Centaur* became a much-loved feature of the Australian shipping scene over the ensuing years, many passengers doing the three-week round trip to Singapore regularly year after year, some coming from as far away as Sydney. She continued to call at Derby until the sea bed started to subside and we had to build it up with sand and cement bags to avoid the ship being over-strained when aground. Eventually we could not keep up with the subsidence and had to relinquish the cattle-carrying service. *Centaur* maintained the Malaysian trade until it was given up in 1982. She was then chartered by Curnow Shipping for use on the rather exclusive UK–St Helena run where there was no air service. Curnow's previous ship, the *St Helena*, had been requisitioned for service in the Falklands war. *Centaur*, however, was not ideal for the service and was sold in 1985 to Chinese owners. Elfrida and I were in Hong Kong in 1992 when, as president, I was representing the Royal Institution of Naval Architects on a visit to China. From our bedroom window in the Excelsior Hotel I could see against the setting sun the familiar profile of *Centaur* far away on the horizon – still running after thirty years. I doubt if over these latter years as much care had been taken with her stability as we had been forced to take by our zealous Government officials.

My office was not wholly occupied with designing new ships and supervising and commissioning them. There were day-to-day tasks; interviewing masters and chief officers as they prepared to join their ships; helping on stability or loading problems; and increasingly I was serving on various national advisory committees. One of the earliest was a Board of Trade (as it then was) working group on Load Line Safety where I attended on Flett's behalf. He obviously could not understand the subject, and I am not sure I did either. I was happier with an early appointment to the BSRA Structures Committee. I have explained how BSRA ran its business through a series of committees of experts drawn from industry and it was very pleasing to be found amongst those I had recognized as the great and the wise when I worked for BSRA.

From all I see going on in business today it is clear that an employee's time and costs are carefully considered and must be evaluated in a way that never applied to me. I marvel now that I was able to attend committees and conferences over the whole of my working life with neither the time I devoted to them nor the travel costs ever being questioned. This covered not only committees directly concerned with my work with Blue Funnel, but also my interests with learned institutions, universities or other outside bodies. Blue Funnel were wholly persuaded as to the overall benefits and encouraged such interests, and indeed, still carried forward the traditions of the Holt family in their conception of civic duties. It was perhaps not surprising that later on I was quietly approached by Harry Chrimes, our manager most closely associated with community interests at the time, and asked if I would consider becoming a magistrate in the Liverpool courts. So I did, and found it a new and perplexing involvement in a city where the courts were already becoming busier than the docks. I only lasted a year or two in the job before I left Liverpool for Newcastle upon Tyne, and although I was invited to continue as a JP there, I felt I should concentrate first on my new appointment.

One of the most serious incidents among those I was daily involved in was a fire on our *Pyrrhus* in the Huskisson Docks in Liverpool on 12 November 1964. I had heard that she was in trouble during that afternoon so I went along to the dock. The ship presented an awesome sight, thick smoke billowing from the cargo hold just forward of the bridge and fire engines and hose lines everywhere. A hold full of rubber and other general cargo was furiously alight and that hold was not only partly under the accommodation, but up against the oil fuel tanks in the engine room. We all knew only too well what had happened in Gladstone Dock in 1952 when the Canadian Pacific passenger liner *Empress of Canada* had gone on fire. In the effort to extinguish the blaze so much water had been applied that the ship capsized and it took a year of expensive effort and grave dislocation to the port to get her lifted and removed.

The same fate was threatening *Pyrrhus*. A fireman's weapon is water, and several hours of blasting water into the ship had put an unknown quantity aboard, not all of it in the bottom of the hold but a lot into the tween decks as well. The ship flopped over slightly away from the quay at one stage, and then rolled back against the quay – all typical of a ship fire where water accumulates at various deck levels and causes unpredictable and sudden changes in the ship's stability. Because the ship was not in our usual berth at Gladstone Dock we lacked our normal facilities for co-ordinating operations and some rapid improvisations were needed. The dock master agreed with our marine superintendents that the level of water in the dock should be run down to make it less likely the ship would capsize. But that meant some of the other ships in the dock system had to be rushed out into the river. Efforts were made to burn holes in the ship's side to release the accumulated water in the tween decks but the presence of the water inside the ship made this impossible. It was one of those occasions when the whole might of Blue Funnel's organization stormed into action.

I found in Firemaster Taylor of the Liverpool fire brigade a strong character. He understood what might happen and throughout the early hours of the evening he helped me continuously with estimates of the water he had put and was putting aboard based on the number of nozzles, the time each had run, and the flow from each. With Harry Goodwin from my department quietly doing his calculations amid the mayhem in a little portakabin we had found on the dockside, we did a running estimate of the stability. Obviously a lot of it was assumption, particularly as to where the water actually was in the ship. The time came when I had to say to Firemaster Taylor that the position was becoming dangerous and capsize looked imminent. For a fireman to lose water is like taking a rifle from the infantryman, but he ordered pumping to stop. The fire took firmer hold and shortly afterwards the sides of the ship were glowing red hot as the hundreds of tons of cargo inside went up in flames again.

But Firemaster Taylor was not to be beaten. He decided to switch to foam instead of water. This would not be a great problem today, but in 1964 fire-fighting foam had only recently been developed, and it had to be emptied from five-gallon drums one by one into the fire engine pumps for mixing with water. For many hours and into the early morning, firemen pick-axed drum after drum until there was a pile of empties soaring high up the wall of the dockside shed. The organization was impressive. First the Liverpool brigade foam was used, then the stock from neighbouring Bootle and then other Lancashire brigades. Taylor told me that if that all went he would call on Cheshire supplies. By morning the whole ship, the dockside wharves, and the dock itself were white with foam, but the fire was under control. It took another twelve hours to extinguish it totally, but I was able to leave and get home at breakfast time. I had not realized the state I was in. Red-eyed and totally covered in soot as I was, Hazel and Ursula could not recognize me.

One particular memory sticks. During the time between shutting off the water and starting with the foam, Sir John Nicholson had arrived to see what was happening. He summoned me to accompany him to the roof of the shed overlooking the ship. As he viewed the dismal scene of one of his great ships belching smoke and flame he calmly said 'Well Meek, what are you going to do now?' I didn't know it was up to me to decide, although it was flattering to be asked. I could only murmur that we still hoped for the fire brigades to succeed with the foam. There was much heart-searching after that incident and our whole system for firefighting was overhauled. We never did discover what started the fire but the ship itself, although severely damaged in the areas near the fire in Number 3 hold, was repaired and sailed for several years after. Remarkably the structure that had glowed red-hot was not impaired at all.

That *Pyrrhus* fire experience meant that on a later occasion when I had to face another such event I was less shocked than I might have been. On 18

November 1987 I found myself staring at a similar blast of incandescent smoke pouring out of the booking-hall stairway leading down to the underground at Kings Cross station. Together with Elfrida, I had intended to go down these stairs. What sticks in my memory was the shape of the smoke plume. It shot up to the roof of the station in the same square shape as the stairway opening, such was the force behind it. A rail staff member was crouching by the stairwell shouting 'if there is anyone there lie down'. It was too late, for thirty-one people had died by then. I had just used the infamous underground escalator where the fire originated to reach the platform from the Piccadilly line and meet Elfrida off the Newcastle train arriving at 7.30 p.m. The escalator must have been in a dangerous condition by then. The train was ten minutes late. We had been due to go back down the same way to the Piccadilly line and it was during those ten vital minutes that it all happened. I try not to be impatient now if my train is late.

As soon as the *Glenlyons* were finished and into service and while we were wrestling with *Centaur*, the call came for a class of cargo liners for both the Blue Funnel and the Glen Line trades to the East. This was to be my opportunity to produce the finest ships we would create from current operating practice and technology. It also gave the opportunity to become involved with Japanese shipyards.

It was always difficult to know the thinking of our management about the cost of new ships. Of course they wanted the best ships possible, but obviously not at any price. It was about this time that the company decided to be somewhat more open with the staff and explain their policies. At one of these sessions on the subject of new ships, I made bold to ask Sir Stewart MacTier (he had received his knighthood by now) how the financial success of a ship was measured. He was quite flummoxed and, implying I was a bit simple, answered that the ship had to make a voyage profit, meaning on each voyage the freight earned had to be greater than the cost of operating the ship. I was never convinced about that simplistic answer because I felt that the cost of the ship should be justified in more precise terms. I always had a feeling that, although there was immense satisfaction in producing magnificent vessels to satisfy what were believed to be company requirements, some less sophisticated ship ordered off the peg from a shipyard, or purchased second-hand at lower price *might* be nearly as profitable.

This was heresy, of course, but I had consolation when certain authorities began to educate shipping people, towards the end of the 1960s, on the economics of shipping. Chief among these were Professor Richard Goss (a remarkable combination of seagoing officer, able economist and civil servant), Professor Harry Benford of Michigan and Dr Ian Buxton, latterly of Newcastle University. These authors showed that there was far more involved in arriving at the most economic ship design than a simple equation of earnings and costs, especially in cargo liner trades such as ours where one ship's earnings had an effect on the earnings of others of the fleet. Items such as the expected life of the ship, and scrap or second-hand sale value, needed to be taken into account; also the estimated distribution of revenues over the ship's life; similarly the distribution of operating costs, involving knowledge of the survey periods. I do not believe such calculations were made at the time the *Priam* class (as they were to be called) were ordered.

In fact at that time Blue Funnel were still clinging to the traditional concept of holding money in the bank and buying the ships as required. I recall Harry Chrimes, who was the manager in charge of the treasury at the time, shaking his head when I gave him my estimate of how much cash would be spent over each of the years of building the *Priams*. It involved estimating (or as it turned out, gambling on) the dates on which each instalment of the ship's price would become due. These were linked to recognized stages of building such as keel-laying, launch, delivery and so on. He was shaking his head because, on my calculations, he would not be paying out enough in each year to avoid, or reduce sufficiently, the impact of company taxation. At that time the thrusting Greek tycoons Onassis and Livanos and their ilk had been building up their huge tanker fleets using money from their banks.

The *Priams* were designed to replace the '*P*' class liners. Whatever means were being used to judge the profitability of our ships, it was perfectly obvious that they were spending too long in port loading and unloading. Reduction in cargo-handling costs had received special attention in the earlier *Glenlyon* class, and now the new class were to be designed with the following as the principal design criterion: 'all other requirements would take second place to those of economic stevedoring and strict care of the cargo.' As ever, speed was the other main criterion. It was to be a minimum of 20 knots, and in accordance with strict Blue Funnel tenets, this was to be no mere new-ship, calm sea-trial condition. Our interpretation of service speed was that it had to be achieved at full draught, in all but the worst weather, and over the normal life span of the ship. In practice this meant that the ships could maintain a 21 knot schedule at almost all times, and so were amongst the fastest afloat. Some of the other requirements were: the ship must accommodate enough fuel to sail from the bunkering point at Port Said, homeward to UK and then back to Aden (this meant over 1,000 tons of oil); cargo tanks must carry 1,000 tons of liquids, palm oil or latex or such, in thirteen tanks; the crew accommodation must be of a standard more than comparable with that in any other cargo ships, based on the belief that it constituted a man's (or woman's, before long) home, perhaps over a period of some years; and because repair and maintenance costs were plainly going to rise over the years, an appropriate degree of first cost must be allowed for to counter this escalating expenditure.

What had the greatest impact on the design was my positioning of the heavily loaded cargo tanks right at the ends of the ships in order to make the 'squarest' holds in the middle of the ships easy for stevedoring. For the same reason the engine room was pushed as far aft as space and the shape of the hull would allow. This meant higher stresses on the hull of the ship and so increased strength of the structure. These are fundamental matters that are always discussed in detail with the classification society and we had a hard time with Lloyd's Register of Shipping. They just seemed so sluggish in comprehending such basic innovation and it took rather too long to reach agreement on the eventual structural design. We received little help from the UK shipyards who had no particular expertise, or even much interest, in these matters. They left such cerebral calculations to Lloyd's Register. We did other things to make stevedoring more efficient such as adopting the latest cargo gear with a combination of cranes and derricks, and squaring off the sides of the main holds. We adopted a double hull so that all the usual obstructions – frames, brackets and ventilation trunking, were buried inside the wing tanks formed by the inner hull. A loss of space was naturally incurred, together with higher first cost of the ship due to increased steel material being used.

Another very radical change was to the outward appearance of the ships. Not only was the engine room moved much farther aft and therefore the whole accommodation block with it, but I replaced the tall cylindrical Alfred Holt funnel by a modern profile. There was no particular fuss from anyone about this major act of sacrilege. It just seemed as if the time for change had come.

There were two exigencies, however, that were to negate the success of this costly venture. Firstly, the UK shipyards' failure to deliver the ships on schedule created intense disappointment, and secondly, the container revolution was looming over these expensive conventional cargo liners which were about to become outdated long before they fulfilled their promise. When we invited tenders for building the *Priams* in early 1964 based on the design my team had been working on since late 1962, we received quotations from Europe as well as UK, but in addition we invited the main Japanese shipbuilders to quote. This was quite unorthodox because no one had built such ships in Japan even though there was increasing evidence that shipbuilding was a progressive, and aggressive, industry in that country. Equally significantly, the industry was viewed very sympathetically by their Government.

Blue Funnel had kept closely in touch with this development and our Far East agents reported favourably. Sir Stewart MacTier visited Japan at the end of 1963 and on his return provided impressive evidence in support of inviting them to tender. The prices submitted showed something of the order of £3 million for each ship from the UK yards and some 12–20 per cent lower from Japan. The managers had decided we needed four ships for Blue Funnel and another four for Glen Line, and the upshot was that two of the eight were entrusted to Mitsubishi's Nagasaki shipyard. Four ships were placed with Vickers Naval Yard at Walker on Tyne, who were anxious to renew links with us; and one with John Brown at Clydebank who, although they had found the going hard and the returns meagre with *Centaur*, were likewise keen to maintain the link. That left one still to find a home. I was with Sir Stewart MacTier when George Houlden, managing director of Vickers Walker Shipyard, took a deep breath, and thinking he was finding favour with Blue Funnel, decided much against his better judgement to take the final order. By doing so both he and Dr John Brown of John Brown's shipyard had sealed the fate of their respective yards. Although they both recognized and were familiar with the heavy demands of Blue Funnel they were wildly optimistic in their estimates both of the cost and the time needed to build the ships and suffered accordingly.

The efficiency of UK yards generally was going steadily downhill, and the improving Japanese performance could be seen in stark contrast. I have highlighted this state of affairs in my earlier chapters on shipbuilding and research and development. The UK shipyard managements were unwilling to pay any heed to what we told them was happening in the Far East. It would have been a golden, although belated, opportunity to learn from the Japanese, but such was the ineptitude and torpor in UK management that they lost the chance of learning and from then on it could only be an increasingly slippery downward slide for their shipyards. Not that the Japanese found it easy to satisfy our specification either. It only took them a few months to realize they could not meet their delivery dates and they came back to us to say so and arrange revised schedules, although that clearly incurred a loss of face on their part. We suspected they fain would have asked for an upward revision in the price as well, but they did not. What did happen was that in our approaches to them for later ships after the *Priams*, they were very cagey indeed and there were to be no further bargains available there.

Falkus points out that Mitsubishi at that time had an order book equal to the total British shipyard capacity. Our shipyards in UK, as well as demonstrating all the management failings I have already referred to, were too small and fragmented and had never had the investment needed to keep themselves up to date. The formation of British Shipbuilders in 1978 was meant to correct this but as I have shown earlier it dismally failed to do so. The dreadful lateness of delivery of the Vickers *Priam* class worsened as time

Priam *berthing at Miami, trying to be a containership.*

went on. The first of the five was seven and a half months late. The last was eleven and a half months late. We had repeated vexatious visits to both UK yards and especially to Vickers on the Tyne where the inability to improve output was palpable. At the launch of one of the five, Sir Leslie Rowan, the chairman of Vickers at the time (and who had been personal secretary to Sir Winston Churchill) publicly apologized to Blue Funnel for the slippage in the programme, calling it a 'stain on our escutcheon which would be removed'.

It never was. We watched their recently instituted planning department under a young graduate called Tony Smith, later to become a failed boss of Cammell Laird, endlessly revise their projections – always 'to the right', with never a glimmer of success in improving any single operation. Dick Rudkin, a younger, intelligent man took over from Houlden, but with no success. Our superintendents reported that he was never seen in the shipyard. He was replaced by Bill Richardson, an old hand from the Vickers Barrow shipyard, and there was some tightening up. But by this time it was too late. Blue Funnel naturally demanded the appropriate penalties for late deliveries. After much wrangling over details of schedules and cost over-runs, Sir Stewart MacTier agreed a final settlement; but when Sir John Nicholson heard the figure he was quite livid and demanded a re-opening of the negotiations. He felt we were being short-changed. I always admired the way Sir Stewart accepted what was a major rebuke from his senior partner and went back to Vickers to re-open the subject. In the end we recouped about one-half of the £4 million loss in earnings that the late deliveries incurred, although there was included a saving in depreciation charges as well.

Both the John Brown and the Vickers Walker shipyards went out of business shortly after, long before the rescue act of creating British Shipbuilders was complete. What was particularly galling was that, as we were taking delivery of the belated *Priam* class ships in 1967, we were well along the way to building the containerships which were to sound the death knell for all cargo liners, including the *Priams*. When I was operations director for our Barber Blue Sea Service later in the 1970s, I had the oversight of the *Priams* which were now on that service. They were carrying containers as best they could, some squeezed into the holds, some in ingenious stowages on deck, but nothing could hide the fact they were outdated in the container age, and so they went all too early to the second-hand market.

In the midst of these fraught years with constant visits to Glasgow, Newcastle and to Nagasaki, there had been developments on the home front. We were getting a bit crowded in our first little home, so we moved to a bigger house in Higher Bebington, still on the Wirral, and only a mile or so away. It was only part-built when we acquired it so we faced the joyless business of persuading recalcitrant builders to finish it – almost as bad as dealing with Vickers. In upper-class Stanley Avenue there were no house numbers so, out of affection for my earlier highland holiday haunts, we called it 'The Cairngorms' – but soon questioned the wisdom of this. It had to be spelt out so often to Merseyside shopkeepers. Shortly before this my brother Max who was working at the National Engineering Laboratory in East Kilbride married Elizabeth Birch, a charming and talented girl who also worked there. Her father, a very modest widower gentleman, was managing director of the Singer Sewing Machine factory in Clydebank. It was not to last much longer in business than that other major Clydebank establishment, the John Brown shipyard. Martha was still living with mother in Auchtermuchty. With a grandma in Fife and one in Purley we knew the roads (and the facilities) well both north and south, and especially appreciated the gradual opening of the motorways which were being built at that time. But now, in addition to work in hand, a new era of shipping was about to unfold.

CHAPTER 14

The first containerships

I HAVE EXPLAINED how in the 1960s the major shipping companies had begun to demand shorter turn-round times and better cargo-handling performance so that the ships could show better utilization. Whatever economic calculations were used by Blue Funnel, it was very obvious that the 50 to 60 per cent of the year spent at sea, although better than most other companies, was just not enough. In our Australian trades the 50 to 60 per cent figure applied not to the time at sea but to the time in port. These dismal figures were in part due to the malign influence of the dock labour force in UK, and even more so in Australia. So studies into improved systems were instituted and Dick Crake who was given a small staff and charged with the task of finding new ideas did his best to come up with solutions. Unfortunately he got it wrong by suggesting that containerizing of the cargoes was too difficult, or the trades were not suited to containers. His thinking, unsurprisingly, was governed by the proposition that containers would be used in our existing ships. It was not realized till a little later that the adoption of larger specialized ships carrying vastly more containers was to provide the answer. There were other proposals around such as using pallets, where cargoes were stacked on timber trays and formed into units, a sort of half-way house on the way to containers. Then there was the more radical proposal to use the roll-on roll-off system, where the vehicle carried the goods aboard. With the able and enthusiastic help of my department I endeavoured to give critical comment on all these proposals.

But in 1965 there was a rapid convergence of view amongst the major shipping companies that the only effective route to more economic sea transport was to adopt containers and find ships that would carry them efficiently. Sir Stewart MacTier had been asking me for advice about such ships during the year but there was not much to go on, since we had no containerships in UK. The only ones around were in US where both Sea-Land and Matson were operating ships mainly converted from cargo liners; and one small specialist containership called the *Kooringa* on the Australian coast. This latter was really the first purpose-built fully cellular container-ship and was something of an experiment – but a successful one. Falkus explains well how it began to look as if the US lines might make inroads into our trades. The very idea of such interlopers met with a robust determination amongst the UK companies that this must not happen. Sir

John Nicholson is generally regarded as being the instigator of discussions with Sir Donald Anderson of P&O who had been thinking on similar lines, namely that nothing other than dedicated containerships would suffice.

None of our UK companies could go alone into these realms because the ships were only the start of the exercise. New port facilities with expensive container cranes were needed, and the thousands of containers themselves had to be manufactured. Costs were far beyond the capabilities of any one company. Two other major companies, British and Commonwealth and Furness Withy were invited to join in. Together, these four controlled about two-thirds of cargo liner tonnage in UK and they set up Overseas Containers Limited (OCL) under the chairmanship of Sir Andrew Crichton of P&O in August 1965. It is interesting that in all of this enormous project the first step was the design and acquisition of the ships. The port and through-transport infrastructure which followed was to alter irrevocably the shape of shipping and the ports. OCL and its parent companies were determined to be the leaders. They set up a small headquarters staff formed from highly qualified members from the administrative, seagoing and technical departments of the four companies. These were to be the link between OCL and the parent companies. Major General Prior-Palmer (whose daughter Lucinda Green is perhaps even more famous in horsey circles) was managing director, and R.B. Monteath from British India (always known as Monty) was technical director. I found these two with their support staff, the principal ones being Harry Lunn and Howard Wilson, excellent people to work with. They carried their authority lightly, were never heavy-handed or demanding, and were always respectful of the technical staff of the companies they were working with.

But who amongst these four great companies was to be responsible for the ships? They all had professional qualified technical departments. P&O ran theirs as a separate consultancy company called Three Quays. Some independent marine design consultancies, such as the highly respected Burness Corlett, were also intensely interested in what was to be the most prestigious ship procurement exercise of modern times. It was decided by the principals (at that stage the four chairmen were closely involved in such matters and they came to be know as 'the grannies') that the design of the ships and their ordering should be in-house to the companies. P&O were already heavily occupied and the options became a straight choice between British and Commonwealth (who were also known by the alternative names of Cayzer Irvine, Clan Line and Union Castle) and Blue Funnel. I believe it was my success with *Centaur* whose entry to service was fresh in people's minds, together with Sir Stewart MacTier's authority and persuasive powers, that swung the decision towards us in Liverpool. We were appointed as designers and procurers in 1966. It was immensely satisfying – and a bit scary.

On the one hand we were facing so many unknowns. We did not know how big the ships should be, nor what speed they should have. We did not know how many ships would be needed because we did not know how much of the existing trades would go into containers. We did not know the size of the actual containers to go into the ships. And most importantly of all, no one at that time knew how to construct large ships where the uppermost strength deck was to be almost completely removed to allow containers to be dropped vertically into the cell guides within the ships. On the other hand, OCL were clear about their requirements. They simply wanted fully cellular containerships as near immediately as was possible, and they were prepared to meet the costs of acquiring them. No naval architect could have wanted a more challenging brief.

Some positioning was required. Ray Adams, my principal assistant, went to OCL for some months to provide a good information feed from them to us and vice versa. Both British and Commonwealth and Furness Withy showed great magnanimity, in spite of their disappointment at losing out on the design contract, by providing senior naval architects such as Jim Ross and Brian Bell to work alongside my staff. My whole department decided we would forget normal office hours and work as long into the evening as necessary and include weekends. I adopted my own design policies. Although what we were doing was novel we *must* get it right first time. For example, it would have been very difficult to live down any loss of containers overboard or indeed any major damage to them on these first ships. It would have knocked the credibility of the whole concept, not to speak of the reputation of the designers. So we made sure, for example, that the ships had good freeboard and that the likelihood of waves causing damage to the forward deck containers was minimized. Almost certainly we overdid the safety margins in several respects but I reckoned it was worth it and at every stage I made sure OCL understood what we were doing. In passing, I should explain that one rather crafty advantage the dedicated containership has is that about one-third of the containers can be carried on deck. Normally you have to build a ship to enclose all its cargo; but with the containership you only use enough steel to enclose the two-thirds of the cargo within the hull – very cost-effective.

My other personal policy was that if something did not work out in the end, I would never be accused of not consulting whatever recognizable source of information and assistance was available. This meant discussing not only with other shipping companies and in particular the US lines already involved, but also the US naval architecture companies who advised them. I visited both J.J. McMullen and J.J. Henry in New York and we fixed on the latter as our own advisers. Bill Dorman and Hank Karsch, who became good friends over the next few years, were solid thinkers on the special problems such as the twisting of the ship hull structure and the loading and fastening of the containers. Both of these companies moved into the World Trade Centre when it was built about that time. It is well recognized that these massive skyscrapers actually sway in strong winds, and using his containership experience Hank Karsch set out to determine how much the rectangular shape of each of the two blocks would not only deflect, but rack or twist in high winds. He wanted to be sure the lifts would not jam in their slides, and that he would get home in the evening. He never divulged what he found. I had my own ridiculous experience when visiting them in their new building. I only needed to descend one floor from a particular shipping company office to reach J.J. Henry's office – on the thirteenth floor, I think it was. With true Scottish thrift I thought I would just use the stairs, only to find I could not re-enter from the stairwell, which was, of course, only used as a fire escape. Against the discouraging reflection that I would have to descend thirteen flights of stairs, I used my trusty pocket penknife to pick the rather simple lock and regain entry.

Then we consulted the classification societies – Lloyd's Register as a matter of course, Germanischer Lloyd (who were far more progressive than our Lloyd's), and also Norske Veritas. Then there were my old friends at BSRA, with George Ward their expert on structures; and various universities, principal of which was Imperial College, London. Here we worked mainly with Dr Jack Chapman a distinguished researcher into structures whom I had first encountered when he was doing work for BSRA in earlier days. One quickly learned to intrude into Jack's thought process or into his discourses with utmost discretion. He gave short shrift to any loose thinking. In due course we were also to harness the energy and dynamism of the German shipyards.

Of all the trades operated by the four parent companies in OCL it was not difficult to decide on the Australian run for the first ships. That was where the greatest gain could be made in reducing time in port, we had the best rapport with managements and authorities, and we spoke (roughly) the same language. In addition P&O and Ocean were predominant in those areas. Even there, however, there were fundamental questions with no immediate answers. An example was wool, the great staple of Australian exports which had always been baled to a certain shape and size. The bales did not suit containers.

Naval architects nearly always have a 'basis ship' to design from. That is what happened with our *Glenlyon* class – they were based on the earlier '*P*' and '*H*' classes of cargo liner. The *Priams* used the *Glenlyons* as the 'basis ship'. Now we had no 'basis ship' that would give us a guide on structural steel weight, or cubic capacity, or propulsion power, or other fundamentals that a naval architect needs. All had to be worked up from scratch and this

General Prior-Palmer, David Moor and MM at the Vickers Experiment Tank, 1966: 'What is the General saying now?'

took time and a lot of careful calculation, and in the end a series of judgements. For the first time, however, we could design a ship with some precision once we knew, or thought we knew, the number of containers to be carried. Even that was a dicey figure because we depended on the OCL freight departments to decide how much of the total UK–Australia cargo might be carried in coming years by our P&O and Blue Funnel ships both outward and homeward, and then how much would actually go in containers. (In the end of course nearly everything did.) Then we had to make the really critical decision on how big the ships should be and so determine how many would be needed.

But to go back to the logic of ship size. For the first time in dry-cargo ship design the nature of the cargo was known exactly. It was simply a predetermined number of boxes of standard size. So by multiplying the number of container lengths, adding the clearances in the cell guides, the structure to support the cell guides and the size of the bulkheads between the holds we arrived at the length of the cargo spaces. The same principle applied to the breadth of the ship. The only problem then was we did not know what size the containers would be. People talked of 20-foot, 30-foot and 40-foot containers, and a 40-foot container is not the same length as two 20-foot containers stuck end to end. Nor was there any agreement on the manufacturing tolerances. Even worse there was no international agreement on the strength of containers, because the depth of the holds and so the depth of the ship depended on the number of loaded containers that could be stacked one on top of the other. However, under the intense pressure of the shipping lines, international standards for containers, both as to size and strength, were rapidly decided – at a conference in Moscow, of all places. The need to cater for 30-foot containers was thankfully dropped. By and large it was only British Rail who used them.

As to the vital draught dimension of the ships, we could never adopt the sort of draughts used by tankers or large bulk carriers even though we were tending towards much bigger ships. Container ports, where the ships have to lie alongside the quay under portal cranes which reach out over the ship, always have limited depth of water. For our ships the River Yarra at Melbourne posed one of the limits. We fixed on 30-foot as the design draught. But just to illustrate the thinking at the time when the whole concept of containerizing was in its infancy, I discussed in confidence with my team what would happen if container transportation did not 'take off'. Just in case, I built into the ship an ability to increase the draught to 35 foot to cover the remote possibility that the ships might have to serve in some other trade at some stage. We considered the most likely might be carrying grain.

For the studies into propulsion of the ships I went back to my old friend David Moor at the Vickers experiment tank at St Albans. Because we did not really know what speed we wanted we had to approach the calculation of the horsepower in a different way. We knew the speed had to be higher than any previous ships. We decided they should be steamships – remember this was before the oil shocks of the 1970s and steam turbines were still competitive. We decided to go for the maximum power that could be effectively transmitted by a single propeller, and this was judged to be 33,000 shp. Then we set out to extract the highest speed at that power for the likely size of the ships. It turned out to be a design speed of 22 knots. We paid particular attention to the shape of the ship at the forward sections so that the containers on deck would be protected from heavy seas as much as possible. The pronounced flare at the bow was based on aircraft carrier practice. I took General Prior-Palmer to see some of the tests at St Albans and together we watched the carriage repeatedly towing the model along the length of the tank at the different speeds. Amidst the conglomeration of probes, gauges, wiring and instrumentation there were two household scrubbing brushes mounted ahead of the wheels of the carriage, presumably to sweep clear any minor obstruction on the rails. Said the General *sotto voce*, 'It's the only bit I understand'.

By far our most severe hurdle was to design such a large ship with very little top deck. Because the whole cargo of containers was to be loaded vertically into the ship the hatches had to be as big as possible and we were faced with a critical decision on the minimum amount of actual steel deck that could safely be left in place to hold the ship together. This had never been studied before, but it did not take long for everybody to realize that the ship would now twist along its length as well as bend in the conventional way, under the influence of the waves – and that the stresses from these two influences were additive. When lecturing on this subject I liked to use an ordinary cardboard shoebox to illustrate the phenomenon. With the lid on, even if it was not a very tight fit, the box is reasonably stiff if it is twisted by hand at the ends. When the lid is removed the floppiness of the cardboard structure is immediately evident, and that is what happens to a containership structure. Then, just as in the original Comet aircraft where structural failure initiated at the corners of the windows, so the corners of our hatch openings became absolutely critical points of high stress. We had to find solutions as we went along – and fast. Once we had determined the arrangement and the sizes, or scantlings as naval architects call them, of the structural components, normal practice would be to seek corroboration from full-scale test trials. That was only to come later after the first ships had been completed. There are no prototype ships.

I give another example of the way I played safe in the midst of uncertainty. Containers have little strength other than in the vertical corner posts, so, when they are stacked on the deck where there are no cell guides to hold them, they tend to twist, or 'rack' as we call it, as the ship moves in a seaway. After massive calculations involving all sorts of assumptions about the behaviour of the ships at sea we designed a system for lashing the containers, not just to the deck, but vertically between the containers themselves, and diagonally to counter the racking stresses. We had to decide how much the ship would roll and how much she would pitch, and convert this into forces on the containers. After the ships had entered service and run for some time we found they did not pitch and roll to extremes at the same time. This meant we could eventually simplify and cheapen the whole system of lashings.

After the few hectic months of designing in the second half of 1966 (during which I had to visit Japan, US and Australia) the order for six ships was placed, five in Germany and one in the UK at the Fairfield shipyard on the Clyde – although the decision on the latter needed rather longer to decide and it became a political decision rather than a commercial one. The German companies Howaldtswerke, Deutsche Werft and Blohm and Voss, all of Hamburg, formed themselves into a consortium and were then on their way to an astounding shipbuilding success. This was in spite of a comic little episode when the representatives of these shipyards attended the Blue Funnel offices in Liverpool for the first time to discuss their tenders to build. We all stood in the boardroom, surreptitiously eyeing each other up under pretence of admiring the large painting of *Nestor* which was the centrepiece of the décor. Jack Scott, a devoted superintendent on my staff whom I had already marked down for these ships in Hamburg, could not contain his pride in his company and the fact that *Nestor* had outlasted World War II. He burst out, 'Aye, and the Jerries couldnae sink her.' Notwithstanding, he and all of us became good friends of these shipyards. Of course there were a good many teething problems to sort out during the building and then on the entry of these first-of-class ships into service, but the technical capability of the shipyard staff, the thoroughly Teutonic approach with an inflexible construction schedule, and the determined overcoming of many unforeseen obstacles during the building left everybody involved with a real glow of satisfaction.

But the experience of building *Jervis Bay*, the one UK ship placed, for largely political reasons, in a British shipyard, caused heartbreak from beginning to end. The shipyard virtually went bankrupt and then was subjected to a series of bizarre reorganizations, one of which came to be known as the Fairfield Experiment because of its new non-traditional shipbuilding management. The pea-brained nature of the chairman and his approach to running the shipyard could be seen in his diary where interviews would be arranged for times such as 10.12 a.m. A minute of his time was apparently more significant than a month's lateness in the delivery schedule of the ship. At one point early on the OCL principals considered trying to persuade Fairfields to withdraw from the contract, but this was not followed through, again mainly because of possible repercussions with Government. *Jervis Bay* was delivered over one year late in May 1970 and the shipyard accepted liability of almost one quarter of a million pounds for lateness. The German ships, starting with *Encounter Bay*, were delivered on schedule from March 1969 onwards.

As well as being the year when we had the excitement of designing the containerships, 1966 was a year full of incident for other reasons. The *Priam* class eventually began to emerge from the shipyards and I had to attend the acceptance trials, as well as be present at the launch ceremonies, including the two in Japan. We became so cross with the Vickers Walker shipyard and their distressing performance that for the last two ships we abandoned high-powered launch parties and gave the honour of naming them to our long-suffering superintendents in the shipyards, Jimmy Waite and Bob Kay. The first voyage of *Priam* from Newcastle to Liverpool to start loading was memorable. The passage through the Pentland Firth was the very antithesis of my earlier experience on *Glenogle*. It was done on a dead-calm night at full power. The only sound on the bridge was the steady quiet reporting of the frequent marks and lights as they came up. With the ship in the light ballast condition the sense of speed was exhilarating.

Amongst these cargo liner and containership involvements came a request for a study of chemical carriers. Blue Funnel had decided that we should diversify our activities further, and again found common ground with P&O. Their subsidiary, Trident Tankers, were our first partners and we found ourselves dashing from OCL in St Mary Axe where we would be discussing a nice simple clean cargo of containers, to Trident where we became immersed in the study of the rather nasty and dangerous products coming out of modern refineries. Blue Funnel had no experience in such trades but it was clear that there needed to be some outlet for Blue Funnel talents and expertise beyond what was required to operate the relatively few containerships. There was much activity with oil-related developments in the European areas of Rotterdam, Teesside and on the Thames, as well as in the major oil refinery areas elsewhere in the world. The appearance of ever more complex liquid chemicals needed special requirements for their carriage. This was all new to us naval architects and we had to do our homework. The ships themselves were to become very expensive with an exotic selection of coatings – epoxy paints, stainless steel and the like to contain the chemicals and oils, many of which were toxic or dangerous and called for special precautions. Things developed rapidly in those days and it was not long before Blue Funnel and P&O decided on a joint venture into these chemical tanker trades. A new company called Panocean Shipping & Trading was formed.

In the middle of all this Blue Funnel decided to formalize the links with our sister company, Elder Dempster, who shared the top floors of India Buildings with us. There had been a close relationship between our two companies since the 1930s but it was decided that now was the time to acquire the whole of the Elder Dempster holdings. Blue Funnel had already reached the momentous decision to seek a stock market quotation in 1965 and the nature of the company was to change irrevocably. The 'managers' became a board of directors with Sir John Nicholson as chairman. Sir Stewart MacTier, who was to retire soon, and Julian Taylor were my main contacts. The obvious successors as leaders were Ronnie Swayne and Lindsay Alexander with Kerry St Johnston and Richard Hobhouse forming the remainder of the board. The acquisition of Elder Dempster, whose trades were mainly to West Africa with subsidiary services to Burma, was the first major move in this new era.

Elder Dempster employed a competent technical department with George Hunter as their naval architect (a Glasgow University graduate, naturally) and Jack Kershaw as his principal assistant. It was obvious that a merger of

MM makes the farewell presentation to Sir Stewart MacTier on his retirement in 1967.

the departments was the sensible action and this was accomplished reasonably amicably in 1967 with George Hunter partnering Ray Adams as my deputies. The total number of ships in the combined fleets now stood at something like 120, and we had a whole series of new ships (and new names) to become familiar with. We found Elder Dempster included car transportation amongst their interests. A subsidiary called Seaway Car Transporters had a new ship being built at Grangemouth when we took over. She was a smallish vessel called *Carway*, entering service between Felixstowe and Scandinavia in 1967. The trade was to expand and in due course we looked after two more such ships which were delivered in 1970.

Blue Funnel now needed a new management system to cope not only with the enlarged fleet but with the new ventures that would come with diversifying into new shipping activities. So Ocean Fleets Limited was instituted and I became one of the directors. I was responsible for the new naval architect's and ship repair division. Although my naval architect's department remained on the eighth floor amongst the other technical departments, I now had my desk on the seventh floor on the quarter-deck – that hallowed area that had hitherto been the demesne of only the managers. I took tea from the beautiful silver tray that was provided on the side table, alongside Sir John Nicholson and his colleagues. When I let some surprise show on observing him at close quarters crouched on the floor by the open drawers of a filing cabinet, he assured me it was always best to do your own filing – then you knew where things were. There were many other intriguing features about this rather fearsome man. Because there was much rail travel between Liverpool and London, Sir John would work his way along whatever train he was on, spotting Blue Funnel staff and having a talk with each about their work and the particular visit being made. He was in the habit of bringing his own eggs if it was the breakfast train, and handing them to the restaurant-car chef for cooking. I heard a dreadful, but I think authentic, whisper just the other day, that the chef was not averse to throwing them straight out of the window, and then happily accepting the plaudits on how well the eggs had been done. On one occasion when I had been summoned to dine at his table, he complained to the conductor that the carriage was not running smoothly. It was explained to him that one particular bogie did indeed need attention and it would be reported, and apologies for the discomfort were proffered.

Blue Funnel had always taken great care of their ships, and repair and maintenance were important. We had our own extensive facilities in Birkenhead at Odyssey Works and they covered what was known as the shipwright's department, which included the boat shed for lifeboat repairs (now to be known as ship repair and come under my jurisdiction); as well as a large engineering workshop; the linen department where all furnishings and bedding and the like were handled; the stores and victualling department and the widely admired laboratories where our metallurgical and chemical problems were analysed. Unfortunately it was at the time when trade unions were at their most obdurate, and because Odyssey Works was almost a mini-shipyard, we had to endure our share of the frustration and acrimony that seemed to be synonymous with any conjunction of unions and shipyards.

I had very able lieutenants to run my new ship repair acquisition in Harry Wilson and Bill Smith. Both were ex-shipyard men who were highly successful in maintaining the standard of our own ships. But they had then to transform our business into a more commercial organization when the number of our ships reduced due to containerization, and we had to go for outside business to keep the place going. Their culture had to switch from one of sensibly keeping the work down on our own ships, to trying to boost it on third-party ships. The Transport and General Workers Union figured prominently in our affairs, and the name of general secretary Jack Jones was anathema. In a sort of conciliatory gesture Jack was invited to one of our launches about that time and our wives were there too. During the hour of pleasantries, Harry Wilson's wife Phyllis, somewhat flushed and buoyant, was introduced to Jack. When she realized who he was and having, presumably, heard her husband inveighing against him so often, she grimaced and clasped her fingers round his neck in a deadly grip. As Jack's face in turn flushed purple in what seemed to be his final moments I found myself in a quandary – whether to make some move on Phyllis, or just let things take their course. Fortunately the lady relented of her own volition and Jack survived to become in more recent times the principal advocate for decent treatment of old age pensioners. I think he was lucky to become one of them.

Because the Elder Dempster services were rather different from ours, I visited Ghana and Nigeria to see what happened at that end. Their trades had never had to face the sort of competition that Blue Funnel faced in the Far East and so the ships, all cargo liners, were slower and simpler in their outfit and equipment than ours. One of their staple cargoes was timber logs and that did little for the structure and the general well-being of the ships. Tema, close to Accra, was the major port in Ghana but we also called at Takoradi, and I visited both. The excesses of President Kwame Nkrumah who had just departed from the scene were very evident, in particular the ridiculous coffee-bean silos, built so grandiose in height that the beans at the bottom became crushed; and the famous concreted motorway that petered out in the bush only a mile or two out of town.

The state of both Ghana and Nigeria was depressing. The people had achieved their keenly sought independence but both countries were really going 'back to bush'. In Nigeria the Biafran insurrection had just concluded in an uneasy peace and there were a lot of restless armed soldiers around. At one of the road blocks that were still in position one of our local agents had his car examined and the soldier found great satisfaction in playing for some time with the child's toy train that he found in the car boot. When our man arrived home he was horrified to find the soldier's rifle still in the boot. I was taken up country on a day trip by our agent's company driver to visit the university at Ibadan. He made the bush that we drove through most interesting by giving me a running lecture on the growth and the animal life. But when it came to having a picnic lunch by the roadside, I was surprised and somehow disappointed to see him quietly and respectfully take his food box to a spot some way down the road, and we sat silently in our respective private lay-bys.

The many mouths of the Niger river were known to our ships as the Creeks and we had to call for cargoes at places like Sapele and Warri. This involved the most unusual and hazardous navigation procedures. I sailed on the *Deido* from Warri to Lagos and saw the famous bend where the bush vegetation pressed hard down to the water's edge and there were a series of large indents in a saw-tooth formation in the creek banks. It was recognized that the simplest and, indeed, often the only way to get round this bend was to let the ship gently impact the bank and then reverse away and take the next bite at the turn. The bush was generally benign in its texture and the ship only lost a bit of paint here and there.

As a finishing touch to the excitement of all these events, Elfrida and I, and Hazel and Ursula, had the joy of welcoming the birth of our third daughter, Angela, in 1966 and so we completed our household. Like Hazel and Ursula, she was born at home as Elfrida had firm views on hospitals and the desirability of keeping out of them, and so I was at least in the proximity and I suppose, fairly unhelpful at this latest arrival. By this time Hazel was at the local private school and Ursula was shortly to join her. We were not without family problems. Elfrida needed a tonsil removal operation in 1967 and when the mother of three youngsters is laid up everybody notices it. As ever, Grandma Cox was at hand. Then we had the disappointment of finding that Hazel at the age of seven had developed diabetes. Neither Elfrida nor I had any family history of diabetes but it is now accepted that children sometimes develop it after having some other illness. This is what seemed to happen after Hazel had been unwell with flu. We had the unhappy job of learning to do injections, and also of encouraging her to practise her own injections by piercing an orange with the needle. Being a determined little girl she got on with it and was soon doing her own injections, as she has done ever since. She has proved that once diagnosed, in balance with insulin, and with sound health care, diabetics can lead normal lives. She has been remarkably healthy ever since, now married and mother of two of our grandchildren.

Chapter 15

Bigger containerships

We were now approaching the point where the move into containers for the Blue Funnel trades would be decided, and we were all poised for it. There was a general acceptance that, after the short spell of doubt whether the container concept would take off and the building of ships be feasible, the whole enterprise was indeed successfully underway. 1969 was to be the portentous year when we would decide to have our own OCL ships carrying Blue Funnel (and other companies') cargoes and manned by our seamen. The six *Encounter Bay* class ships were already destined for the Australian trade and, although we designed them, P&O were entrusted with their operation. They formed a new company called Container Fleets Limited to run the ships under the direction of Michael Penny, with Captain Paul Ogden as the marine operations manager and Stan Mole as the technical manager. The officers and crew were mainly from P&O and associated companies. In the designing and building of the ships Blue Funnel worked closely with Container Fleets until, on delivery, we handed them over. Not that we were finished with the ships – far from it, because with so many novel features it was not surprising that there were problems to sort out after they began to enter service in 1969.

First off to Australia was the *Encounter Bay* from Howaldtswerke shipyard in Hamburg in February 1969, by which time the thousands of containers had been manufactured, the berths at Tilbury and in Australia with their brand-new lofty portal container cranes had been constructed, the straddle carriers and all the gear to handle the containers around the terminals and the land transportation systems linking with the shipping sector of this new through-transport concept were ready – all of it in just over two years. The darkest blot on the whole exercise was the failure of Fairfields shipyard to build the one British ship of the six on time. The inept performance and the incompetence of the management, and the sheer sloth or obstructiveness of the work-force were beyond any prodding, cajoling or threat that we could employ, even when it came direct to their chairman from Sir John Nicholson himself. After all the other ships and the vast array of associated equipment came into service in 1969, the *Jervis Bay* limped in from Fairfields in May 1970, over one year late.

But not all the troubles OCL had to accept lay in that shipyard. The sorry history of UK trade union behaviour further records that the dock labour at

Tilbury refused to handle the ships because of a national dispute that was running at the time. For over a year OCL was forced to use Rotterdam and Antwerp at the European end of the service and tranship the containers to ports other than Tilbury in UK. Then the refrigerated containers, which formed a significant proportion of the total cargo, were found to have been constructed of styrene insulating materials that seriously tainted the contents of the containers. OCL had to charter conventional refrigerated ships till they overcame the problem. The financial loss to OCL from all this was over £2.5 million, a very hurtful amount in those days.

The ships themselves had various technical problems that took some months to sort out, and this was one particular period in our dealings with OCL when the understanding and forbearance of the principals was deeply appreciated by me and my engineering colleague Willie Falconer, and all of us in Ocean Fleets. We were never subjected to complaint or harassment because the novel nature of all that we were faced with was always fully appreciated by them. I am not sure I could say the same about our own new management that took over from Sir Stewart MacTier. There were difficulties with the gearing of the main machinery, and with turbines and boilers. And the bane of all fast single-screw ships that I have referred to before, propeller-excited vibration, was with us again. These all took some months to resolve, but the most insidious and most difficult problem to explain to non-technical people concerned the level of stress in the main-deck structure. It had always been the aspect of the design that troubled me most and I have tried already to show that we used every source of advice and every current technology available to us in the design process to get a satisfactory ship. But unlike the designers of all other vehicles whether road or rail or aeroplanes, ship designers do not enjoy the assurance that comes from building a prototype. So I was most anxious, as was the shipyard, to get, as early as possible, some idea of the real stress levels in the real ship and compare this with our calculations.

As the *Encounter Bay* neared the point of delivery, very near indeed to the moment of starting to load her first cargo, we conceived a method of testing the structure of an actual ship. *Flinders Bay*, the second ship in the class, was afloat and nearing completion at the shipyard, so we set out to physically twist the ship by loading very heavy weights on the deck on one side, and filling selected tanks within the ship on the other side in a sort of diagonal configuration. The resultant stress in the steel structure at critical points was measured with about 180 strain gauges, and the deformation of the ship across the diagonals of the large hatches was also measured. The end result showed that, after taking into account the expected weight of the cargo of containers in the loaded ship, the fuel oil and stores, and then adding the worst wave-induced forces anticipated at sea, the stress in the critical hatch

Flinders Bay *under Sydney Harbour Bridge, 1970: 'Will the mast hit?'.*

corner areas would be too high in actual service. With OCL agreement we had regrettably, as an interim measure, to give instructions to the masters to take precautions on the first voyages – to reduce speed or alter course if the instruments we put on board showed excessive stressing.

This of course was unpopular both operationally and commercially, and we needed a longer-term solution – and quickly. We decided we must add more structure to the top of the hull at the ship's side to give greater strength. It took the form of a massive steel member running the length of the ship and replacing the conventional bulwark. We called it the 'strength bulwark'. Actually, it yielded a bonus which countered the cost and delay incurred in constructing it. We could now add a whole new tier of containers on each side of the ship straddling the walkway along the deck. I had taken the precaution of giving the ships a built-in margin of stability at the earliest stage of fixing the dimensions and that now allowed us to accommodate these extra containers. Ray Adams and I had often discussed such margins, reminding ourselves that you can calculate to the ultimate using the most reliable information available, but in the end someone has to decide whether to 'add on a bit' – just in case. And to avoid any unnecessary or dangerous duplication of such margins, it must be done by only *one* person – and that was me.

These tests produced another landmark in the development of ship structures. When it became clear that the stressing of the hatch corners could exceed the yield strength of the steel there was a fair degree of concern. During our rather agitated discussions Jack Chapman of Imperial College, always a steadying influence, quietly said, 'Well there is no need to panic even though we are facing a high stress regime, but now we must study fatigue'. This was the first time fatigue had been seriously considered in merchant ship construction. Up till that time it had always been assumed that fatigue of metal components where repeated stress applications occur only applied to rotating or reciprocating parts of machinery. In other words it was an engine-room problem, not a 'deck' problem. Now that it was indeed the deck that was subject to higher than normal stress under the repeated passage of the waves, we had to look very carefully at all the welded connections in the regions affected and get them absolutely right. Nowadays fatigue of the hull structure is routinely examined in the design stages of most ships. Even at that time everybody knew that under high stress, cracks were more likely to start at imperfections, whether at faulty welds or at flaws in the steel surfaces. Now that we knew that we did have higher stresses, it was decided to examine every one of the many hatch corners and make them as smooth as possible. I was dragged across to Rotterdam by Julian Taylor in the sort of dramatic gesture that he enjoyed, to see *Encounter Bay* when she was just about to load her first cargo for the maiden voyage. I remember it well because Elfrida and I lost our wedding anniversary dinner that night. We could have gone to Rotterdam equally easily next day. But I did see an impressive sight next morning when a coachload of German workers from the Howaldtswerke Shipyard, having travelled all night, disembarked with every man clutching a file or other tool. They straightaway attacked every one of the hatch corners in order to impart as near a mirror finish as possible to the steelwork – not an easy task because into every corner there was tucked a massive container cell guide.

And so this group of ships, the first ocean-going vessels of their size and type, entered service. OCL, considerate as ever, gave all the Ocean Fleets technical staff, mine and our engineering colleagues and our wives, a very grand lunch party at the Café Royal in London in celebration. When the first ship returned to UK after her inaugural voyage the master was asked how much clearance he thought he had under the Sydney Harbour bridge. He reckoned about six feet. I had a moment of horror being unable to recollect discussing that at the design stage, until Ray Adams reminded me that he had taken care of this particular dimension, knowing it would be tight, but confident in his figures. When the second ship returned home it was with a severely bent topmast. When passing under the bridge she had hit the underside of the painters' stage which runs at a level below the actual structure. It was supposed to be moved clear of the fairway during navigation hours but someone had blundered. When the minute size of the stage is compared with the great span of the bridge it was very bad luck. OCL sued the bridge authorities.

I treasure a letter I received, completely unsolicited and dated as recently as October 1998. It came from P&O Nedlloyd, the current operators of these same ships, and it read:

> Re: *Encounter Bay*
>
> Dear Mr Meek,
>
> By way of introduction I am writing to you as Operations Manager of the Australian/New Zealand and Latin America Services at P&O Nedlloyd.
>
> I think you will be interested to know that *Encounter Bay*'s career will finally come to an end on 12th January 1999 some thirty years after first entering service. Not only the first of her class, but as I understand it the first purpose-built containership, she will also be the last to retire from P&O Nedlloyd service, *Discovery Bay* and *Moreton Bay* having been sold several years ago and *Flinders Bay*, which was not converted from steam propulsion was withdrawn three years ago for disposal.
>
> My colleagues in Australasia together with those in London as well as serving officers in the fleet join me in congratulating you on producing a series of ships which has served both this company and the trade extremely well. As far as is possible in a new design we all agree that you 'got it right first time', all subsequent cellular ships being a variant of the principles employed in *Encounter Bay*. The only significant departure from this basic model as you will be aware is the hatchless container-carrier which has enjoyed limited success in certain trades.
>
> *Encounter Bay* together with *Botany Bay*, have latterly been employed on the Australia/New Zealand to Mediterranean service. They are being replaced by standard designs from the Kvaerner Warnow yard; their refrigerated capacity is however almost the same as the *Encounter Bay* class, as is their sustainable service speed, a clear indication that your original assumptions were correct.
>
> Once again, I would like to thank you on behalf of those in P&O Nedlloyd who have had the pleasure of serving on and operating the *Encounter Bay* class ships.
>
> Yours sincerely
> Peter D'Arcy

I could not ask for stronger vindication of all that my team achieved in 1966–9. I was able to reach most of them and tell them of this letter through the Blue Funnel old-boys' *Nestorian Newsletter*, and through the RINA journal, *The Naval Architect*. When I wrote to tell Monty (Monteath, OCL's first technical director) of this complimentary letter he, from his great age, said 'I didn't know companies of today did that sort of thing'.

But well before the *Encounter Bay* entered service in early 1969, the OCL principals had made their studies, gauged the measure of success already made, and hearkened to the promptings of Sir John Nicholson. The Far East Blue Funnel trades were to come next, and as far as we were concerned, these ships were to be 'the big ones'.

I had been wondering how we would decide this time how big and how fast the ships should be, remembering the rather *ad hoc* approach to the Australian ships' design parameters. A curious episode intervened. I was on one of my frequent trips to Hamburg in December 1968 when I met in the hotel where I was staying one of the New York consultants we had been working with. He was not there on our business and he was carefully confidential about the purpose of his visit and who his clients were. We talked far into the night. Without my appearing over-interested, and with his excitement barely concealed, I could gradually glean that he was working on containerships, that they were for some well-known and established US company, that they were to be very big, and they would be very, very fast. Over the weekend, after a night during which my journal entry records 'Ursula sick six times and Elfrida same', I composed a memo which was directed to Lindsay Alexander who, as deputy to Sir John Nicholson, was in charge of new developments in Blue Funnel. It explained that I believed a major US company was intent on taking the lead with larger containerships with speeds, unbelievably, well above 30 knots. When JLA, as he was always known, read it he pursed his lips in his precise style and quietly spoke four words, 'We must beat them'.

Falkus tells us that an OCL Board Minute dated 20 December 1968 (four days after my memo) recorded 'Ocean and P&O agreed on the feasibility of containerising this (Far East) trade and, bearing in mind the threat from Sea-Land, had recognized the urgency to develop in the first instance a container system in the Japan–Hong Kong service'. From that moment on, Blue Funnel were seriously into designing our new containerships which everyone now agreed must be world-beaters. And beat Sea-Land we did. Our ships were delivered in 1972, a long way ahead of what turned out to be the illustrious Sea-Land SL7s with their incredible 33 knots. They were never a success and ended up as support vessels for the US Navy.

My memo to Lindsay Alexander also suggested that we should just go straightaway to the uppermost sensible limits of size and speed. I saw no point in the perpetual competition on size and speed that existed between Ben Line and us and others such as the Japanese NYK Line. Why not make it impossible from the start for any one else to beat us? As to size, there was one obvious limit that would apply to any ship on a possible round-the-world service and that was the size of the locks in the Panama Canal. The OCL 'grannies' accepted that argument. As to speed, I had been talking with Dan Wallace, the quietly competent Scottish naval architect of Cunard Line, about the *QE2*, then not long entered into service. As the ships I envisaged were to be of roughly the same size (unheard of for any cargo ship other than tankers), we talked about the 120,000 horsepower of the *QE2*. I felt we did not quite need that much power – after all we were merchant ship people. So I indented to the Blue Funnel and OCL seniors for 100,000 horsepower. The 'grannies' considered this seriously but concluded that this young naval architect was getting a bit above himself. They cut me down to an arbitrary 80,000 horsepower. I was well enough content because nobody had ever envisaged propulsion power of such magnitude in the cargo sector of merchant shipping.

The trouble with the Panama Canal locks' length limit was that nobody knew what it was. The Canal authorities would never lay down a limit for the very simple reason they did not want long ships. The limit on breadth was obvious. The width of the locks was 110 feet and the authorities demanded 2 feet of clearance on each side in case the ship listed somewhat. That gave the maximum ship's beam as 106 feet. As to the maximum draught of the ship, this too was clearly specified because it was related to the depth of water in the Canal at any one time. That depth depended on the rainfall held in the Gatun Lake which was integral with and fed the Canal. But there was no such guidance on maximum length. To understand the reason for this one has to picture the vast amount of tonnage traversing the Canal and the ever-present danger of the lock gates being damaged by an errant ship. This would seriously disrupt this crucially important flow of both US and international traffic. When the canal was built in 1914 ships were prevented from contacting the gates by massive protective chains, but these were dispensed with when the Canal operators started to use the 'mules', small powerful locomotives which ran along the lock side. These are attached to the ships with hawsers and provide a much more positive control over ship movement. But the gates must still be treated as utterly sacrosanct and the obvious way to avoid risk of damage was to avoid having long ships. I return to the actual determination of the length of our ships later.

Once again, our most acute problem was how to design the structure of such massive ships when there was virtually no top deck to give rigidity. On my usual principle of never neglecting consultation with any likely expert, I did another round-the-world trip, this time with our adviser and friend Dr Jack Chapman of Imperial College. As well as discussing structural design, I was commissioned to sound out the interest amongst Japanese builders in building such novel and large ships, and so had discussions with our old friends Mitsubishi and Mitsui, as well as new ones IHI, Hitachi and Kawasaki. Of all these major shipbuilding companies only Mitsui showed any real interest in quoting. They all cited difficulties with meeting our requirement for early delivery. I think the truth was that these canny shipbuilders were not ready to take the risk of building such novel ship types, especially for Blue Funnel. Our demanding standards were by now known throughout Japan following Mitsubishi's *Priam* class experience.

From Japan we flew to San Francisco to speak about structures with Henry Schade and his colleagues at the University. During that visit Jack Chapman and I viewed the city from the top of the Mark Hotel, a well-known viewing point. As a strong wind was blowing we had the idea of using one of the viewing telescopes to detect the relative movement of the skyscrapers as they swayed in the wind. We failed because there were no crosswires on the lenses to show up such small movement. But we then became aware of one particular tall building where the main structure was not vertically and horizontally arranged as is normal; the main skeleton of the building was clearly visible and it was diagonally disposed. We assumed it was so designed to resist the racking tendency that is generated by earthquakes. And so our new large containerships, when they came out of the shipyards, had some diagonal stiffening on the bulkheads instead of the traditional vertical and horizontal stiffening because they too had to resist racking forces. This was quite novel.

After a call in New York to check developments with J.J. Henry in the World Trade Centre Jack Chapman left and I flew to Panama. There I met up with Captain Colin Sparkes our nautical adviser. We had decided the only way to find out the maximum ship length that we could be allowed by the Canal Authority was to confront them. They were an intimidating lot. In 1969 US still controlled the Canal and we found a group of close-cropped bull-necked US Navy brass in charge. I explained how we were about to commit the most powerful UK shipping companies to their most expensive-ever commercial enterprise, that the length of the ships was one of the most important parameters that we had to decide on, and they alone could adjudicate on that. So they generously agreed that, yes, we were the customers, they were the providers, and they would give us a figure. Having obviously already put their heads together they said, 'The locks are 1,050 feet long, we feel we need 50 feet at each end in case the ship goes walk-about, and so you can have 950 feet for your ships'. This was more than we dared hope for, and so it was that that overall length applied to all large containerships for the next quarter of a century. We made the stern vertical and the stem as vertical as practicable, and squeezed on to that length every container we could.

The trouble was that ships built to the dimensions of the Panama Canal locks were all of the wrong proportions. They were not wide enough for such a length. Presumably when the locks were built the intention was to accommodate two ships of normal size end-to-end in the lock. Perhaps it was not surprising that as we stood at the Miraflore locks watching the unending stream of ships moving gently through, an American lady tourist, disappointed at being faced with the mere 110 foot lock width exclaimed 'Gee, is *that* the Panama Canal?' With such a limitation on width we had to

Liverpool Bay, *achieving over 30 knots off Norway, 1972.*

take special precautions to ensure adequate stability of our ships and compensate for the lack of beam. We did this by using empty spaces in the bottom of the ship for water ballast and filling them as the oil fuel in the bunkers was consumed during the voyage. This was not efficient design since extraneous deadweight was being carried for part of the voyage, but the overall result was beneficial.

Like the year 1966 when we designed and ordered the *Encounter Bays*, 1969 was to be equally memorable for similar reasons. The five *Encounter Bays* were delivered from the shipyards in Hamburg at regular intervals during the year, yet at the same time we were finalizing the design of the much bigger Far East ships without the opportunity of learning from operating experience with the first ones. These same Hamburg shipyards led by Howaldtswerke entered into the spirit of our new studies with enthusiasm, being very keen to be involved in the new ships, even though the date of completion to satisfy OCL's schedule was demanding. We reached the stage at the beginning of May when OCL felt they must decide whether to go ahead with serious procurement.

Together with Willie Falconer, I was in Hamburg at the end of April charged with satisfying the OCL principals on two points, firstly that the concept of building such enormous ships was supported by the Hamburg shipyards; then that these German yards were competent to build them. In that case OCL would decide on the number of ships required and then work together with the shipyards in the final stages of design leading to submissions of tenders. The formal meeting of the OCL Board to whom we were due to report was convened for the next day, 1 May. There was a surprise airline strike that morning and so not enough seats for London. Willie Falconer had got wind of this and had sloped off early and managed to get a seat. I had to charter a small aircraft in an effort to get to the P&O offices for the afternoon meeting. A Piper Aztec takes three hours from Hamburg to Heathrow compared with one hour in a Trident, so as I and my three companions fluttered on to the runway amongst the Boeing 707 jets, I was running late. In spite of the taxi to the city breaking down en route, I arrived at the meeting in time to share the satisfaction of hearing the 'grannies' decide to build four of our big ships, and to continue with the final stages of design up to the placing of firm orders later in the year.

Then just as we were tidying away our papers Sir Freddie Harmer of P&O suggested that we might actually consider a fifth ship. This was heady stuff and all the great men were obviously mightily attracted to the idea, even though we were talking of well over £10 million per ship, equal to something much in excess of £100 million today. Caution prevailed however, on that occasion, but that fifth ship was added by the time OCL came to sign the contract with the two shipyards of Howaldtswerke and Deutsche Werft in December. What is still astounding to me is that an order of such magnitude was placed without seeking alternative quotations elsewhere, such was the trust that had been built up during the building of the *Encounter Bays*, and such was the haste to get the ships into service. That trust was fully vindicated in our dealings together over the next few years. The new ships were called, justifiably, the *Liverpool Bay* class. They were steamships (later to be converted, like the *Encounter Bays*, to diesel propulsion after the 1970s oil shocks); they had a fully loaded service speed of 26 knots but were capable of more; they could carry a design load of 2,300 containers (but were to reach 3,000 in service); and they were twin-screw following my discussions with Dan Wallace of Cunard about similarities with the *QE2*. It was unheard of for merchant ships to be bracketed with the crack passenger liner of the day!

There was still much to do, particularly in satisfying ourselves on the structural design. Jack Chapman ran a research project at Imperial College where large models of both the *Encounter Bay* and the *Liverpool Bay* hulls were made from perspex and araldite material for testing and comparing with our calculations, and with what we had found from the shipyard tests on *Flinders Bay*. In addition we employed BSRA to instrument up the *Discovery Bay* with a full set of measuring equipment. Dave Tucker sailed out to Australia on a round voyage to see that it worked. Although we were working with Lloyd's Register of Shipping who would class the ships eventually, we were helped rather more effectively by the German society, Gemanischer Lloyd. Then in June of 1969 I flew to Australia to learn more about that end of the *Encounter Bay* service and see the actual container ports in operation; also to have a few days at sea. This I did sailing from Melbourne to Fremantle on the *Encounter Bay*, crossing the Bight in fairly heavy weather. It was here that I experienced the unusual whipping motion of the ship in a seaway and it confirmed to me the urgent need to study fatigue stressing of the hull.

It was a marvellous experience to find all the crew so enthusiastic about their pioneering service, but my trip came to a rather miserable ending. I had had an injection operation for varicose veins in my right leg a few weeks before and the aftermath was unhappy. I flew back to Sydney from Fremantle and, showing obvious circulation troubles, was quickly put into the Waverley Hospital, Kings Cross with severe thrombosis of the leg diagnosed. There I was most solicitously cared for by our Sydney agents, both P&O and Blue Funnel. Things seemed to have improved after two weeks and I set off for home via US with a short stopover in San Francisco. By the time I reached London I had become a victim of what is now well recognized as in-flight deep vein thrombosis. After struggling home I was soon in the Birkenhead General Hospital with a pulmonary embolism and thereafter out of action for some months. At my lowest point very soon after admission I dimly recognized that the nurses were talking excitedly about the comical way the US astronauts hopped about on their first landing on the moon. It had taken place during that night. Although I tried to keep up with developments in the office from my bed I was only too glad to let Ray Adams take over, which he did right well. So much so that by December we had a ship design ready to build and the order for five ships was placed with the German shipyards. These were worrisome days for Elfrida as she bravely cared for our three little girls, with Grandma Cox helping when she could.

The ceremony of signing the contracts, attended by the shipyards, OCL and Ocean people was memorable. Sir Andrew Crichton signed for OCL as chairman and there was a sort of juvenile, semi-intoxicated exuberance about the occasion. Sir Andrew taunted Sir John Nicholson about Ocean being the austere northern calvinistic member of OCL. He was, I think, a little jealous that the big ships were going to Ocean. He quoted from Psalm

84: 'I had rather be a doorkeeper in the house of my God than to dwell in the tents of wickedness...' I failed to see the relevance. The whole event took a long time because he insisted on signing each document with his full name of Andrew Maitland McGill Crichton.

The builders set up a joint venture between Howaldtswerke and Deutsche Werft to control this massive exercise and appointed Herr Kuhl, who had just retired as managing director of Deutsche Werft, to head the project. He was the ideal man for the job – precise, knowledgeable, respected by the work-force, and a delight to work with as far as we were concerned. Elfrida and I kept in touch with him until quite recently when both he and his wife died at over ninety years of age. The project went even more smoothly than the *Encounter Bays*' building, and the five ships entered service within the year of March 1972 to March 1973. We had to go up to the Norwegian coast to do the sea trials of these ships because with their speed and size they needed deeper water than that around the Elbe. It was thrilling to be running at over 30 knots. Aircraft carriers would be the only comparable ships afloat for size and speed. And there were none of the problems that had plagued the earlier class. We had conquered the structural stress troubles; because the ships were twin-screw we had no propeller-excited vibration; boiler and gearing difficulties had been solved; again with the fruitful relationship with Neville Ward we had produced accommodation for the crew that was the quite the best afloat. For a good many years thereafter the German shipyards were the world-wide leaders in containership building and they deserved to be.

I had the history of these latest technical developments written up in a further paper to the RINA. It gained something of a place in the history of the Institution because it had five authors – Ray Adams and I from the shipowners, H. Reibel and P. Wieske from the shipbuilders, and Jack Chapman as consultant. The discussion did not quite match in length the one that followed Alfred Holt's paper to the Civil Engineers in 1877 but twenty-two people took part. Since many of these contributions were themselves learned treatises, the amount of work involved in answering them, let alone bringing together the responses of five authors, was a major effort. I have always felt, as have done others, that we merited the Institution's gold medal. That rather impoverished body had not at that time the wherewithal to fund gold medals in bulk, so we had to make do with the Institution's Premium which involved handing over five pounds sterling plus a certificate to each of us. As Jack Chapman said it was not surprising that the German authors were not moved to come across to UK for its presentation.

The consequences of building these containerships were soon felt over the whole shipping scene. As to the recasting of the efficiency of shipping they were strikingly successful. But for thousands of people the sequel was catastrophic. I gave a lecture to our North East Region of the RSA a few years ago in which I was describing my role in the naval architecture of these ships, and I talked about the impact of the container revolution. In the discussion Professor Brenikov of Newcastle University explained how he had been born on the dockside in Liverpool and he wanted to know if we understood what we were doing when we designed these ships. He was referring to the way the port of Liverpool was doomed to near extinction because of this metamorphosis in transportation. I could only say that we were just doing our job to the best of our ability. I well remember the economic calculations I made during the design period for the scheduling of these new Far East ships, based on their exceptionally high speed and heavy oil fuel consumption of 400 tons per day. It did not take long to prove that for ships trading to the Far East, Southampton was the right port and not Liverpool. And so when this became the decision, it was to be an immense and cruel blow to the prosperity of the whole of Liverpool and Merseyside. Of course the Liverpool docker had not helped himself or his fellows during all the previous years of mindless dispute and acrimonious relations. There was little attraction to shipowners who were pushing into new ships and new systems, in continuing to use the port, but such was the labour relations ambience nationally at that time that no one was brave or rash enough to put this into words. Even at Southampton there were problems with dock labour in the first year or so as the unions tried to milk the new systems while they could.

Before long we could see the new statistics forming. The *Glenlyon* class of cargo liners spent only 191 days at sea per year. The expensively designed *Priams* increased this to 216 days at sea but even that reduced to 201 days in 1969 because of worsening dockside labour relations. The *Liverpool Bays* increased the time at sea to 300 days per year, the sort of impressive and unarguable improvement that justified everything we had done. If the carriage of cargoes is expressed in tonne-miles per year, to use latter-day terminology, the *Liverpool Bays* carried between six and seven times more than the *Priams*, the greatest of the conventional cargo liners. Small wonder then that the repercussions on Blue Funnel itself were severe, with one containership replacing seven or eight or even more conventional ships. Chairman Sir John Nicholson, nearing the end of his illustrious career, had the unenviable job of writing to the staff, and particularly to the seafarers, to explain the impending changes to the company and the inevitable redundancies. Sir Lindsay Alexander who followed him as chairman is known to have confessed that the saddest day in his career with Blue Funnel was when he had to admit that the company could no longer offer or speak of jobs with the company for life. For a company bearing such shining traditions of service and loyalty these were bitter days.

It seems almost indecent against that background to say I have enjoyed much satisfaction over my career, with the success of the containerships as the sweetest moment. I have referred to the *Encounter Bays*' exceptionally long and successful life even though they were 'first of class'. After some twenty-eight years, more than even Alfred Holt's ships averaged, the *Liverpool Bays* have only recently come to the end. Other companies in the UK quickly followed our lead into containerships and then in Europe, Japan and the Far East. I was particularly incensed when our old competitors Ben Line went along to Howaldtswerke shipyard in Germany and coolly ordered 'the same'. I made bold to express my dismay to Sir John Nicholson at the way they so easily fell heir to all the development work and research cost we had put into the design. I got short shrift. I had failed to grasp said he, that unless we drew them alongside in joint Far East services they could well join up with others in competition to us. I still think they got the better of an unfair bargain.

Naturally, there have been many improvements in the design of containerships since we pioneered. With much greater knowledge of the way ships behave and with better means of calculation, ships of today are able to carry more containers. And most importantly there was never going to be a repeat of the high speeds we designed for. Fuel cost was now too high. Slower ships could be made 'fatter' on the same overall dimensions and so carry more containers. But with the economics prevailing in the late 1960s and early 1970s, we wanted to be first and fastest, and I wanted to get it right – and we succeeded. It is fascinating to see that just recently some ship-owners have decided to ignore the Panama Canal limit on size altogether and restrict their vessels' trading either to the east or to the west of Panama. They are therefore building far bigger 'post-Panamax' ships, but because they have no recognizable physical limit these operators are all at sea as to how big to build their ships. Compared with our 3,000 containers on the *Liverpool Bays* there are now ships carrying 5,000 and 6,000 or more and there is talk of 8,000 or 10,000. They cannot make up their minds about the optimum number because there is no obvious limit to size at the moment.

By now Blue Funnel saw very clearly that once these Far East container-ships entered service there would need to be urgent reappraisal of the shipping businesses. I shall describe later the almost frantic efforts that followed in trying to diversify out of cargo liner shipping in a way that would retain and give employment to so many loyal staff both ashore and afloat, but meantime I remind you that this search for other outlets and other ship types was taking place during the building period of the Far East *Bay* ships. It was a pressurized era for those of us involved in the acquisition of the ships. The overall value of all the ships we were involved with over those few years would today run into billions of pounds.

Elfrida launches Anchises at Fujinagata, 1973.

To revert to family affairs, we had decided it would be nice to have a little retreat somewhere to which we could decamp reasonably easily for a breather. People on Merseyside tended to divide into those who sought solace in the Lake District to the north, and those who chose North Wales to the south. We chose North Wales, and bought a bungalow in the little village of Gaerwen in the middle of Anglesey. It was easily reachable, and gave us many happy holidays over the next ten years until we moved to the North East. We enjoyed both seaside and mountains, the glorious sands of Rhosneigr and the sweep of Snowdon's slopes, and discovered that the Welsh language is very much alive. Through our continuous association with our Christian Brethren we attended assemblies first at Holyhead then at Llanfairfechan and formed happy links with a new set of friends in those areas.

We had another reason for choosing that direction for our leisure time. Hazel, our oldest daughter, had started at Howell's School in Denbigh, one of the Haberdasher Guild schools, and Denbigh was on the way to Anglesey. Her younger sister, Ursula, was to follow her to the same school shortly. They were happy there and we enjoyed our visits to see them. We were always impressed by the discipline exercised at the school. Perhaps it was easier to impose than in a boys' school. At one of the Parents' and Prize-giving Days the whole school was formally arranged in rigid tiers in the rocky amphitheatre that faces the main entrance. Before the mass of parents and friends one little girl fainted at a particularly solemn moment during the service. She lay amongst the heather with the bees buzzing round and not a soul around her flinched or moved an inch.

My mother had kept the old home in Auchtermuchty going since father died in 1955 and Martha still lived with her. But in the late 1960s mother became increasingly troubled with heart problems and she died of heart failure early one morning in December 1970. Thereafter Martha carried on alone, having been left the house. I suppose it was somewhat unusual that mother was buried alongside father in Muchty cemetery, under a gravestone that he had himself made and erected in the first place for his own parents. Around it there were the peaceful grounds that Max and I had cared for in earlier years.

Mother was the dominant one of my parents. Having faced hardship in early life, losing her mother when she was only eighteen, having to care for her brood of little brothers and sisters until a stepmother came along, she was quietly determined; and because her own mother had already imparted her strong Christian faith she reflected the same. Without education beyond that of Muchty school (in itself not to be underrated) she had a deep Scottish appreciation of learning. I have always been impressed with her erudition, gleaned from I am not sure where. In brethren circles the name of John Nelson Darby figures largely as one of the founders in the early 1800s. A man of remarkable intellect, he single-handedly translated a version of the Bible from the French (which I find today is very similar to the New International Version produced by a large committee of academics). Darby wrote the most beautiful hymns and poems but his letters, lectures and massive biblical expositions are widely recognized as turgid, convoluted and desperately hard to absorb. My mother read them copiously and enjoyed them. She was always ambitious for the family to succeed as long as any success was contained within her Christian principles, and it is due to her urging and encouragement that we gained the education and formation for which all three of us are most thankful today.

Before I describe the maritime ventures that followed the advent of the containerships, I run a retrospective eye over other interests of that time. I was appointed visiting professor in naval architecture at Strathclyde University at the instigation of Professor Chengi Kuo. An appointment for three years, it somehow stretched to ten. I was invited by Wedgwood Benn at the Ministry of Technology to join his advisory committee on marine affairs; I became a member of the Ship and Maritime Technology Research

Board (SMTRB). This was in the days of Prime Minister Harold Wilson's white-hot technology, when everybody recognized there was great need to understand and develop technology, but there would be near total failure to follow through with it to the production line. I served on the Structures Committee and the Design Committee at BSRA and chaired for some years the highly effective group studying propeller-excited vibration until we found how such vibration could be 'designed out'. I chaired the International Chamber of Shipping Marine Safety Committee and our own GCBS Technical Research Committee. I was elected a member of Council of RINA. I continued with my series of papers to the RINA describing my activities, and there were others like the one to the Royal Society on ship design. It was all very satisfying.

Chapter 16

Containership aftermath – the end of Blue Funnel

After the major effort of designing and building the *Liverpool Bay* ships and seeing them into service in 1972 there was never to be the same excitement and sense of purpose and achievement again. It had taken just over six years from the first concept of containerizing in 1965 to the full burgeoning of world-wide container transportation. Clearly shipping had been ripe for change. Blue Funnel were now facing a more difficult scenario where many staff, both seagoing and shore-based, were plainly in danger of being made redundant, and the available financial resources needed to be re-directed into other than the traditional cargo liner trades. It was an exceptionally difficult commission for Sir Lindsay Alexander who had taken over as chairman from Sir John Nicholson in 1972. Lindsay had always held Sir John in complete adulation but I had a feeling he had modelled his career and conduct on him perhaps rather too closely. Everything was about to change in shipping and there was little point in hoping that Blue Funnel principles and practices would still apply in the totally different trading environment. In addition there were to be convulsive international events in the form of the oil crises of 1973 and 1979 that would shake up all previous assumptions. I did not fully appreciate it at the time but we were now set on a tortuous but quite short path to extinction, and we were not alone. UK was to disappear as a force in world shipping remarkably and disappointingly quickly.

My last years with the company through the 1970s saw continual searching for profitable enterprises both at sea and land-based. Diversification was the prevailing word, and the company still had cash reserves. In the investigations into the procuring of new ships my own department took care of all the naval architectural affairs. We were to become involved in ships such as we had never known; we had to learn a lot of new technology; and we became familiar with a host of shipbuilding companies all over the world. Yet at that moment I was asked to assume new responsibilities in addition to naval architecture. I suppose it could be construed flatteringly that I was regarded as a versatile sort of chap, but nothing surprised me more than being asked to take over the whole of the storing, purchasing and victualling of what was still a very sizeable fleet of about 100 ships. I had never been over-interested in our domestic 'food supply chain', being very happy to leave all such matters to Elfrida. Now I had to study not only the menus on the ships but the sources and quality and distribution of supplies, and then I had to interview the catering officers as they came into head office voyage by voyage to report on their performance and expenditure. They had to give a valid explanation if, for example, they incurred more than 7 lbs of meat including bacon per man per week – a quantum that sticks in my memory.

It all felt very odd, but I was greatly helped and supported by Gordon Smith, the head of the victualling department, and by Peter Gannicliffe of stores and purchasing. These men dealt most graciously and patiently with their rather naïve naval architect boss, and I learned a lot. Exchange rates were extremely variable at that time and we had to be very flexible in our purchasing policies. It was really impressive to see the great trucks rolling out from our Odyssey Works in Birkenhead laden with stores for ships as far away as the Black Sea ports since at the time it was beneficial to do the purchasing in UK. We were moving rapidly away from the years of concentration on the Far East trades.

A second new task given to me was to act as operations director for all our foreign-based ships, and also the remaining passenger ships in the Elder Dempster fleet. This meant I was responsible for the running of the ships but not for freight matters. I enjoyed this tremendously, particularly because the eight *Priam* class ships that I had designed so carefully were now under my guardianship. They were scheduled into the Barber Blue Sea service and ran between US and the Far East. Captain John Robinson, a splendid operations manager, was my mentor here. He had earlier been one of the many chief officers who did a spell in the naval architect's department – an enlightened move that was beneficial to both sides. Now I was able to learn at first hand from the masters and officers what happened on every voyage, which was a satisfying and sometimes humbling experience not often given to naval architects. It was becoming apparent even then however, that these proud ships, designed all too obviously for break-bulk cargoes, and suffering from their lateness in delivery into service, were not going to have a long life now that containers had arrived with such momentum.

Then I had the laboratories, also at Odyssey Works, to look after. Because of our meticulous approach to safety and efficiency we had for many years enjoyed in-house advice on both metallurgical and chemistry matters. The former tended to relate to the ships and the latter to the cargoes. John Deegan was our metallurgist and Harold Critchley our chemist, and my job at this particular time was to encourage these men to turn what had been a purely inter-company service into a commercial unit doing third-party work against the time when our own ships would start to disappear. Before long I was finding cog sections from the Snowdon mountain railway, failed axles of

Liverpool Corporation buses, and broken children's scooters lying around what had hitherto been very much a marine establishment. John went on to become an influential consultant and expert witness in inquiries and court cases. We found ourselves together more recently in the *Derbyshire* inquiry where he was acting for the relatives of the victims and I was doing the same for Lloyd's Register. But I come back to that later.

Because I already had under my care the ship repair and maintenance department at Odyssey Works, who too had to learn to seek out third-party work, the addition of these new interests meant I had a pretty full portfolio. I could only subsist because of the wonderful support of so many Blue Funnel departmental managers. The old loyalties and traditions still prevailed everywhere. Yet looming over all was the growing recognition that we were now set on a path of irrevocable change which could only lead to fewer ships and, unbeknown to us at the time, to the eventual demise of Blue Funnel as a shipping company. But before that destination was reached there were valiant and almost frantic efforts at diversifying into other shipping operations and these involved my naval architect's department heavily. I could not now take direct personal interest in all the detail of the acquisition of the new ships and I delegated much to Ray Adams, and also to Jack Kershaw, a delightful and able companion from the Elder Dempster line-up. Others were Bob Brown, who had joined me away back in Sir Stewart MacTier's day; Ken Chapman, an ambitious, highly qualified and extremely hard-working man who rightly went on to become a director of the Swan Hunter shipyard; and Dave Tucker, always willing, helpful and a real goer who is now a director of Three Quays Marine Services.

I can only tell the story of these increasingly fraught years as I saw it. For the reasons behind the decline of Blue Funnel (and all other UK companies) one has to look elsewhere. Falkus in his otherwise marvellously wide-ranging *Blue Funnel Legend* comes to a stop about this time, and I find the best and most balanced record of this period is in Professor Peter Davies' *The Trade Makers*. Although this recently re-edited volume primarily describes Elder Dempster's history, it gives a very good summing up, from that semi-detached viewpoint, of the Blue Funnel problems and the attempts at solutions. From my own line of sight over the years I see two images – firstly, the almost frenzied efforts to diversify into related marine, or indeed non-marine, activities which were only partly successful. And secondly, the rather agonizing ship purchasing programme that took us into ship types and trades new to the company, but which likewise were only partially or temporarily successful. I agree with Peter Davies when he refers to the exceptional reputation of Blue Funnel as cargo liner operators but suggests that that expertise extended only to liner shipping. What was really happening was that Blue Funnel were going into the risky and hitherto

Nestor, *the LNG carrier that broke our hearts.*

despised tramp shipping and charter business, and with ships of very high value.

As a director of Ocean Fleets I had Richard Hobhouse as chairman. He was son of Sir John Hobhouse, the senior partner before Sir John Nicholson. Richard was not an effective leader. He was indecisive, too discursive in his deliberations and tended to be querulous on technical matters. When he resigned in 1976 and Bill Menzies-Wilson succeeded him as chairman of Ocean Fleets, he confessed to Ray Adams 'I haven't been a very good boss' – further proof that son succeeding father is not always successful. But on ship design and procurement matters I missed Sir Stewart MacTier greatly. He understood how to get the best out of technical people – encouraging, asking the right questions at the right time, gently rebuking if necessary, and issuing concise and understandable orders. A little note from him to me on his retirement recorded 'I have taken a very special pride in the naval architect's department because I do think you and your team are most certainly the leading designers in the country and perhaps in the world' – and that was before the success of the bigger *Liverpool Bays.*

I now had Julian Taylor to contend with and he was quite different and very difficult. I think he felt inadequate in some way when up against qualified professional people, and to compensate he tried too hard to be original, active and questioning. Hours were wasted in needless explanations and argument. But he had a lively although somewhat illogical mind. One of the few things I learned from him was the importance of getting out of the office chair and on to the field of action if there was trouble anywhere. It was not surprising that he was diverted in 1975 out of the main line of succession on the main board to be head of a new ship procurement department where he was joined by Willie Falconer who had been director of engineering in Ocean Fleets.

It was during the completion of the *Liverpool Bays* that it had become increasingly apparent that our very considerable resources, both in finance and in qualified people, would now need some other outlets. So the board decided to make a move into large tankers. I and my staff had to do some rapid homework. We knew little about the tanker trades and when *Titan* was purchased in 1971 from the AB Gotaverken yard in Sweden we were no little impressed with the immensity of the vessel which became ours. She was 100 feet longer than the *Liverpool Bays* and was a typical VLCC of her day (very large crude carrier of about 250,000 tons deadweight). Alongside the enthusiasm of us technical people to get involved in such ships, there was no lack of seagoing staff who were keen to take charge where no Blue Funnel master or officers had ventured before. We played little part in the design of the ship and it would be the same for many of those that followed. The major shipyards had their own designs which were only subject to minor alteration to suit any particular shipowner. We did supervise the construction in some detail however.

Next came *Tantalus* in 1972, of similar size, from Nippon Kokan's brand-new shipyard at Tsu in Japan. Blue Funnel were not allowed to superintend the building (shades of *Glenalmond* and *Pembrokeshire* from Mitsubishi still lingered). She was a more complex ship, being able to carry both oil and ore, and so was more versatile. Fortunately *Tantalus* only ever carried oil and we never had to face alternate oil and ore trading. It seems incredible now that just as the 1973 oil crisis was about to break, Japan and some other countries were not only churning out supertankers and even readying themselves for ULCCs (ultra large crude carriers up to 500,000 tons deadweight), but they were building shipyards to build ever more tankers. There was to be a rude awakening shortly. The trouble with Blue Funnel was that we had no apparent logic to our purchases other than to find someone who would sell us a ship at what was deemed a favourable price and then see if we could charter it profitably. Not many shipyards in Japan were willing to help. The *Priam* class building experiences were too fresh in the mind.

Since the time when the two *Priams* were built at Nagasaki in the mid 1960s we had available to us the services of a very superior Japanese gentleman called Admiral Takahashi who had been identified by Butterfield and Swire, our agents in Japan. I was never sure just what naval history lay behind the title of Admiral, but he served us well and became a good friend, acting as a very effective go-between in dealings with the shipyards by whom he was patently highly respected. He was just as mystified about Blue Funnel policy on new ship acquisitions as any one else and came to the carefully articulated and confidentially expressed conclusion that 'Ocean seemed to have a policy only of opportunistic purchases'. He was right. Next came another tanker *Troilus* in 1974, from Mitsui this time, and biggest of all. None of them were to serve anything like a full span. They were steamships and uneconomic after 1973, and there was a glut of tankers anyway. *Titan* was sold in 1975. *Troilus* went within a year of building. *Tantalus* after being laid up in Southampton for two years was sold in 1984. Blue Funnel were losing money on tramp-style shipping.

Meanwhile we were building five smallish bulk carriers at Mitsui's shipyard at Fujinagata on the Inland Sea. These were the *Agamemnon* class, Alfred Holt's most famous ship name given to a group of rather mundane shipyard-designed bulk carriers. They were the first ships following the Mitsubishi *Priams* experience where we were allowed to have a superintendent – nominally only to 'observe'. Russell Knight, ever the diplomat, was in charge of that delicate exercise. They were of the maximum size to use the St Lawrence Seaway and found themselves in various trade groupings such as the Scanscot bulker pool. Elfrida was invited to launch one of them called *Anchises* and did so in April 1973. The previous *Anchises*, a Holt 'A' class ship, was completed at Caledon shipyard in 1947 while I worked there. We were handsomely entertained by Mitsui at that launch, having made it a round-the-world trip.

We went outward bound via US and back via Hong Kong and Singapore; and we enjoyed two short sea trips, one from Hong Kong to Taiwan on *Liverpool Bay* with an impressive and rather frightening entry into the ridiculously tight approach to the container terminal at Kaoshsiung. Container terminals always seem to be in the most inaccessible reaches of the ports. We were due to fly from there to Japan but on going ashore our agents somehow allowed us to get separated from our baggage. We immediately became suspects at immigration. Sleeping pills, which I never used, in my briefcase were objects of highest suspicion. We shall ever be most grateful to Captain Vic Moore of *Liverpool Bay* who, having left his ship on hearing we were in trouble, strode into the immigration offices to determine the position. The majestic sight of a full white uniform bearing down on the miniscule Taiwanese customs people did the trick and we were released immediately. The other trip was on my own familiar *Centaur*, up the coast from Singapore to Port Kelang and back. As ever, the hospitality on board was warm and delightful. These Mitsui bulkers were to be no more successful than the big tankers. It was a bad time to try new ships because the trade just was not there. *Agamemnon* lasted only six years, *Antenor* lasted five, and the best of the others no more than eleven.

Before I complete this lengthening list of acquisitions, and I am by no means finished, I record the 1972 takeover by Blue Funnel of William Cory and Sons Limited as one of our more successful diversifications. Cory's background was in the coal trade but they had themselves diversified into a good many other businesses and there was a fair common interest between them and Blue Funnel. The units within Cory that interested me directly were the tugs in their Cory Towage company, and the little shipyard they owned in Wivenhoe in Essex under the name of James Cook. After the expected and understandable reluctance to have us oversee them had been overcome by these two companies, we had very useful collaboration. Jack Kershaw went off from my department to run Cook's shipyard, although it really was too small and primitive to last long in the modern shipbuilding world.

I enjoyed rather more the study into modern towage practice and trends, and we produced a major strategic plan for Cory Towage. They had been very conventional in their tug design but we gradually got them to look at the new propulsion devices and systems that other competing companies were adopting. I am glad to say that Cory Towage eventually came round to a really progressive attitude and outlasted all the other marine businesses in the Ocean Group. The company was only fairly recently sold to the Wijsmuller Groep of Holland which in turn was purchased six months later by the A.P. Moller Group. So was to end all Blue Funnel links with the sea.

Meanwhile there were more ship purchases and more joint marine ventures, all of which demanded my attention and the resources of the naval architects. In 1969, during the hustle of designing the *Encounter Bays*, we had formed the alliance with P&O in the building and running of chemical carriers under the name of Panocean Ltd. Our first ship was *Postrover*, built in Spain, and others followed. We set up a joint company with Inchcape called Ocean Inchcape (OIL) to run a series of offshore supply boats for the oil and gas industries. The first ones were *Oil Prospector* and *Oil Producer* from Holland and others followed. We had another stab at bigger bulk carriers, two this time from Burmeister & Wain in Copenhagen, named *Hector* and *Helenus*. Both struggled to make a decent return and *Hector* was sold in 1979. *Helenus* was converted, to our design, into a large car carrier in 1978 and managed to survive till 1983. Next came two smaller and specialized tankers, *Cyclops* from van der Giessen in Holland and *Charon* from Sasebo in Japan. Things became almost bizarre when Blue Funnel then ordered two vessels from the Kherson Shipyard in Russia. These were delivered in 1976 and 1977, cargo liner type ships with some ability to carry containers, and they were built surprisingly strongly. Both moved over to the

Elder Dempster fleet for two years and then played a part in the Falklands war where their solid construction helped. But they were sold shortly afterwards. All a far cry from the traditional Blue Funnel manner of ordering and running the ships.

Alongside these Blue Funnel acquisitions there were developments in the Elder Dempster camp as well. Their older ships were being disposed of from 1972 onwards and I found myself advising John Robertson, the director of Elder Dempster responsible for new ships. John was an enthusiast and it was difficult to keep abreast of his ideas, or to keep him abreast of practicalities. We enjoyed working together, always in the hope that the company would be able to acquire ships suitable for the West African trades which did not seem ready for full containerizing. The solution at that time was to purchase so-called 'combo ships', part-conventional, part-containers. So we acquired two combos in the form of re-purchases from H. Schuldt of Hamburg with whom John had worked his charm.

To look after them during building and delivery we had to make regular and rather unpleasant visits to the Stocznia shipyard at Szcecin, usually flying to Berlin and then onwards by car, struggling through the grim check-points into East Germany and into Poland. The whole place was dismal, grey and depressing and the ship completion trials with their primitive feeding arrangements were particularly awful. There were to be five of these *Shonga* class ships in service in the end. One was launched by the wife of Geoffrey (now Sir Geoffrey) Ellerton, managing director of Elder Dempster. As a memento she was given a large and very heavy glass vase and she had to carry it all the way home unwrapped in any form. Geoffrey, always the perfect gentleman, was given a rather unattractive wooden model of the ship. He thought to be free of it when he inadvertently left it in the coach to the airport. At the last minute of passing through the boarding gate an attendant rushed up with it. 'How could I be so careless!' gallantly exclaimed Geoffrey.

But the *Shongas* weren't big enough for the job and another 'opportunistic' purchase followed. Sir Lindsay Alexander was a non-executive director of BP and when BP were forced to cancel two VLCCs at Mitsubishi in Japan he engineered an alternative order of cargo ships from Blue Funnel. A deal was set up between BP and ourselves to the advantage of both and I was pleased to find we were actually to design a batch of combo carriers, larger than the *Shonga* class, in conjunction with our old friends at Mitsubishi. We now co-operated famously, even succeeding in incorporating John Robertson's demands for a very curious type of cargo gear which, combined with an unusual hatch stowage arrangement, produced assuredly the most inelegant Blue Funnel ships every built. How the master could see

Tokyo Bay, *a snug fit in a lock in the Panama Canal, with a first generation US containership conversion alongside.*

forward to navigate his ship through the forest of derrick posts and rigging was a mystery. Four ships in this *Menelaus* class were built in Japan, and a further three of mainly the same design from Scott's shipyard at Greenock. These were to be the last Blue Funnel ships built in UK, and from the same shipyard as the first, the *Agamemnon*, some 120 years before. As ever with UK shipyards, it was a slog to get them delivered by 1980 and I had departed Blue Funnel by then. None of these ships were to guarantee the salvation of Blue Funnel. They were all sold before reaching anything like a full lifespan.

I suppose I could have produced a treatise called something like 'a comparative study of shipbuilding methods and practices throughout the world', but it was all too hectic at the time. I have now only general reflections: on the fairly harsh dealings with the Spanish who were so anxious to catch up and succeed in shipbuilding; the much more congenial relations with the Dutch and in particular with the van der Giessen shipyard who were always closest to us in attitude and mentality, and friendships lasted there – with a touch of Bols 'turbine oil' to help; the straight but firm dealings with the Danes at Burmeister & Wain, and their Friday lunch of pea soup with ham; the Poles, a battered people living on gristle; and the Germans again, because after the happy co-operation over the *Bays*, we helped Ellerman Line with their containership at AG Weser – and grew tired of wurst, especially in the soup; the Japanese, by now supremely confident and on their way to becoming world leaders in shipbuilding, but still as inscrutable; and the French whom I now want to tell about – proficient and carefully friendly but still very French and *supérieur*. They helped to bring Blue Funnel to its knees. I am glad I escaped before we received our very last ship in 1984 from South Korea, another country displaying its own privations. One of our superintendents mistakenly turned up for a launch accompanied by his wife. He was rapidly re-educated on the place of women in Korea. Ships seemed to be best built in developing countries by hungry, striving people.

It will be obvious that only a very wealthy company could have countenanced such expenditure on new ships, especially if I say that various other non-marine acquisitions were in hand at the same time. It was intensely satisfying for me because I ended up with knowledge of virtually every type of ocean-going ship, and of shipyards in every major shipbuilding country. By now I had as large a staff of qualified naval architects as any shipping company, a fair proportion being scattered round the world supervising these ships.

Blue Funnel first began to look at carrying liquefied natural gas (LNG) as cargo in 1970, when it was becoming clear that the containerships were going to be successful and we would need other kinds of ships to keep occupied what was still very much a shipping company. LNG is simply what we would call household or North Sea gas, but carried in liquid form. This makes it easy to carry large amounts because 600 cubic metres of gas can be turned into one cubic metre of liquid. The trouble is that it is then at a temperature of –160 degrees centigrade. This extreme cold will not mean much to the average reader, but to the naval architect it means that no ordinary shipbuilding steel can withstand it. At such a temperature steel becomes so brittle it loses its strength altogether, so very special precautions have to be taken to protect the double-hulled structure of the ship, with massive insulation round the gas tanks. This makes for an incredibly expensive ship.

Then there is the safety aspect in operation. The two ships we ordered from Chantiers de l'Atlantique at St Nazaire were to carry the amount of gas that would fill many hundreds of the sort of gasometers you see close by the Oval cricket ground. It does not need much imagination to picture what might happen in a collision or some such marine emergency. We studied this in utmost detail and the general feeling was that if anybody could carry LNG safely it would be Blue Funnel with their traditional record of safety and care behind them. Blue Funnel joined with Nederlandsche Scheepvaart Unie of the Netherlands and ordered *Nestor* for Blue Funnel, and *Gastor* for NSU – ships of 122,000 cubic metre capacity, meaning they were amongst the largest of the relatively few LNG carriers around at that time. We formed a joint technical team with NSU where Blue Funnel led on naval architecture and cargo containment and control systems, and NSU on the engineering side.

I had not dealt with French shipbuilders before and found we were up against an astute negotiator. All the detailed contract discussions were done by one brilliant man, M. Regard, at their head office in Paris. He ran rings round us. He included clauses covering himself for escalation in price just when we were about to enter the period of greatest inflation and adverse currency movement. He wrote in a clause beneficial to him if the cargo capacity proved greater than specified, and a penalty against him if the ship speed was deficient. The former was out of all proportion to the latter, so he set out to make the ship big and fat to gain capacity at the expense of speed. When in the end we found the ships marginally deficient in speed, the gain to him from the greater than specified capacity worked wholly in his favour.

Then, beyond the control of even M. Regard, we had the rise in oil price in 1973 that transformed the market in energy during the five and more years of building the ships. The hoped-for contract to carry gas from Venezuela to the US Gulf disappeared almost as soon as the ink dried on the shipbuilding contract. There was a change in Government in Venezuela that killed the project. For the whole of these years of construction there was an urgent search to find work for the ships. David Graham, one of the intake of more sensible managers, was made head of a company called Gastransco, specially set up to market the ships. The next proposition was for US West Coast utilities to import gas from Indonesia. A twenty-five year gas purchase contract was agreed and a corresponding charter for shipment. But it all depended on both State and Federal Governments being satisfied with the result of public hearings on safety. After five years of these there were no permits.

I was appointed operations director of the *Nestor* and it should have been a marvellously satisfying job – building and running the most expensive and complex merchant ship Blue Funnel and probably the UK ever had, with the need for a level of safety in operation away above anything elsewhere in the fleet. But it wasn't satisfying, for we began to realize we had a disaster in the making.

Nestor was built in St Nazaire over the years 1971 to 1976, and *Gastor* was finished in 1977. I had many visits to the yard and we sometimes stayed at La Baule which was next door and a pleasant seaside place. That was when we used to visit the site of the commandos' successful raid on the St Nazaire dock. I had excellent superintendents in charge – Dave Tucker, before he went off to Gastransco to help David Graham; Russell Knight; and in the early stages Ken Chapman, before he left us for Cammell Laird and then Swan Hunter. In due course I had Captain Gwyn Pari-Huws as an

A place for meditation: the interior of one of Nestor*'s LNG tanks.*

enthusiastic operations manager when we came closer to the delivery date. There were stalwarts like Steve Sprague and others on the engineering side.

The sea trials on completion showed a deficiency in ship speed. Speed had been sacrificed by the builders in favour of cargo capacity where the contractual gains were greater. After painful arguments and repeated speed trials we invoked the terms of the contract which plainly allowed us to reject the ship. I personally drafted the telex to the shipyard declaring that we were rejecting the ship and asking for all payments to be refunded. There was never any chance it would happen. The shipyard simply turned to the arbitration clause and we and NSU were faced with a long, utterly miserable and expensive legal battle conducted in French and, even worse, under French law. We had to share the penalties written into the contract between us and the shipyard.

Even then we were not finished. Outboard of the ship's LNG gas tanks there was a double hull and this created enormous ballast spaces of irregular shape and with some almost inaccessible corners. All had to be coated with paint material for protection and just at delivery we found the coatings were failing. The shipyard agreed that all had to be recoated. There followed one of the most dismal episodes. The ships were taken to Marseilles and there, in the heat of summer, the tank interiors with all their intricate steelwork, in darkness and confinement, had to be shotblasted, cleaned out and recoated. My superintendents monitoring all this had one of the grimmest tasks I have known – and all the time we suspected it might well be pointless.

On completion everything felt unreal. Everybody knew the ships had no work in view. *Nestor* was sailed to the gas terminal at Canvey Island where a part load of gas was bought from British Gas and the whole ship and its systems were tested. It was a strange experience actually to see in a bucket the innocent-looking but hazardous cargo we had designed and built for. And then as operations director I had the final lugubrious task of laying up *Nestor* in Loch Striven off the Clyde estuary. That in itself was a new experience because conservation of the ship for the unknown years ahead was crucial. Everything was protected, oiled, greased, painted, covered and sealed against Scottish weather. The vital innards received special care. Much of the engine room was opened up – the boilers, turbines, pumps; and a dehumidifying system was put into action. To go round the engine room in that condition was like visiting some progressive science museum where you could look inside everything. A generator had to be mounted on deck to supply the power for the dehumidifying and for the needs of the skeleton crew who were then to live aboard in hermit style. Even the generator had to be contained in a sound-proof housing to avoid abusing the intense silence of the remote Scottish loch.

Gastor followed in due course and there the ships, which had each cost way above £70 million even in those days, remained over the years until both were written off the companies' books. *Nestor* was sold in 1989 to Shell for a pittance. Blue Funnel never really recovered from this hammer blow and I think Sir Lindsay Alexander, who had been the main promoter of the project, never rediscovered his former enthusiasm and verve. None of us blamed him, for we had all been behind him in this brave and pioneering project.

It was to be downhill from then on for this proud company. The conventional ships steadily disappeared both in Blue Funnel and Elder Dempster, and other UK shipping companies shared the same fate. One of my last special efforts came when I was appointed to lead a little group which would look at all possible diversifications for the company. I had a select band in support – Phil Foster, a bright business-orientated graduate brought in via the central think-tank the company had now set up; Ron Obree, another quietly determined management and business campaigner as secretary; and Ron Gooseman, one of the more intellectual managers from Corys. It was a kind of impossible and depressing commission. Although I had a free hand to look at anything and everything, a despondency pervaded all our work and we sensed, unsurprisingly, a reluctance on the company's part to commit further large sums following the only very modest successes of all our recent ventures. I looked at a great range of business from recycling waste to offshore oil and gas but could not come up with any proposal that fired up the main board to some fresh challenge. We were on an inexorable slide towards our exit from shipping. The last Glen Line ships were sold in 1977 and the *Priams* followed. Odyssey Works closed in 1981, and *Aulis* our training establishment for officers likewise. The last Blue Funnel ships disappeared in 1988 and Elder Dempster's in 1989. So ended Alfred Holt's dream of 1865.

One could adopt the harsh view and suggest, as some have done, that Blue Funnel should have taken the firm text-book businesslike action earlier of making the office and sea staff redundant, accepting the cost, and straightaway put their capital into some other activities. Two things would not allow that – the decency of a management still tending towards paternalism who wanted, in the tradition of the company, to do their best for their staff; and a certain lack of confidence and expertise that prevented them, in spite of academic brilliance, from venturing further into unknown territory. The distressing period of diffuse effort and uncertain direction followed.

I had left by this time, having agreed with Sir Lindsay Alexander at the end of 1978 that I would accept the offer of the technical director's position at British Shipbuilders. As he did so he breathed: 'Thank goodness we've got one away safely.' It might be questioned whether British Shipbuilders was all *that* safe, but the comment reflected the concern for staff that had always permeated Blue Funnel. He then summoned John Parker (now Sir John) of British Shipbuilders to his office to discuss my pension and ensure I would not lose out. I didn't. The notice that Sir Lindsay circulated to Blue Funnel staff regarding my resignation referred to my services as being of incalculable worth to the company – and I appreciated that greatly.

During these years when the company became so troubled our family of three girls were growing up. Hazel finished at Howell's School in Denbigh and set off for London where she enrolled at the London Secretarial College. The same lady interviewed her as had interviewed her mother a generation earlier. Ursula was still at Howell's and Angela at Wirral Grammar School when the call came for a move to the North East. I suppose I line myself up with other colleagues of my time and way of life, and have to admit with some regret that I did not spend enough time with my children nor encourage and help them more in their education. We normally had the weekends together but I was away somewhere for a few days in every week; and most evenings were spent on office work or in the writing of publications or technical papers. Yet we, family and all, felt part of a great company, and friendships, particularly with my own naval architects' team, were close and have lasted to this day. Several of them, Ray Adams, Bob

On holiday in France, 1980: Angela, Ursula, Elfrida and Hazel.

Brown, Howard Jones and Mike Burkett, joined me at British Shipbuilders in due course. I felt this a considerable responsibility at the time, but they have all progressed and prospered here in the North East.

I travelled from the Wirral to Newcastle to take up my new job on the bitterly cold and snowy evening of 1 January 1979 when, due to strikes, there was a national panic about petrol supplies. I had recourse to extracting petrol, with the help of the night watchman, from my Ocean Fleets company car to get me to Newcastle in my British Shipbuilders car. I felt just as a school-leaver does on exchanging the sixth form for his first job. But I have told my story from here onwards in the earlier chapters on shipbuilding and then research and development.

Part V

Warships

CHAPTER 17

Entry to the warship scene

FROM MY EARLY DAYS at Caledon shipyard in Dundee through to the days of the modern cargo vessels in the 1960s I had been involved only in merchant ships. That was to change. The Chamber of Shipping was the body that had represented British merchant shipping in the eyes of the public, the Government and outside partners for many years. To become its president was the pinnacle of a shipowner's career and ambitions. Needless to say, Blue Funnel enjoyed its share of the occupancy of that position and this usually carried the statutory knighthood at the end. Sir Stewart MacTier, who had been my main board director, Sir Ronald Swayne and Sir Kerry St Johnston all found recognition through this route. At the time of my busiest period at Blue Funnel, the Chamber decided it needed a new image and gave itself the title the General Council of British Shipping (GCBS). I had been involved for many years in various of its committees and especially its Technical and Research Committee which did good and useful work. But the expenditure incurred by this committee gradually came under closer examination by the GCBS management. Was it necessary for shipping to spend its own money on its studies? Should not the producer of the ships undertake any research necessary? Or could the Council contract in other parties to do its investigations? In the end, as someone pointed out, the budget allowed for technical projects and research was getting to be almost less than the telephone bill for the organization.

It was at this time, and shortly before I moved from Blue Funnel to British Shipbuilders, that the GCBS put forward my name as their representative on the Ministry of Defence (MOD) Fuel Sub Committee. This rather arcane body considered in detail the Royal Navy's requirements for fuel for its ships. Such was my ignorance about MOD that I was surprised when I found the Navy, for their own very sound reasons, used something called 'dieso' to fuel its engines. It sounded a rather puerile title, and rather an expensive fuel compared with the heavy fuel oil that merchant shipping used to propel its ships. Heavy fuel oil was low cost, at least before the oil price rises of the 1970s. It was what remained after almost every vestige of distillate virtue had been extracted from crude oil. But this choice 'dieso' fuel merited detailed discussion apparently, to which I regret I could contribute very little. But from that small beginning I then found myself, while still with Blue Funnel, invited to join the Hull

DSAC Hull and Machinery Committee visiting Vickers Barrow, 1986: on MM's left, 2nd David Watson, 3rd Roy Burcher, 5th Ian Buxton, 6th Ross Goodman, 7th Eric Tupper; on his right, 2nd Roy Turner, 3rd Jim Glasgow, 7th David Goodrich.

Committee of the Defence Scientific Advisory Council (DSAC). I was to remain closely involved with this council and its committees for the next twenty years.

The existence of the DSAC was supposed to be 'classified' in MOD terms, but its cover was shortly to be blown because of the activities I want to describe. It existed to provide a totally independent view of the technologies associated with MOD in all its diverse affairs, and to comment on MOD scientific and technical progress. It included in my area of interest the most effective and knowledgeable members of the maritime technical world. So I entered at the modest level of membership of the Hull Committee. There was a Machinery Committee running parallel with it and sadly there was little association one with the other at that time, although I was able to change this a little later. There were other committees within the DSAC dealing with land warfare and air warfare. Throughout all my references to the MOD and to the DSAC and its committees I should make it clear that I am giving my own personal views and my side of the story. This may not necessarily be the MOD view.

At first I could see little value in or application for the committee's deliberations, but this was partly, I suppose, because of my own lack of knowledge of naval affairs. Professor King of the engineering department of Edinburgh University was chairman of the Hull Committee, soon to be followed by Professor Faulkner of the naval architecture department at Glasgow University. I still found little real substance in its discussions. More time seemed to be spent discussing the agenda for the next meeting than discussing anything useful at the current meeting. So much so, that I got round to considering resigning. Just at that point Professor Faulkner left for a short-term appointment in US and I was asked, to my total astonishment, to be chairman. I agreed, and it did not take long to find at least one topic that gave me and the Hull Committee, and many others, a very real purpose for years to come. This topic was what came to be known as the 'short-fat' versus 'long-thin' controversy and it related to the basic design of the Royal Navy frigates which were the mainstay of the fleet.

Royal Navy ships had been developed over many years to their then current design by costly experimentation, detailed calculation and rigorous examination of performance and operations at sea. The typical hull of a frigate had ended up with a length to breadth ratio varying between 7.6 and 9.2 or thereabouts, depending on which frigate was referred to. That meant that the length was roughly 7 to 9 times the breadth (or beam) of the vessel. In the late 1970s a certain David Giles started to persuade some less knowledgeable but influential people into believing there was merit in a shorter and 'fatter' (meaning wider) ship with a length to breadth ratio of about 5 instead of somewhere between 7 and 9. From the start I believed him to be wrong, as did all other professional naval architects. I never found, during all the years that the argument raged, a single properly qualified naval architect outside his company (and I think I can say I have either known or known of them all) who, having become familiar with the case, was prepared to support Giles's idea – or 'concept' as he insisted on calling it. Yet it took enormous effort and cost, it involved the resignation of several people in very senior positions, vast sums in legal fees, and in the end a very expensive inquiry conducted at the personal request of Prime Minister Thatcher to show the whole thing was a nonsense. I shall come back at the end to the lessons from this astonishing episode, but I particularly wanted to tell the story because I saw it unfold from three separate viewpoints, and not many others had that opportunity.

I had first become aware of the existence of David Giles through references to him by Julian Taylor just about the time I was leaving Blue Funnel in 1978. I heard more about that link between Julian and Giles after I joined British Shipbuilders, and my fears of some malign outcome increased. This feeling was shared by Ray Adams who took over from me when I moved to British Shipbuilders. Ray and I watched one of our respected staff, Len Buxton, recently retired, being sucked into talks between Julian Taylor and Giles. This concerned the quite small protection vessel *Havornen* and three sister ships built at Frederikshavn in Denmark to Giles's design. *Havornen* remained in Denmark while the others were destined for Burma. I remember very well Ray advising Len to 'be careful' and not get too involved. I think he, wise man, pulled out shortly after when he found he was getting out of his depth.

To this day I wonder if Julian had some influence over the wide-ship idea because of my expressing views to him, many years earlier, that increasing the beam of a ship might not always be disastrous as far as the propulsion power was concerned. And of course, it provided greater stability. But any view I expressed back in the days of the Alfred Holt '*D*'class of cargo liners in the 1960s which were deficient in stability, and by inference in beam, never countenanced the extreme length to breadth ratios which Giles was now advocating.

David Laurent Giles had an Oxford BA, had served in the submarine service, had an aeronautical background and although his business stationery carried the bold description of his company as Naval Architects, Consultants and Agents, he himself is clearly on record as saying that he was not a naval architect. His co-director in Thornycroft, Giles & Associates Ltd. was Commander Peter Thornycroft, a famous name in the marine world. He *was* a naval architect, but he never seemed to play any very obvious active role in the short-fat controversy and died at the age of seventy-three as the whole affair was about to end in 1988. Thornycroft had been closely involved in earlier days in the design of smaller craft such as pilot boats and was very successful. I think the trouble originated when Giles claimed that such successful small craft could be scaled-up to the same size as frigates and still be as successful. There are several reasons why ships do not easily scale up and he should have known that the required horsepower would be very high.

But he also claimed that the vessel would have the benefit from 'lift'. In other words it would start to 'plane' on the surface of the sea. He did not seem to realize that to do this the propulsion power would be enormous, roughly double the power of a conventional frigate, and so be quite uneconomic and unrealistic. There were many other features such as the ability to carry enough weapons, seakeeping and noise reduction, that needed exploring. But as I have said, it took nearly ten years and vast cost to disprove his subtle arguments. They were subtle because he made a speciality of avoiding full and open discussion based on real data with contemporary naval architects. He concentrated on influencing those in high places where he had some strange credence. Geoffrey Pattie, Minister for Defence Procurement at the time was one such. Also, Giles had some mysterious entry to the press. To read the columns of *The Times* Diarist, in particular, over that long period is quite comical when set against the now accepted view that the whole thing was never going to be a runner.

There was another aspect of Giles's conduct that affected the full and proper discussion of his claims and that was his propensity for issuing writs or threatening to do so. This was very effective in stifling proper discussion. He was engaged in such an exercise when I was with British Shipbuilders. There was a requirement for patrol vessels for Hong Kong in 1980 and Giles naturally took an interest. There were discussions between him and British Shipbuilders and his design was included under the name of *Osprey*. During its examination by British Shipbuilders the St Albans experiment tank became involved and David Moor the superintendent, who was ever seeking to expand his knowledge and his data base, had taken more interest in *Osprey* than Giles had expected, to the extent of testing it without permission. Most designers would have been grateful to have a hull form tested at no cost. Model testing is an extremely expensive exercise. However, Giles sued British Shipbuilders for breach of copyright.

That legal case then rumbled on with increasing costs and growing rancour right through till 1985/86, on the basis that *Osprey*, according to Giles, had some mysterious qualities that held enormous promise not only for its designer, but for the nation. Although the surreptitious testing of the *Osprey* hull form could not and did not in any way help British Shipbuilders, since there was no particular merit in it, Giles sought to inflate and exaggerate the case and use it to embarrass the corporation. This is when we find Admiral of the Fleet Lord Hill-Norton becoming very vocal in support of Giles's design, and needless to say Tam Dalyell MP, the inveterate critic of all things military, asking questions during defence debates in the House. *The Times* Diary of January 1985 advised us that the forthcoming trial *British Shipbuilders* v. *Giles*, which Lord Hill-Norton was incensed about being held partly in camera, would 'make Clive Ponting's trial look like a vicar's tea party'.

The next day *The Times* Diary told us that the case was making it difficult for British Shipbuilders to sell the Hall Russell shipyard in Aberdeen because the yard had won the contract for the *Peacock* class of patrol vessels and they might have been based on Giles's *Osprey* – which was a nonsense. The following day *The Times* Diary told us that Lord Hill-Norton had said there was a cover-up about Giles's design being rejected by the Navy as an alternative *Type 23* frigate. It pointed out that Marshall Meek, who had been chief naval architect with British Shipbuilders, was now head of the National Maritime Institute (which was true), and had been chairman of the DSAC Hull Committee (which was also true) when it rejected the Giles design. And so it went on day after day in *The Times* until its leading article on 5 February 1985, referring to the Speaker of the House refusing to allow a debate on *Giles* v. *British Shipbuilders*, wanted Minister of Defence Michael

Heseltine to answer to the House on the subject. He did not, being rather more careful than his Minister for Procurement.

A comic side of the reporting began to appear in *The Times* Diary of 29 May 1985 when a Treasury Solicitor, it was claimed, had been found as an interloper at a High Court hearing in chambers when preparations for the court case *re* British Shipbuilders were in hand. The Treasury, the Diarist said, had admitted sending 'an observer'. Then on 11 June *The Times* suggested there had been evidence of Brooks's Club being bugged when an independent committee was being set up to pronounce on the Giles controversy. We shall come back later to the end product of this particular committee, which became known as the Hill-Norton Committee Report.

During all this time there was an inordinate expenditure of time and legal costs on this case within British Shipbuilders. Such was the internal pressure that David Moor, the superintendent of the St Albans experiment tank, a colleague of mine since university days and a man whose life had been dedicated to the study of hull forms, felt obliged to resign. Shortly after, Jack Daniel who had earlier been Director-General Ships at MOD and was now director of British Shipbuilders' warship-building division, and necessarily a party in the dispute, also felt he should resign. These were regrettable losses of eminent men in the profession and, as I shall show, were quite unnecessary. I myself was called upon from time to time to comment on the technicalities and worked closely with Geoff Mills who led our legal team in British Shipbuilders.

The Times Diary had, however, not given up. In November 1985 it suggested there were problems with British Shipbuilders selling the jewel in their crown – the Vickers Barrow shipyard, and these problems might be because Vickers was a defendant, as part of British Shipbuilders, in the forthcoming *Osprey* copyright trial. We were told that an embarrassing forty-five day trial scheduled for January 1987 (over a year away) was to open and this would affect Mrs Thatcher's expected general election date because senior Government ministers would be involved. There never was going to be such a trial, but the arguments – and costs, dragged on till January 1987 when British Shipbuilders settled. I had left British Shipbuilders by that time. I feel it was probably sheer weariness that prompted the settlement which was on the basis of each side recognizing the professional integrity of the other, and there was no order sought as to damages or costs. There was, of course, reputed to be some undisclosed payment by British Shipbuilders, which I think they were wrong to make. By that time the final conclusion that there was no value in the Giles design proposal was about to be announced.

On leaving British Shipbuilders in 1984 I had become managing director of the National Maritime Institute (NMI) at Feltham, West London. Here was David Giles – again! His concept had moved on from being called

Osprey to *Sirius* and then to *S90*. He had commissioned NMI to carry out model tests for resistance, propulsion and seakeeping for his *S90* hull form in the experiment tanks before I arrived at Feltham. After making part payment, I found he had refused to pay the balance because he did not agree either with the actual results, or the way NMI staff analysed them. In other words they did not support his claim of having found some unique hull form. After much discussion with solicitors we decided in the summer of 1984 that NMI would commence proceedings against Thornycroft Giles. As we might have expected, years of argument and toing and froing between solicitors followed, and the general effect was to severely inhibit rational discussion on these matters.

Throughout all the arguments about the *S90*, Giles only once to my knowledge ever put into print a reference to the horsepower his hull form would need to drive it. I shall come back to that reference later, but it was enough to show that he required about double the horsepower for a normal frigate and this fact made the success of the design very doubtful indeed. I was able to point out to him in an open letter in *The Naval Architect* of May 1985 that he was merely using a hull shape that was very close to what NMI had in its data files. Two eminent experimenters at NMI, Marwood and Bailey, had earlier run a very full series of tests on small craft hull designs very similar to those Giles was promoting, and they had published their findings. These hulls were never intended to be blown up to the size Giles was proposing for modern MOD frigates, simply because the horsepower would have become prohibitive. Giles never accepted my letter nor indeed any other NMI explanation.

Instead of rational discussion he involved us in bitter disputes not only about the validity of the NMI tests themselves but also about the mysterious factor naval architects know as (1 + x). It was clear that Giles never really understood what it was because he seemed to argue that it was itself a measure of success or performance of a hull design. In actual fact it is only an empirical correction factor, obtained from years of experience, which links the power predicted from model tests with the actual power determined from the ship's full-scale trials. There is usually a slight discrepancy between the two, remembering that naval architects have to use the results from a model probably not much more than 3 metres long to predict the power of a ship possibly 300 metres long. Naturally, it is always very near to 1.0 and only varies between extremes of 0.9 and 1.1. Yet we had endless discussion, all conducted through solicitors, on the merits not only of the NMI model results themselves, but on the (1 + x) used. So it dragged on till, late in 1986 after my retirement from NMI (by which time NMI had become BMT), sheer weariness again set in, I suspect, and a form of settlement was reached. NMI did not recover full payment.

Chapter 18

Short-fat versus long-thin

My experiences with British Shipbuilders and NMI and Thornycroft Giles as recorded here were, however, mere peripheral skirmishes compared with the main battlefield where Giles was engaged directly with MOD, and consequently with the DSAC. From the moment DSAC took an interest in the argument, I was involved throughout, firstly when at British Shipbuilders, then when I was at NMI, and latterly in (so-called) retirement.

Just at that time the Royal Navy were to have a new class of frigate, to be known as the *Type 23*. The concept and initial design had been developed in the normal way by MOD's own in-house resource, the Royal Corps of Naval Constructors, using the vast resources of knowledge and experience contained within that body. But their performance and abilities were being questioned. I had been familiar with members of the RCNC for many years, mainly through contacts within the Royal Institution of Naval Architects. There is no doubt these people were superior. The trouble was they knew it and tended to show it, and the rest of the maritime world would sometimes resent this superiority. I quote one little illustration. I referred once in open discussion to the role of the DSAC in advising MOD after its existence had been exposed by Giles. Ken Rawson, who was the senior designer at the time, loftily dismissed the DSAC as 'a useful irritant'. A bit rich, I thought, as I and my colleagues had by that time spent countless hours defending his department against the allegations of David Giles.

The Royal Corps members were selected and trained to highest standards. They originally had their own educational route through the Royal Naval College at Greenwich and their practical training was, naturally, through the Royal Navy. But they had been obliged to leave Greenwich and their educational route then ran through the naval architecture section of the department of mechanical engineering at University College London. This had been astutely arranged by Professor R.E.D. Bishop of UCL when he heard of the need for the Royal Corps to leave Greenwich. I shall have more to say of him later. I myself have never had the slightest doubt about the technical competence and the integrity of the RCNC. It therefore came as a surprise when I found in 1982, when the *Type 23* design was nearing the point at which tenders to build would be requested from warship-building yards, that urgent questions were being asked about alternative designs, or at least one alternative design. This was of course, the Thornycroft Giles concept of a shorter wider ship.

There had been discussions between Thornycroft Giles and MOD as far back as 1981 with Giles offering his *Sirius* short-fat hull as a cheaper alternative to the conventional *Type 23*. The Minister for Defence Procurement, Geoffrey Pattie, had obviously been strongly influenced by Giles's competence as an eloquent salesman. He was clearly persuaded that here was something that offered a possibly better, and above all, cheaper alternative to the product proposed by the orthodox and allegedly over-conservative MOD/RCNC designers. Battle was joined, with MOD naturally arguing their case for a design based on years of experience and technical achievement as against what was merely a 'concept' with no firm data to back it up. They rightly believed, as I always have done, that a proper ship design must be expressed in at least an outline plan showing the layout; a lines and body plan, as naval architects call it, defining the hull form; and evidence in actual numbers that the weight and buoyancy, the stability, the propulsion power and speed have been calculated and proved acceptable. None of this was forthcoming from Thornycroft Giles. Instead, there were only strongly expressed claims as to the superior but highly confidential merits of what they themselves described as a 'concept'.

Actually, Thornycroft Giles were not alone in questioning MOD designers. I had done the same at times, believing that they should, if necessary, be prepared to justify their views. Others had queried certain aspects of MOD ships. In particular YARD, a powerful naval architecture and marine engineering consultancy based in Glasgow, and originating in the former Yarrow Shipbuilding Company, had made bold to suggest possible alternatives to the MOD design for the *Type 23*. They believed, for example, that MOD had traditionally striven too hard for the smallest and lightest ship for the best balance between cost and capability. YARD suggested there could well be merit in allowing the size of the ship to increase somewhat, and using more conventional hull structures rather than the more sophisticated and expensive structures developed by Navy designers. In other words, a more commercially oriented approach could be considered and indeed several of YARD'S ideas were incorporated in the *Type 23* design, especially in the ship structure. But nowhere did YARD (or I or anyone else) ever countenance anything so totally different in its dimensions as the Giles concept now being put forward.

With MOD encouragement YARD had completed their own full study of the proposed *Type 23* design and gave their views to MOD in mid 1982. Although it made proposals which, if incorporated, would have delayed the construction of the *Type 23*, MOD considered it very carefully and, putting YARD's views together with their own, concluded that their own basic design, as compared with the Thornycroft Giles concept, was wholly satisfactory. This conclusion sent Thornycroft Giles into their customary fury, coupled with frantic media activity. By the end of the year the press were in action again. Bridget Bloom of the *Financial Times* and Lindsay Vincent of the *Sunday Observer* wrote advising readers that the Government were to give Thornycroft Giles an opportunity to validate their design 'in the teeth of opposition from Navy designers'. Also that 'bitter rifts were developing within the Royal Navy, MOD and British Shipbuilders'.

At the beginning of 1983 Controller of the Navy, Admiral Sir Lindsay Bryson, asked the DSAC Hull Committee, of which I was chairman, to take up the matter as an independent body and advise on the relative merits of the Thornycroft Giles proposals. Controller of the Navy carries the ultimate responsibility for the providing of all naval vessels. Knowing how slippery Thornycroft Giles could be in discussion, I thought quite hard before inviting Giles to give a presentation to the committee. I was extremely fortunate in the membership of my committee, having built it up with people I knew: Rodney Eatock-Taylor of UCL, now professor of engineering at Oxford; Ian Buxton of the department of marine technology at Newcastle University; David Watson of YARD, Glasgow; Professor Louis Rydill of the department of mechanical engineering, UCL; George Ward of the British Ship Research Association; Roy Turner, chief naval architect at Vickers Shipbuilding and Engineering, Barrow. These were the independent naval architect members who were best able to support me, and there were in addition the MOD representatives who provided the link with, and the necessary entry to, the official side: David Brown of Ship Department, MOD; and the late Professor Roy Burcher of what was at that time the Admiralty Marine Technology Establishment at Haslar. The Hull Committee had already commenced a study of ways to make ships of the Royal Navy cheaper because new ships, demanding increased sophistication and ever higher performance, were becoming alarmingly expensive. The suggestion from Giles that he could put forward a design that he claimed would cost only half as much as a conventional design was therefore one of particular relevance to our studies.

What we found from our eventual meeting with Thornycroft Giles was disappointing, but not surprising to me. The voluminous documentation put before us did not explain in recognized technical terms why they claimed such benefits for the short-fat ship. In fact, the investigatory tests on models of the Giles form that I have referred to in the previous chapter as being carried out at NMI were only being commissioned at that very moment. So Giles had been able to convince the principal Government minister involved and various other high-ranking people that he had some revolutionary concept long before there were any hard facts and figures available to prove or disprove his case. We have already seen that these model tests did not

MM at Buckingham Palace in 1989, with Ursula, Elfrida and Angela in support.

prove what he wished to see and that they became a source of dispute. It became increasingly clear as time went on that Giles, perhaps having to concede in his own mind that there was less merit in his wide hull form by way of providing better resistance characteristics and so less horsepower than he hoped for, began to repeat and press his claims that his ship would benefit from the hydrodynamic characteristic known as 'lift'. Some of us recognize it better as 'planing', seen for example in the way that fast speedboats lift out of the water when running at high speed. It is accepted that smaller vessels, perhaps even up to patrol boat size, might be able to plane to some extent. But we all knew it would only be possible to get a frigate-sized ship to plane if it was given an extraordinarily high propulsion power, beyond anything remotely acceptable as to cost either in engines or fuel.

Yet one of Giles's supporters, a certain Richard L. Garwin of the IBM Thomas J. Watson Research Center in New York thought otherwise. I never did discover how Giles found his supporters but they seemed to fall inevitably to his blandishments. Garwin was a physicist and specialized in military technology. He was certainly not a naval architect, so he wrote with great conviction: 'The simple fact is that whatever benefits are demonstrated by a model in the use of dynamic lift to reduce propulsive power requirements, are also available in a similar full-sized ship.' What he failed to mention was that the power needed to generate this dynamic lift in a full-sized ship was beyond any acceptable limit.

I have concentrated so far on the resistance, the horsepower required and the speed of the Giles hull form almost to the exclusion of other warship features. This was because we were being offered some reputedly novel hull form, and it is the hull form that determines the speed and power required. But Giles also made claims regarding the superior performance in seakeeping and also in the weaponry that could be carried. The Hull Committee therefore spent a lot of time investigating these matters, and always came back to the view that Giles's claims were not supported by authentic evidence. For example, amongst the scanty information we were given there was a plan of the *S90* vessel. It was the sort of thing a school-boy would be severely rebuked for in an elementary engineering lesson. The *S90* was actually shown as having all the decks of the same shape. This was manifestly ludicrous. It can readily be pictured that the front of a ship, the bow, is always raked to some degree, that is, sloped upwards and forwards. This means that each deck below the main weather deck must end at the fore end further back than the deck above. This then means that the sides of the ship are narrower at each deck as one descends into the ship. Yet Thornycroft Giles's plans showed each deck to be of the same shape and size as one went lower down into the ship. This made for a very nice series of spaces for accommodation, stores, services and the like. Unfortunately it was quite impossible and the whole interior of the ship as they had drawn it was therefore ridiculous. In the normal way, I prepared a Hull Committee report on our findings for the Marine Technology Board of DSAC to whom we reported, all of this being reasonably confidential to the parties involved as befitted DSAC business. I was a member of the Marine Technology Board by virtue of being chairman of the Hull Committee.

Then two events occurred out of the blue in May 1983. Firstly, Ken Rawson, the deputy director ship design in MOD resigned. Secondly, David Fishlock of the *Financial Times* gave full publicity to the substance of the Hull Committee's critical findings on the *S90*. I never discovered how he gained access to our discussions. As can be imagined it sent Giles into further enragement. I received a letter from him assuring me he would now only release what he chose to call his 'validation report' on his hull form to the MOD on condition it was not divulged to the Hull Committee of the DSAC. He wrote complaining to the DSAC secretariat; he wrote complaining to the editor of the *Financial Times*, in which letter incidentally, he admitted that his design was 'only in the rudimentary stage'. Yet he had managed to convince Government that he had a worthy competitor to the fully designed *Type 23* frigate. All this now exposed DSAC to a wider public than it had ever faced before.

The resignation of Ken Rawson who had ultimate technical design responsibility for the *Type 23* was something of a tragedy. There was no conceivable justification for anyone to seek his resignation, but his departure illustrated the hidden pressures that had been exerted over a long period, all generated by the short-fat long-thin argument. Ken was a brilliant naval architect, well recognized throughout his profession and completely above the sort of innuendo and skulduggery that seemed to pervade these years of conflict with Thornycroft Giles. I suspect he had found he was not being supported by the highest levels within MOD who seemed somehow paralysed in the face of the Thornycroft Giles attack. I think he was wrong to resign. We needed every ounce of effort available to resist the 'false teaching'. It sent out wrong signals, as the many critical references in the press demonstrated at the time. But I can fully sympathize with him.

Whatever may have been the clear direct criticism of the *S90* expressed in the DSAC report, there were still to be years of conflict on the subject and untold manhours to be needlessly expended. That DSAC report, with all its criticism and reservations, naturally went into the MOD system and to the Minister for Defence Procurement, Geoffrey Pattie. Still Giles kept on arguing his case. So much so, that an unclassified version of the DSAC Hull Committee report was issued by MOD in an effort to explain the weaknesses in Giles's proposition. The conclusions are worth recording because they still held good after the next four years and more, of bitter argument:

- We consider the *S90* has no advantages in terms of hydrodynamic performance over the conventional design concept for frigates. It is substantially more resistful and has excessive stability (i.e. because of its width).
- The space available in the *S90* would not be sufficient for it to fulfil the functions required by the Royal Navy.
- TGA's (Thornycroft, Giles & Associates) assessment of weight and power requirements are too low.
- Various features such as shock protection, noise suppression, damage survival, had not been shown.
- Lastly, the short wide hull form of the *S90* has such fundamental drawbacks as a concept for a modern class of frigate that no amount of further testing or detail designing is likely to affect our conclusions in any important respect.

It becomes tedious to record in detail the ongoings over the rest of 1983, so I tell only of the main events. Press references favourable to Giles's unusual design proposal continued. With threats to me and to DSAC because of the earlier leak to the *Financial Times*, I was presumably meant to go quietly on the subject. But I remained determined that this grotesque saga must come to a sensible conclusion, if only out of respect for the reputations of colleagues that had been damaged already. In July I was invited to a meeting with Minister for Defence Procurement Geoffrey Pattie, held at MOD in Whitehall to explain the Hull Committee report. He had in attendance Ian Stewart his Under-Secretary of State for Defence Procurement, and the private secretaries. A Mr Ling, a rather unknown supporter of Giles, was present. He was not recognized by me or my colleagues as a naval architect of any great prominence, and as far as we could see, not at that time a member of the Royal Institution of Naval Architects. He was employed by the British Ports Authority and was the only known technical supporter of Giles, who himself was not present. I had Professor Bishop of UCL in support. Controller of the Navy, Admiral Sir Lindsay Bryson was present together with Professor Norman, MOD chief scientist; R.J. Poole, director defence science; and P. Jarvis, director general ships. Capt. J. Moore, editor of *Jane's Fighting Ships* had been expected to support the minister but did not turn up.

The meeting started with a silent video of a model of the *S90* afloat in the English Channel. There had been an attempt to study this model in actual sea conditions and compare it with a *Leander* class ship, but it never served any useful purpose as there was no satisfactory means of correlating what was observed with controlled tests in an experiment tank, nor of comparing it with a conventional hull form. The minister had clearly been instructed by the absent Giles to show it, I think to demonstrate seakeeping abilities. After we had sat in silence for a while watching this primitive yellow-painted model aimlessly bobbing about in the waves, the minister opened with 'Well Mr Meek, she looks very stable does she not?' The pseudo-learned comment was so unexpected – and so ridiculous – that I found myself without words. Professor Bishop chipped in with some comment – ambiguous, as tended to be his style, but it tided over the silence. During my subsequent presentation of my report, it was very obvious that the minister was not going to be over-impressed. It was clearly going to be very difficult to adjust his mind-set.

The next significant meeting was a few months later when Ian Stewart, Under-Secretary of State, conducted a meeting intended to convey finally to Giles that his proposal was not going to be further embraced by MOD. They now wanted to get on with the ordering and building of the *Type 23* frigates. Giles turned up with an astonishing array of thirteen people in support. They included H. Metcalfe, chief executive of BAe; A. Thatcher, managing director of Dowty Electronics, with two others from the same company; Gillespie of NEI; Laite and Williams of Graseby Dynamics. Commander Peter Thornycroft actually materialized for once; and as I expected, my old boss Julian Taylor, who by this time had left Blue Funnel as others of his managerial colleagues had. On the MOD side, in addition to the under-secretary, there was a formidable attendance: Admiral Sir Lindsay Bryson, controller; Professor Norman, chief scientist; Mumford and Poole, senior department staff; Professor Bishop, now vice-chancellor of Brunel University; and the three technical representatives – Bill Sanders of MOD Forward Design; Jan Neumann managing director of YARD; and myself from DSAC.

The Under-Secretary of State started by asking for a detailed technical appraisal of the *Type 23* versus the *S90* from Bill Sanders. This was the MOD view. Then a resumé of the independent YARD studies of Thornycroft, Giles and Associates' (TGA) validation report from Jan Neumann. And lastly, my summary of the critical DSAC Hull Committee report. TGA were invited to reply. Each member of the TGA team answered in turn to form a weird amalgam of subjective offerings. Commander Thornycroft quoted his family associations and felt that there was merit in the *S90* 'from the seat of his pants'. Julian Taylor felt that minds were closed from the MOD side, and then went on to prove his credentials by claiming he had been responsible for procuring sixty ships while with Blue Funnel (they had all been my design responsibility), and he had been on Lloyd's Register's Technical Committee for many years (during all of which time I supplied him with the appropriate comments on ship design). Many on the TGA side were, on their own admission, only interested in specific aspects such as sonar, weapons or sensors. Metcalfe of BAe clearly wished he had not come. In the end and after some rancorous exchanges, Controller Bryson made it clear that the *Type 23* would go ahead and TGA would do well to direct their sights on some other class of ship. But in spite of the mass of expert evidence against him, and with no single recognized designer to support him, Giles was determined to press on. He was not going away.

CHAPTER 19

End of short-fat

A PERIOD OF press silence on the subject was broken when Admiral Bryson presented a very full and lucid paper to the Royal Institution of Naval Architects in 1984 on *The Procurement of a Warship*. Obviously he would have had RCNC assistance in the writing of it. It put on record in great detail the way in which naval ships are designed and later procured. Quite naturally, the question of the TGA *S90* proposal arose and the Admiral confirmed in his paper how it was not acceptable to the Royal Navy. As is usual there was discussion on the paper, both verbal at the meeting and in writing thereafter. I contributed to the written discussion, made reference to the misconceptions within the *S90* proposal as I saw them – and made Mr Giles very angry again.

I was not the only one at that time who took legal advice before either writing to Mr Giles or writing about his proposals, such was the climate surrounding everything to do with the *S90*. When I mentioned the word 'quack' in my contribution to the discussion I received a very hurt response from Giles in the form of a letter to the editor of *The Naval Architect* when it published Admiral Bryson's paper and its discussion. I should have been glad it was not a writ. 'Few if any, of your Members, let alone your guests can have been the subject of such contumely as was implied concerning the *S90*'s designers in Marshall Meek's contribution to Admiral Bryson's paper', he wrote.

Unfortunately for him he published an article in the magazine *Naval Forces* just at that time, with a certain diagram in it which became known to many of us as Figure 13, and he actually repeated it in his contribution to the written discussion of Admiral Bryson's paper (that is where Figure 13 got its number.) For the first time Giles showed speed and power performance for the *S90* in actual numbers, including also certain seakeeping results. But it was his very own Figure 13 that proved conclusively that his *S90* would need at least twice as much horsepower to drive it as any conventional frigate. By any normal naval architectural reasoning this ruled it out – more and bigger engines, higher operating costs, less capability in weapons and so on inevitably followed. The strange thing is that Giles did not even seem to understand the significance of what he was publishing.

What he did was use what naval architects call a non-dimensional presentation. This is used to compare for example, the horsepower required for two similar ships of rather different sizes. But Giles used it in a foolish way to cover both his ship and an American frigate (the *FFG7 Perry* class) where the dimensions were very different indeed. On the face of it, using the particular coefficients he chose, the power required appeared to be similar. But when *actual* figures for speed and lengths of ship, which of course were very different, were fed into the calculations it proved conclusively that the *FFG7* needed 38 lb of thrust per ton of displacement and the *S90* 92 lb per ton – more than double the power. Giles never seemed to understand this. It confirmed what I already knew to be the position, and this encouraged me to carry on the battle against this nebulous but persistent proposal.

Still Giles did not give up. He resorted to influencing his friends in the press yet again in a series of articles, mainly in *The Times* Diary such as I described earlier. Then an article in *The Times* by Stephen Aris showed the way the wind was blowing. He told us there was a private lunch at Brooks's Club in St James. Among the guests were Admiral Hill-Norton, the former chief of defence staff; Professor R.V. Jones of Aberdeen University and renowned for his work on radar in World War II; the above-mentioned physicist Dr Richard L. Garwin; Lord Strathcona and Mount Royal, former Junior Minister for Defence Procurement; unbelievably, Sir Terence Conran of Habitat Mothercare; also Christopher Monckton, a member of the Downing Street policy unit. The purpose of the meeting apparently was to decide how to promote the *S90* in the face of all the powerful and authoritative opposition which had decided it had no merit. Here we recall the comic *Times* Diary suggestion I have referred to earlier, to the effect that Brooks's Club was bugged at one point by someone.

In January 1986 *The Times* confirmed that Admiral Hill-Norton, former Sea Lord, was to prepare a secret report for the Prime Minister on the short-fat ship proposal and show how the Royal Navy and the Government had been misled by their own advisers. My family have used the term SOA on the quiet, for some years. It stands for Silly Old Admiral, and I fear the usage of the term as applied to these retired gentlemen began about that time. And so we were subjected to the Hill-Norton Report which came out later in 1986. When it did, a massive leading article referring to it in *The Times* expressed the view very forcibly that our country had a sorry reputation for wasting its inventive genius by bureaucratic ineptitude and lack of official imagination. The report included the make-up of the committee which now lay behind it. Sir Terence Conran had become merely an adviser on accommodation within the ships, and Christopher Monckton's name had evaporated, leaving only Lord Strathcona and Mount Royal, the illustrious professor of physics R.V. Jones, and the US physicist Richard Garwin to tell the Prime Minister how to design Her Majesty's ships.

Figure 13, the only diagram in the whole Report, appeared yet again in all its mistaken glory in spite of Admiral Bryson's detailed explanation in his reply to the RINA discussion showing how it actually disproved the *S90*. One can hardly be surprised that a mere retired admiral should refer to it so proudly and so erroneously, but could not Lord Strathcona and Mount Royal have understood the mistake being made, or even Sir Terence Conran of Habitat Mothercare? Presumably Christopher Monckton harboured a suspicion of trouble ahead and lay low. A summary of the most important findings of the committee included gems such as the following: (comments in brackets are mine)

- The rejection of the TGA claims (note only *claims* after all these years when facts and figures should have been available) by DSAC was unsoundly based.
- The short-fat hull form offers enough advantages for ships up to destroyer size to merit much more serious consideration than it has so far been accorded. (This, after years of patient study of the TGA statements and clear exposition of its weaknesses by every authoritative source available in UK.)
- The short-fat hull form may (note *may*) offer a significant increase in top speed over the long-thin hull of similar size.
- If the 25 per cent saving in cost suggested (note *suggested*) by Frederikshavn of Denmark can be confirmed a wide degree of flexibility is offered to the Royal Navy.

Then followed the pompous recommendation, in spite of all that had gone before:

> We recommend that an official Committee of Inquiry be established under the Chairmanship of a learned Judge or Queens Counsel with independent members expert in relevant fields, to validate or reject our detailed conclusions and report the results urgently to the Prime Minister.

It was to be, of course, total rejection in the end. And I might say here that in other countries, US, France and the Netherlands, there were expressions of amazement – and amusement – from naval architects that such an absurd debate could run for so long in UK and reach such high levels.

Meanwhile I had become chairman of the Marine Technology Board of DSAC and so found myself successor to David Penny, recently managing director of the National Engineering Laboratory. David had been most helpful to me when I was chairman of the Hull Committee which by then I had managed to merge to become the Hull and Machinery Committee. I had also by now acquired fresh representatives on the naval architecture side to support me: Dr Ross Goodman of Lloyd's Register; David Goodrich, managing director of BMT Ltd; Tony Dorey, technical director of Vosper Thornycroft (not associated in any way with Thornycroft Giles).

An award from the Hong Kong Shipowners Association, 1992.

All my earlier advice rejecting the *S90* had gone through the normal route of the Marine Technology Board to the DSAC Council. The chairman of the DSAC was Professor John Cadogan (later Sir John), director of research at British Petroleum. He was always acutely conscious of the significance of what I was doing and was most supportive at every stage. He in turn, reported to the MOD chief scientist who was responsible for advising Government. So we found ourselves yet again having to prepare a DSAC paper in the form of a response to Hill-Norton. I formed a Hill-Norton Working Party and together we got down to a critical examination of his report. There was, however, to be a different recipient for our work.

Prime Minister Thatcher decided she had had enough of this incessant arguing. I think she must have echoed the words of Achish, King of Gath, when David fled from Saul and feigned madness before him: 'Wherefore have you brought him to me? Am I short of madmen that you bring this one to me to rave in my presence?' So she set up an inquiry at the end of May 1986. *The Times* and the *Daily Telegraph* and others construed this as a critical turning point in naval design, assuming the short-fat ship would prevail. As Lord Hill-Norton put it so elegantly in a *Times* main-page article: 'The Navy must be given bloody good ships, and if vested interests get a bloody nose in the process, then so be it.' Unfortunately for him, the blood was to end up on the wrong nose.

The crucial decision then was who would chair the inquiry. After long deliberation Professor John Caldwell of the naval architecture department of Newcastle University was appointed. I had known John for many years, a man of highest repute and an internationally recognized authority on naval architecture and in particular on ship structures. He was at the time president of the Royal Institution of Naval Architects. His new appointment as chairman lasted all of three weeks. Mr Giles objected to him as chairman because, for a short period, John Caldwell had been a director of a small subsidiary of British Shipbuilders. He was therefore sullied and not independent, according to Giles – a gross calumny. John would have been an excellent chairman, but probably it was all for the best since the chairman who was appointed eventually, towards the end of 1986, was Roderick McLeod, chairman of Lloyd's Register of Shipping. From his greater resources he was able to put together a very large and powerful team, probably more so than John Caldwell could have done. So my DSAC response to Hill-Norton now became a submission to the Lloyd's Register inquiry. The terms of reference of the inquiry were:

> To consider the advantages and disadvantages of the *S90* hull form for the purposes of meeting the naval staff requirements (NSR 7069) for an anti-submarine frigate (insofar as the current state of the development of the *S90* permits), taking account of the independent assessments made in 1983 by YARD and by the Marine Technology Board of the Defence Scientific Advisory Council, and of the Hill-Norton Committee Report *Hull Forms for Warships*, published in May 1986, and to identify any implications for the design of future destroyers and frigates for the RN.

The inquiry, which ran until March 1988 when it reported, was conducted in a punctilious and rigorous manner. Every word was documented. Visits were made to four ships and a very large number of external parties were involved in doing supporting work. TGA were involved at every stage and had nine meetings with the inquiry. DSAC submitted my formal report to the inquiry at the end of 1986. We had prepared it meticulously, fed up as we were with fighting over the same ground time after time. DSAC were invited to discuss it with the inquiry in April 1987. Professor John Cadogan attended and I had Professor Louis Rydill of UCL, Dr Ian Buxton of Newcastle University, and Dr George Ward of BMT in support. I was well satisfied with the conduct of the meeting.

As might be expected the Lloyd's Register inquiry report turned out to be a majestic piece of work. They handled it in a novel way by keeping TGA closely involved throughout and showing how the original *S90* design was just not capable of fulfilling the naval requirements. It was too small. Therefore a scaled-up version was developed and it, of course, had to be a longer ship to do the job. This was the *S102* and it had Giles's approval. But when compared with the RN *Type 23* frigate design, the *Type 23* was cheaper and more effective. From then on a series of designs was produced with TGA working alongside until the last, the *S115*, was the nearest that could be matched to the naval requirements. By this time the length had increased to almost the same as earlier conventional and successful frigates, for example, the *Leander* class. Yet still the horsepower required was 35 per cent more than the *Type 23*. Other features such as noise levels did not meet requirements. It would also certainly cost more to build than the *Type 23* and cost more to operate. Other important aspects of design were considered in great detail – seakeeping, habitability, manoeuvrability. But in the end, the 'Firm Conclusion' of the report, published in July 1988, says: 'The Inquiry could find no reason to disagree with the MOD's preference for the *Type 23*.' A particularly telling sentence is: 'The dispute about the optimum frigate design for a given requirement would have been much shorter if fully worked out comparisons between the different proposals had been made.' This was an observation I had pressed consistently over all these years on anyone who would listen.

True to form, when Mr Giles saw the way the design development was going, he himself having to concede that step by step he was getting back closer and closer to a *Type 23*, the *Daily Telegraph* told us he had pulled out of the inquiry. Also, now that the report was out, he was refusing to accept the findings – and was issuing a writ against Lloyd's Register for libel. The *Daily Telegraph* had the grace to add Lloyd's Register's response: 'This is not the first time that Mr David Giles has made allegations of this kind and they are completely without foundation or justification.' As for Admiral of the Fleet The Lord Hill-Norton GCB, he toddled off muttering that he was glad his main recommendation for an official inquiry had been met; but the Lloyd's Register report had concentrated too closely on a comparison between the Giles hull and a conventional design for a *Type 23* frigate – which was, of course, what it was all about. *The Times*, after many years of loyal support for Giles, seemed to be silent.

So ended one of the longest, most expensive, damaging and useless arguments I have been involved in. The inquiry alone was reputed to have cost at least £1 million, to which must be added the cost to British Shipbuilders and NMI in their legal settlements. Also the countless man-hours spent and expense incurred by MOD, the Royal Navy and the DSAC, not to speak of the ill-effect on the reputations of a number of senior and respected people. I learnt a lesson. It was that a Government minister, ignorant of scientific and engineering technicalities and who will not accept the advice of his professional advisers, is a very dangerous person; and especially so if he is predisposed to listen to his own friends to the exclusion of qualified people. Geoffrey Pattie's defence, we have known him to say, was 'How am I to know whether this designer, with a brown paper parcel of plans below his arm, is not another Frank Whittle?' There were plenty of people able to help him. On the other hand I do believe the Royal Navy's own designers, much given to studying their own concepts in utmost detail, were too readily bogged down with studying what was never more than a TGA 'concept'. There seemed to be a reluctance at the highest level in MOD to accept the simple fact that, if one ship needs twice the horsepower of another, supposedly doing the same job, it cannot compete, and that was always the position with the Giles proposal.

Roderick McLeod, chairman of Lloyd's Register, received his knighthood. Sadly he died too soon thereafter. Some people are not sure why they are awarded an honour, but receive it gladly from Her Majesty. In my case, the citation for my CBE was very clear. It simply read 'Chairman of the Marine Technology Board of the DSAC'.

A little postscript. A year or two ago I had a call from a BBC reporter who wanted my view on a new proposal for very fast passenger vessels to be re-instituted on the North Atlantic run. As he spoke I was moved to suggest this sounded very similar to a case I was familiar with. The answer was 'Yes – and Mr Giles suggested I speak to you!' I excused myself with what must have seemed undue haste and rapidly replaced the receiver. We still await the advent of such ships.

Chapter 20

Cheaper warships and the Falklands

As a member of DSAC I did some other things as well as cope with Mr Giles. The study into the short-fat ship originally started because the Hull Committee was already looking at ways to make warships cheaper and Giles was discovered to be advocating a frigate design that would not only be more effective but would also be cheaper. To use his own phrase he was 'offering more bangs for fewer bucks'. Having disproved his concept at very considerable time and cost, as chairman of the Marine Technology Board I went back to studying ways in which HM warships could be procured at lower cost. This was a much less satisfying exercise than I would have liked. Nobody could deny that costs of military hardware, including ships, were steadily increasing to the point where it appeared we might no longer be able to acquire enough to satisfy requirements. There are always pressures pushing up costs, in particular the eagerness to have the very latest weapons for the ships, coupled with highest propulsion and seakeeping performance. But nobody seemed particularly keen actually to do anything about reducing costs. So I chaired a little working group. This time it included David Penny who was always a tower of strength in these studies; also Jan Neumann, formerly MD of YARD, and Michael Valentine of Hunting Engineering. David Brown, deputy chief naval architect and a weel-kent figure within the Royal Corps of Naval Constructors, was our liaison officer with MOD.

We struggled on with this difficult subject for almost three years and it was obvious from the start that it was going to be a battle to get the various parties even to consider, let alone accept, stricter discipline on costs. Obviously the shipyards were not going to be the leaders in cost reduction – life was too comfortable for them to want to upset things; and the Navy themselves were always bound to seek the best in military terms. But what disappointed me was the reluctance among MOD civil servants to consider altering their methods or their thinking. I remember in particular one numbingly negative discussion at MOD on the relatively minor matter of paying, during the building process, the many instalments to the shipyard as decreed in the shipbuilding contract. I suppose there always is the necessity for public monies to be carefully monitored, but the complications attached to deciding at which point the inordinate number of instalments would be paid were unbelievable compared with the simplicity of the merchant shipbuilding system. We could change it not a whit.

What is often not realized in discussing warship costs is how small a proportion of the total lies in the hull itself, and how difficult it is to achieve savings by better shipbuilding practice alone. So much of the total cost lies in systems and weapons and these should obviously be the areas to concentrate on. Yet these are the items where only the best and most sophisticated will do. Roughly speaking, one-third of a frigate's cost is in its weapons, and only 10 per cent or so is hull cost. Over half of the total ship cost is in propulsion and electrical machinery and auxiliary systems. It is no longer sensible for the shipbuilder to be the main contractor when so much of the ship is not his direct responsibility. Nowadays a prime contractor such as BAe is appointed and he has to control and work closely with the shipyard and all the other major contractors. The question then is, does the prime contractor want, or try to give us cheaper warships?

The enormity of the costs, and the associated risks and uncertainties in the light of continual improvements in weapons and systems both before and during the procurement period, have always caused great problems. There is no possibility of producing a prototype unit. Hence great minds have been exercised over the years on how to manage and control these major projects. Because we had become aware of a very large offshore energy project undertaken by Esso in Fife, we went to see it and were greatly impressed. Then we looked at the way these large energy companies handled new projects. I got my working group to arrange a presentation by very senior directors of both BP and Esso to the DSAC, together with MOD, explaining their systems of procurement and handling of such major projects. They are of the same order of value and complexity as warships and these companies do it successfully and within restricted time scales. They use a customer-led project management system embracing a cost-plus-fixed-fee principle, quite different from MOD practice. We recommended that it should be looked at more closely. Mr Levine (now Baron Levine of Portsoken), recently appointed to the new position of head of MOD procurement, abruptly dismissed the suggestion. I felt in the end that our report made rather little impact, which was disappointing to me and my colleagues. It was to take years for real action to happen on this front. I note with interest that now in 2003 the MOD are suggesting some novel joint arrangement between purchaser and suppliers of the new large British aircraft carriers.

However, I had another much more exciting and shorter-term task. It followed the hard-won success of the Falklands campaign of 1982. Immediately it ended the Government wanted to know from the DSAC what was wrong with the ships – the same question as Admiral Beatty implied in his famous comment during the Battle of Jutland in World War I – 'There seems to be something wrong with our bloody ships today.' The

MM signing the agreement of co-operation with the Society of Naval Architects of Korea, 1993.

DSAC responded to this particular commission by setting up a working group under David Penny this time, with three other members – Stewart Leach, professor of metallurgy at Nottingham University, Professor Dick Bishop of UCL and then Brunel University, and me as the naval architect.

Because this campaign was waged far from home, the Royal Navy figured largely, and we need reminding just how largely. There were forty-four Royal Navy ships; twenty-two ships of the Royal Fleet Auxiliary; and forty-five ships 'taken up from trade'. These were merchant ships taken over for this campaign, but operated by their owners' crews as volunteers. It was some fleet! We lost six major ships (and thirty-four aircraft as well). Such losses had not been experienced since World War II and obviously the scale of the sinkings caused great concern. The order for the next class for the Royal Navy, the *Type 23* frigates whose design had been the subject of the troubled arguments with David Giles, was about to be firmed up. MOD wanted to know if anything in their design needed modification in the light of the Falklands experiences. It was a very important question because of the heavy costs and urgent delivery dates of the new class of frigate. We were not involved in the study of the two non-RN ships, *Atlantic Conveyor* and RFA *Sir Galahad*, although I was personally much interested in these losses. It was the loss of the four major Royal Navy ships that we were asked to concentrate on, as well as the fighting experiences of other ships of the RN fleet and the damages many of them sustained. My firm and long-held conviction that the officers and ratings of the Royal Navy are a very superior genre was confirmed by what we found. But in some respects the ships themselves did not measure up to the same high standard. I was reminded of Admiral Viscount Cunningham's motto: 'It takes the navy three years to build a ship but three hundred years to build a tradition.' In other words, the men count for more than the ships. However, there were indeed design lessons to learn.

The campaign started in April 1982. Hostilities at sea began on 25 April with a submarine action. On 2 May HMS *Conqueror* sank the *Belgrano*. On 4 May HMS *Sheffield* was targeted by aircraft launching Exocet missiles. Fuel tanks amidships were hit and serious fires started which so filled the central part of the ship with smoke and heat that the ship had to be abandoned. On 21 and 23 May respectively we lost HMS *Ardent* and HMS *Antelope* due to bombing. On 25 May HMS *Coventry* was attacked by Skyhawk aircraft and was sunk. Fifty-three men died in these attacks.

Our investigation was really very intensive and demanding, not just on our time, but on our physique. There were a lot of ladders to be climbed. Everything was done with naval efficiency and with class. As we boarded the several ships as they came back from the South Atlantic we were piped aboard in formal naval style. We then had a detailed description from the commanding officer of how the ship prepared for battle. Some had already been on the Naval exercise 'Spring Train' in mid-Atlantic when summoned to the South Atlantic, and were readier for action than others. It was fascinating to hear how each ship prepared. After this introductory address we inspected the damages inflicted on the ship, and finally we had a full discussion in the ward-room on ways to improve the ships and what there was for MOD to learn.

The surrender of the Argentine forces took place in June and the ships were arriving back by the end of July. Our first visit was to HMS *Plymouth* in Rosyth, then to HMS *Glamorgan* and HMS *Glasgow* in Portsmouth. I remember *Glamorgan* particularly, where the path of the Exocet missile could be traced as it bent over the upstand of the hull plating at the after deck, and then passed into the helicopter hanger with serious consequences. Then on to Plymouth to see HMS *Arrow*, HMS *Ambuscade* and HMS *Broadsword*, the last of which had been in such close company with HMS *Coventry* when she was sunk. As well as visiting the ships, we had discussions with Yarrow Shipbuilders, the various dockyards, Vosper Thornycroft, and various MOD establishments, rounding off with a visit to HMS *Intrepid*, HMS *Hermes* and a final interview with Admiral Woodward, who had been in charge throughout the campaign. I was a bit surprised, but should not have been, to find he was rather more interested in what he had to do with the ships than in the ships themselves. I realized how admirals, as they make their vital operational decisions in action, have to assume they have been given sound and reliable warships.

Our report was delivered to MOD in October. I could not help noticing that Dick Bishop, who attended most but not all of the visits, not only never wrote a word during the studies, but nor did he contribute at all to the final report. I never could understand him. The White Paper entitled *The Falklands Campaign: The Lessons* was published in December 1982. It incorporated our submission as far as could be publicly disclosed. I think what surprised me, as it did most people, was how the dangers of fire and smoke figured so largely. I had been accustomed to endless arguments and discussions over the years about fire and smoke in merchant ships, with quite severe restrictions to counter these dangers being imposed by international regulations. I felt strongly that what had been achieved in merchant ships had not been transferred across to warships. Below the waterline there had always been excellent design against flooding in warships from mine, torpedo or grounding. But the White Paper had to admit that improved fire zones, making bulkheads more smoke-tight, reduction in flammable materials, additional fire pumps and breathing apparatus, and other measures would be taken to correct the deficiencies now recognized. Admiral Bryson, in his paper to the RINA that I have referred to earlier, explains all this very well. For the *Type 23* class which was about to be built, there were to be five sections within the ship contained by fire-proof bulkheads instead of three sections in the original design. This was a really major change, not only because of the effect it had on the runs of ventilation trunking and key systems such as electrical cables and water distribution, but on the movement of personnel across the zone boundaries. Naval personnel had long been accustomed to the inconvenience of passing through access doors within watertight compartments. They now had to accept similar inconveniences in moving between fire zones. Another simple-sounding change, but one that meant much to the design and operation, was the re-siting of the mess decks as high in the ship as possible to speed movement of personnel when going to action stations.

The inflammability of materials received a lot of thought. It transpired that improvements in habitability throughout previous decades had led to increased use of combustible materials. For example, the bulkhead and ceiling linings fitted in the accommodation were re-examined because they were found to hinder damage control. In the *Type 23* they were minimized even though this meant the interiors were less pleasant decoratively. Electrical cabling as fitted in the older ships was another item that had proved to be flammable and changes were introduced. We must remember, however, that the RCNC would have wanted many of these improvements, but were continually thwarted by cost restrictions in their implementation.

People today still recall the references to the reputed burning of aluminium structure. It was pointed out in the White Paper that aluminium was in fact used in the superstructure of the *Type 21* class which included HMS *Ardent* and HMS *Antelope*, and to a smaller extent in a few other classes, but not in HMS *Sheffield* and her sisters in the *Type 42* class of destroyer; also sometimes in non-structural minor bulkheads, ladders and ventilation trunking. This was to reduce weight, which is important in warships. It had been recognized that aluminium loses strength in a fire more rapidly than steel does and so its extensive use was discontinued several years before the Falklands event. There is no evidence that aluminium contributed to the loss of any vessel.

As a sort of summing up it would be difficult to deny that the Royal Navy had faced real problems in this campaign. I suppose the service had become a little short of actual warfare experience in the previous decades. However thankful the rest of us may be for this, military hardware and personnel are best tested in real live conditions. In the Falklands I believe that of the two, naval personnel came out of it somewhat better than the ships. Altogether this was a very satisfying exercise for me, and the White Paper made generous reference to the work of the DSAC Marine Technology Board. I continued to serve on the DSAC Council as an independent member until 1998 when, my secure filing cabinet no longer having the capacity to hold my accumulation of documents, I resigned.

PART VI

Professional Interests

CHAPTER 21

Institutions

I HAVE NOW LAID OUT the broad tapestry of my professional activities. There have been some strands (whether of gold or silver I am not sure) that interweave the whole picture from end to end. From my earliest days after starting work I had become aware of bodies such as the Institution of Naval Architects, later to become Royal (RINA), and the Institution of Engineers and Shipbuilders in Scotland (IESS). They were referred to in magazines like *The Shipbuilder & Marine Engine Builder* and *The Motor Ship* that you could buy, or find in libraries, or occasionally come across at work. I must have studied these publications rather closely because I still have copies of *The Shipbuilder* from the 1950s that I bought regularly and then had bound into annual volumes. There was no particular inducement from my shipyard bosses to take an interest in professional institutions nor indeed in technical magazines. That in itself may have been indicative of the blinkered vision of UK shipbuilders of that day.

At university, however, we were encouraged to take an interest in these professional institutions, of which the RINA and IESS were the principal ones for us Glasgow undergraduates. Then I soon became aware of the North East Coast Institution of Engineers & Shipbuilders (NECIES) and through them the Society of Naval Architects & Marine Engineers (SNAME) in US because there was an affiliation between these bodies. Ever since, I have found that my colleagues, and the wider maritime engineering industry, fell into two groupings. Either you believed that professional institutions were important and you took an interest in them, paid an annual subscription, read the transactions, attended meetings where possible, and joined in discussions; or you didn't. It is regrettable that in UK those who did not take such interest, and only glanced at the ongoings of the institutions from afar, achieved about as much by way of advancement as those who did.

There have been immense struggles by the engineering institutions, not only to disseminate knowledge, but also to initiate training schemes and install qualification and registration systems so that highest standards will be maintained, and benefit will accrue to the members and to the engineering profession. But until the topmost managements shed their worn-out attitudes to technology, until there is a national recognition of the value and importance of qualified engineers, and until they require national registration to be allowed to practise like some other professionals such as doctors or

Admiral Kime acknowledges MM's congratulatory address at the SNAME centenary in New York in 1993.

lawyers, there will always be less than complete support for our institutions. Meanwhile the nation continues to accept lower standards of service from its engineering professionals than it should.

I joined the Scottish institution (formally inaugurated in 1895) as a student member in 1948 and have been a member ever since. I have seen the institution pass from being an internationally recognized body full of life and ideas, with transactions that recorded advances on all fronts, to a rump that as I write is convening a brainstorming event to try and find a consensus on the way ahead – or just disband. Not really surprising when set against the decline in shipbuilding and ship operation that I have already described. I like to think one of the most informative technical papers I have written was to the IESS in 1975 describing the operation, behaviour and performance of the OCL containerships. It gained the institution's premier W.W. Mariner award.

MM while president of the RINA in 1990, with Elfrida.

I joined the North East Coast Institution in the 1950s and remained a member until it folded in 1992. I never held any official position in the IESS but I was closely attached to the NECIES. They seemed to attract interesting technical papers that were both theoretical and practical, and helpful to people actually doing things as well as to the more academic fraternity. I have already mentioned that my very first contribution to this elevated professional scene was my paper to the NECIES in 1954 on the stresses experienced during the launching of a tanker. I was not to know then that with a steady progression I would reach membership of council of the NECIES and then become president in 1984. Such honours were not sinecures. My job as president, chairing council and guiding progress generally, was played out against the unsettling backdrop of the decline in the marine industries. I was landed with the task of trying to decide how the institution should go forward in these difficult days. It did manage to carry on with reducing membership and tightening finances for a few more years until, after a lot of heart-searching, we felt we could only bow to the adverse winds. Rather than be forced into an irreversible loss of members and an undignified and unhappy submersion into bankruptcy, the NECIES wound itself up in 1992 after 108 years of usefulness and formed the North East Coast Engineering Trust which would use the residual funds for the encouragement of maritime engineering in the North East.

Running alongside the naval architectural institutions there was the Institute of Marine Engineers (IMarE) in London. I joined in 1968. There has always been a sort of needle between this body and the Royal Institution of Naval Architects. I know sniffy colleagues who have dubbed IMarE colleagues mere marine lorry drivers, whereas we were *designers*. This is altogether unfair, for marine engineers are just as essential in the scheme of maritime things as naval architects – yet there exist real blockages between us. I shall come back to our long, disappointing discussions and negotiations with them about a merger.

The Royal Institution of Naval Architects has always been the senior body among the maritime institutions. When the US Society of Naval Architects and Marine Engineers celebrated its centenary in New York in 1993, I attended as president of the RINA and had the honour of addressing them on behalf of all the other younger sister international institutions. RINA has a long and proud history. Again, when I was president we celebrated in 1991 the three-hundredth anniversary of the inauguration of the Society for the Improvement of Naval Architecture. This was really the forefather of the RINA and had the Duke of Clarence as president with a string of notables in support such as the Earl of Stanhope, Lord Mulgrave and Sir Joseph Banks. It apparently ceased to function in 1799 but had a lasting effect on British warship design. Various luminaries carried forward the development of the design of ships until, under the stimulus of the Great Exhibition of 1851, the Institution of Naval Architects was formed in 1860. It gained the accolade Royal in 1960 in recognition of the contribution of its members to the nation's marine successes.

The names of the early presidents sound like a roll call of the nobility of the day. The first was Lord Hampton who did the job for twenty years; Earl of Ravensworth; Earl of Hopetoun; Earl Cawdor; and one that appeals to me, Duke of Northumberland 1921–8. When I joined the institution my certificate was signed by Admiral of the Fleet Viscount Cunningham of Hyndhope. When I eventually reached council Sir John Lang was treasurer. He had been secretary of the Royal Navy – a distant successor to Secretary to the Admiralty Samuel Pepys – and he prepared his annual statement of the accounts in his very own crabbed handwriting. He was content if he succeeded in matching income from subscriptions against expenditure on the tiny staff and the publication of the transactions, all a far cry from what is needed now to run any professional institution. After the expansive years when famous shipbuilders made generous bequests to the institution it became somewhat grounded in the 1960s and 1970s. Perhaps it is no coincidence that this was during the period when the shipbuilding industry was losing its way and ceasing to become as closely involved with the advance of technology as it should have been. It took rather a long time for the RINA to realize that the days of big ships and big shipyards were passing in UK and that small ships of every type, yachts and leisure craft and eventually fast ferries, were appearing; that the whole vast offshore oil and gas industry was arriving; and that we had to become much more international in our outlook.

I joined as a student member in 1949 and the customary advancement followed – associate member, member and fellow. Then election to council in 1967 and so entry into the policies and doings of the institution, and I have been there ever since – a seat on the membership committee, chairman of the publications committee and chairman of council, leading eventually to my succeeding Viscount Caldecote as president in 1990. It was not a propitious time to take over. We had a new secretary, my old BSRA colleague Peter Ayling having just retired; a new treasurer as Michael Everard of Everard Shipping had resigned at the end of his stint; a brand new chairman of council in Gary Beaumont of Lloyd's Register – all a piece of maladroit management if ever there was. Fortunately I was able to call on my old colleague Ray Adams, a naval architect for sure, but one who knew his way around the finance world, to become treasurer. It did mean, however, that I had to become much more of a hands-on president just at a time when the institution was being forced to change its ways.

We had already recognized that we could no longer be a cosy kind of club where old friends could listen to each other expounding their latest findings from the ship experiment tanks. Under Peter Ayling's guidance a more commercial approach was in hand. The excellent *Journal* was admired by all but it needed advertising revenue to keep it going. The dissemination of technical know-how was increasingly coming from conferences, but they had to be profit-yielding. We needed yet more finance to do the things professional bodies were doing in addition – setting standards, encouraging training and, a real and dangerous novelty for RINA, speaking out publicly for the profession of naval architecture. So we had to attract more advertising for our *Journal* and we had to earn even more money by running conferences. I had retired from NMI/BMT by now, otherwise I doubt whether I could have found the time for these more intense activities.

One particular event pushed the institution more visibly on to the public stage. On 6 March 1987 the *Herald of Free Enterprise* capsized outside Zeebrugge. Elfrida and I had been on holiday on Loch Lomond and on our way home the day after the disaster we listened on the car radio to the continuous reporting of the rising loss of life. On arriving we found Hazel and Angela had left a note: 'Beware, the press are after you!' They certainly were, and it was because they had traced things I had been saying for many years, namely that ro-ro ships were dangerous vehicles. Together with Ray Adams and the rest of my colleagues in Blue Funnel I had realized away back in the 1960s and 1970s that ro-ro ships, which had originally been quite small and incurred a relatively small risk, were now becoming very large indeed. They broke no regulations for the simple reason the regulations had not kept up with the developments in shipping. We in Blue Funnel believed the current ro-ros infringed a basic principle of naval architecture – that large open spaces near the waterline were dangerous in the event of the hull being penetrated. No doubt this was a reflection of Blue Funnel caution and the policy of self-insurance. In the event of damage from collision or other flooding incident, the ships could well not remain upright. Very few people paid any heed – why should they, if the statutory regulations did not demand any precautions?

Now, after the *Herald* sinking, the world knew that we were right. The RINA took this disaster very seriously and decided to set up a standing 'safety committee' to study the whole question and make recommendations for reducing the risk of capsize. But in addition Viscount Caldecote, our president at the time, pressed the institution's council to make a public statement on the matter. We had never spoken out like this before, believing it would be difficult to formulate a corporate RINA view; and in truth we were loath to become embroiled in nasty controversies. But thanks to our president's prodding, and because we now had our safety committee backed by council to provide just such a unified opinion, we adopted a totally different stance from then on and started to make our mark more effectively. It took years of argument and persuasion, and it needed the additional tragic loss of *Estonia* before there was international acceptance of the need to make ro-ro ships less vulnerable. The UK Government played a lead role in these long-running international negotiations and remarkably, paid close heed to the advice of their own technical advisers within the Department of Transport. This was in marked contrast to the regrettable breakdown of trust between ministers and advisers in the case of the short-fat versus long-thin warship dispute that I have already described.

In my earlier days on council naval architects were supremely confident in the recondite conjunction of art and science which they believed underlay their profession. They had not generally seen themselves as belonging to the broader engineering profession. This was to change when UK engineers began to appreciate the desirability of acting together, and they managed to institute the co-ordinating body which was later to become the Engineering Council. RINA had to accept, rather reluctantly, that its place was in engineering and within the Engineering Council. Engineers in UK have never enjoyed the sort of recognition their colleagues receive in Europe and such attitudes are not easily altered. However, engineering *is* slowly making an impact now on the national consciousness, although I still find it feeble when I hear bleats from engineers that they do not have sufficient status in society. It's up to us to generate respect and justify our status.

I look back with regret on an over-long and unhappy episode – the attempt at a merger between the RINA and the IMarE. I supported and encouraged the concept of a unified institution right from the start because there is so much common interest between the two bodies; the things naval architects and marine engineers do are complementary; and at the time when engineers needed to speak with a stronger voice, a single institution would have been more effective. Although the IMarE seemed wealthier, we knew they were running at too high an expenditure and that they could not always rely on their property for security and income. The RINA had no great resources other than their valuable leasehold, but we were a lean organization. I did believe that together we could create a long-term soundly based institution. It was not to be. We wasted years of effort, and probably we lost opportunities of progressing our own institution in the futile negotiations.

There were two distinct campaigns. The first started in 1980 and, in the nature of such negotiations, dragged on until 1985 during which time I led the RINA side in the discussions. The second round started in 1988 and ended in failure in 1993, the main discussions being held while I was president from 1990 to 1993. I was therefore deeply implicated again. On the first round we came a long way towards reconciling our differences and

MM at the RINA Annual Dinner in 1993, with Field Marshal Lord Carver and Admiral Kime of the US Navy.

could see our route towards a merger. But in spite of protestations of a strong desire to merge from both sides, the IMarE were happy to see progress fizzle out through a series of miserable niggles and trivial disagreements.

After the second attempt we were almost there by 1993. Dr Ross Goodman of Lloyd's Register led from our side and did a tremendous job, dedicated to the task, skilful and masterly in negotiation. We agreed how a joint council would be formed, how the grades of membership would be reconciled, how the finances would be handled even to the point of receiving a realistic valuation of the RINA leasehold from Grosvenor Estates – not something lightly achieved. Referenda simultaneously conducted by both institutions showed overwhelming support by the members on both sides for a merger. My opposite number as president, Rear Admiral Mike Vallis, declared many times in my hearing that he was wholly behind a merger, and was urgently pressing his institution towards it.

In the end two things became obvious. On the RINA side I could speak for a council who, after full and sometimes heated argument, were totally united behind me and were willing to merge on the agreed basis. On the IMarE side there was never such a serried front. We had excellent relations with the members of their negotiating team, but in spite of their president's assurances, somewhere in the background there was always a shadowy group who were apparently determined to block a merger. They won in the end. After a vast amount of man-hours and expense we discovered IMarE were, amongst other prevarications, not willing to tell us about their finances (which were becoming less assured). We decided very firmly that enough was enough. RINA has gone on since then with very reasonable progress, particularly under the new chief executive, Trevor Blakeley – membership increased to its highest level ever, more joint branches both in UK and internationally and, initially under Ray Adams' influence as treasurer, far more respectable finances. IMarE has changed its name to IMarEST, the Institute of Marine Engineers, Scientists and Technologists in an effort to widen their membership; and they have had to move from their prestigious building in Mark Lane.

It will be obvious that I did not lack association with professional bodies. The last, and with a proper sense of finality, was the Royal Academy of Engineering, a body instituted with the direct support of His Royal Highness the Duke of Edinburgh in 1976 to provide for engineers the equivalent of the scientists' title FRS. Its objectives are 'to pursue encourage and maintain excellence in the whole field of engineering in order to promote the advancement of the science, art and practice of engineering for the benefit of the public'. It does this, it bestows the designatory letters FREng, it has become a valuable and recognized source of engineering expertise. I was elected Fellow in 1990 and have served from time to time on its panels and committees, including one specifically set up to comment on the safety of ro-ro ships.

CHAPTER 22

Universities

IN SPITE OF BEING a graduate of Glasgow University I have had no particular association with that establishment over the years – other than keeping in touch through the newsletter and annual reports. Because naval architects form an intimate group in UK however, I knew the senior staff well – Professor John Conn who had been my boss at BSRA, Neil Miller his principal lecturer also from BSRA in my day, and later Professor Douglas Faulkner, originally from the RCNC.

My more active links have been with the sister University of Strathclyde. Dr Chengi Kuo (later Professor) was the go-ahead lecturer under the kindly Professor Ian Bridge who had the idea I might be appointed the first visiting professor to the department of naval architecture. Chengi was one of the naval architects who saw very early on the potential of the computer in the study and practice of ship design, and he produced various publications that greatly influenced our thinking. Then he was instrumental in guiding the department into the new and exciting realms of offshore engineering. I was very happy to take up this appointment in 1972 even though it was during my busiest days at Blue Funnel. It was a three-year appointment, but it was to last ten years because of Chengi's skilful manipulation both of university regulations and also of me. There are not all that many schools of naval architecture in UK so it was always a bit odd to have two in Glasgow. We often spoke about joining up but academia is just as sensitive about its status and traditions as are professional institutions. It was to take until 2000 before the two departments came together. I feel I became more of a figurehead over these years than a practising lecturer, but I am glad that during my professorship the student numbers remained high with a big percentage of overseas people. To this day I am regularly accosted by students who remember me – and I have forgotten them.

The moment I relinquished my Strathclyde appointment I was gobbled up, again as visiting professor, by Professor Louis Rydill of the naval architecture department at University College London. Louis is one of these determined, calm and very knowledgeable RCNC men I have been so pleased to work with. He was especially helpful to me during my DSAC work and his logical approach and clear exposition were much appreciated when I was feeling overwhelmed with service jargon and the MOD mentality. I have explained how the RCNC was originally based at the Royal

Naval College at Greenwich until, under official pressure to economize, Professor Dick Bishop was able to inveigle them into his department of mechanical engineering at UCL. It was a different atmosphere from Strathclyde, not so much bustle and competition, and the students were probably a little older on average and somewhat more dignified as befits the Royal Corps.

Dick Bishop, who was there at the time, remained to me a baffling figure. Eventually vice-chancellor of Brunel University, FRS, FREng, he was a respected figure – except by some of us. I first met him when Julian Taylor, who had somehow got in tow with him, invited Willie Falconer our engineering director and me to dinner at the East India Club in November 1970. Julian had told Bishop about the performance of our new *Encounter Bay* ships and especially the description I had given of the unusual whipping motion of the hulls when in waves. This generated a train of thought in Bishop's mind which, I think, was the start of his infatuation with the concept of hydroelasticity as applied to ships' structure. He produced many papers thereafter in support of his theories but they were never wholly accepted by the ship structures establishment, which included Lloyd's Register.

Geraint Price, his respected and closest associate, read a paper to the RINA, just after Dick Bishop died, giving their research team's explanation of why mv *Derbyshire* sank without trace in the Pacific. I shall talk about the loss of this ship which became a *cause célèbre* shortly, but this effort by Price represented a kind of culmination of Bishop's work up to that point. With John Prescott prominent as Secretary of State for Transport in the front row, he sought to show that *Derbyshire* almost certainly broke up with fractures starting from one of three possible points, which they defined. Unfortunately for the hydroelasticists, the *Derbyshire* wreck was found and photographed, and they were proved quite wrong. It had not broken up in the way they postulated. One ironic phase of Bishop's career intrigued me. Being a friend of Julian Taylor he was in a fine dilemma at the time of the short-fat versus long-thin ship argument. On the one hand we had Bishop, supposedly advising MOD through the DSAC Marine Technology Board which I chaired, against the short-fat ship. On the other hand, across the table, was Julian Taylor supporting Giles, the proponent of the short-fat concept. No wonder I could get few positive helpful statements from Bishop.

Newcastle University's naval architecture department was always strong, with well-known figures marking out its history – Professor Burrill and Willie Muckle for example, and in my time at Blue Funnel and then in the North East, Professor John Caldwell, who built up a formidable departmental team. Amongst them were Professor Bob Townsin (how the names of old colleagues of BSRA days keep cropping up); Dr Ian Buxton from Glasgow University, a pillar of the department for years; Professor Bill Hills, a Sunderland man through and through and highly motivated. I was on Prince Philip's selection committee when Bill won the Duke of Edinburgh's Prize for Designers recently. I met all these friends at the meetings of the North East Coast Institution regularly. The after-lecture dinners were thoroughly enjoyable occasions. I never held any particular position at Newcastle University other than external examiner and adviser on various occasions, but they were wonderful people to be associated with.

Which brings me to a concluding judgement on UK's maritime-oriented universities and schools of technology, which include Southampton, Cardiff, Plymouth and others. They have done and are doing remarkably well. There is no reflection here of the rundown in the maritime industries even though the natural expectation would be that the prevalent decline would have an adverse effect on the universities. What they might lack in home student numbers they compensate for by attracting overseas students. I have over the past few years helped to adjudicate on the award of bursaries at Newcastle. I am impressed by the immaculate turn-out of the student applicants – jacket and tie, of course, and a very impressive explanation of their ambitions for their careers. So many were from overseas, from Cyprus, or Singapore or wherever, with parents advancing very large sums to get them to UK – and to Newcastle – and these young people wanted to repay them. It does seem that the sea still has enormous attraction for young people and our universities have cleverly adapted to this by widening their courses as well as linking in the offshore oil and gas and energy aspects. It used to be that graduates mainly went into the shipbuilding industries, but now there are far more opportunities open to them; and some have not seen the naval architecture course as particularly vocational at all and gone off to do other things after graduating.

CHAPTER 23

Committees

TO ELABORATE ON THE multitude of committees, sub-committees, working groups and panels I have laboured on would be tedious beyond forbearance. I have mentioned some of them along the way. I do not think I can now even remember some of them, but the fact that I was so implicated meant that, although obvious success may not have by any means attended every meeting or committee, I always enjoyed a very fair knowledge or feel for what was going on. So I touch only on one or two of my later exertions.

When the rundown of UK shipbuilding and of the UK fleets, both merchant and naval, was gaining momentum it was pretty obvious that Prime Minister Thatcher was not going to hearken to noises from the defenders of these 'sunset' groups, as she saw them. In what to some of us was a belated and despairing move, the British Maritime League was instituted. In any other era than hard-line Thatcherism it would have appeared an influential body, since it incorporated senior figures from every sector of our maritime interests. I was asked to serve on it. Admiral Sir Anthony Griffin with whom I had had such close relations, both when he was chairman of British Shipbuilders and then president of the RINA, figured right at the forefront of the BML. He was naturally alarmed at the rundown of the Royal Navy and he was equally determined to trumpet opposition to the merchant fleet's rundown. The league produced some very good reports highlighting the consequences of Government policies on our maritime businesses, ranging from the basic manufacturing industries through the merchant and naval fleets, and on into the infrastructure of designers, consultants, insurance companies and the like. Unfortunately, nobody in high places paid any attention and the BML died.

In the meantime, Admiral Griffin, being a man of action, had been seized of several notions that he felt could greatly benefit the marine industries and he wanted them progressed. He seemed to see me as one, even *the* one, who could help him. So I became the reluctant recipient of several of his proposals. He was most anxious about two in particular. One was to design a ship made of concrete instead of steel; the other was to run a ship on hydrogen instead of oil. The first I could live with and look at. The second was hallucination. Together with many others I have hankered after a better material than steel in the manufacture of ships because steel corrodes, especially in saltwater conditions, and needs perpetual painting and conservation. Against that, however, it is a wonderful material, easy to work, and all its properties are well understood. Concrete ships have been tried before and I saw it as quite sensible to have another look at them; after all, the nature and properties of reinforced concrete are nowadays also well known and it has been greatly developed as a material. It comes down to the matter of its weight versus steel and that tends to be the problem. So I had some studies done but they gave rather inconclusive results, and as usual no UK shipbuilder was interested in following it up.

The hydrogen proposal was different. Here the Admiral was unreasonably influenced by a Frenchman who claimed he held a patent for producing hydrogen as a fuel for vehicles – supposedly easy to produce and very efficient in combustion. The concept involved unwinding a type of aluminium wire from coils held in a sort of bunker compartment of the ship, and feeding it into a container of sea-water where an electric current was introduced. By a process of hydrolysis, hydrogen would be given off. This, Admiral Griffin believed, could be collected and used as fuel for the engines. It would revolutionize ship propulsion. I was expected to make it happen for the benefit of the nation. He had also brought it to the attention of the RCNC in Bath and I was glad to have some collusion with them because I, and they, had strong reservations about the whole concept. We persuaded the Admiral to take advice on the physics of the scheme from the most authentic source he could find. Being a friendly neighbour of Sir Arnold Weinstock down in Sussex, the proposal was referred to him and onwards to the laboratories of GEC, than whom there could be few more qualified to pronounce. The answer came back promptly from the head of the laboratories – it wouldn't work.

The Admiral was wholly unpersuaded and pressed on. I was dragged down to his home in Bosham to witness the Frenchman do a test run on his vehicle. It was a blue Ford van, and in spite of garbled assurances from the inventor that its running demonstrated some part of his process, the engine was patently not running on hydrogen. I felt thoroughly mean in expressing my doubts, especially while partaking of a very elegant tea from Lady Griffin. Sir Anthony was not only a naval gentleman in the finest tradition, but he had enormous powers of persuasion. He kept on with his campaign in spite of every criticism and warning right up to the time of his death, at which moment by a strange coincidence his Frenchman was convicted of fraud. Tony Griffin was such an impossibly decent chap that if I class him as one of my SOAs, I do so with profound regret. Hydrogen propulsion has never happened; and the British Maritime League soon became just a tiny snippet of history.

Some people still remember the Board of Trade (BOT) when they oversaw shipping, with their rather officious surveyors waiting to pounce on misdemeanour or fault. In the way that Government departments change, the Department of Transport (DTp) later became responsible for shipping, and the surveyor general carried the ultimate executive authority. He needed a research committee to advise him and control the spending on investigations and developments. I was appointed to it as one of the two outsiders in 1992, six years into my retirement. Professor Richard Goss was the other. Very shortly the surveyor general's department was hived-off, like many another supporting arm of Government, to become a semi-independent agency – the Marine Safety Agency (MSA) under Robin Bradley as chief executive.

I was pleasantly surprised in my dealings with these semi-detached civil servants. Gone were the stuffy attitudes when the potentate within the sanctuary would bawl 'come!' when you knocked. Here was a group of friendly faces, pulling well together in making the new agency a success: Tom Allan, an old naval architect friend, most helpful to me in the RINA, and now the UK's leader at the International Maritime Organization (IMO); Alan Cubbin, Doug Bell and Bill Graham dealing with all the technical stuff and Roy Padgett the money and administration. The research programme was beautifully presented and controlled, much better than it was back in my BSRA or Chamber of Shipping research days – but spending of public money needs, I suppose, to stand up to closer scrutiny. I enjoyed this job, the only problem being I had to get from the depths of Northumberland to the Agency offices in Southampton several times a year. MSA not only controlled their research expenditure tightly but also their travel expenses, in true civil service fashion. As with every other committee I have ever served on, there was no remuneration, and Elfrida eventually suggested after six years of such travel that I seemed to be taken for granted. So when MSA became transformed yet again into the Maritime and Coastguard Agency (MCA) on joining up with the Coastguard, I resigned. Maurice Storey the new chief executive rewarded me for these years with an invitation to lunch in Southampton. He didn't say who would pay the fare – and I couldn't go anyway.

My longest spell by far on such activities was on the Technical Committee of Lloyd's Register – some twenty-one years. Actually it was longer, because before I became a member in my own right on joining British Shipbuilders, I had been helping Sir Stewart MacTier and then Julian Taylor when they in turn were the Blue Funnel representatives on the committee. What they contributed was based on my, and my department's, comments; and they culled similar support on engineering matters from our engineering colleagues from across the corridor. There was no way they themselves could discuss the sort of detail that Lloyd's Technical Committee handled. LR existed at that time in an elevated, unreal, over-respected layer of the heavens when other more down-to-earth but forward-thinking classification societies were, in an increasingly competitive world, overtaking them not only in technical advances but in the volume of shipping they classed.

The meetings I attended were for years just rubber-stamping occasions. The chairman I first sat under was the quiet and rather ineffectual Ronnie Punt, just retired from heading Harland & Wolff, and the members of the committee included every respected figure from shipbuilding, shipowning and allied institutions. A later chairman was Gerrit Korte, an old friend from the Howaldtswerke shipyard in Hamburg. It was a delightful club of everybody I knew from the technical side of shipping plus many others I didn't know. Granted, the main business was supposed to be conducted by correspondence before the meeting, and any comment on changes to Lloyd's Rules (the ultimate expression of LR requirements) were supposed to have been submitted beforehand. Yet it was still impressive to observe the sheer inanity of the meeting. The chairman and the chief surveyors, ship and engineering, had to stand up to make every statement from the platform. They would rattle through a presentation of each proposal for change to the Rules using the form of words provided to them by the staff, and ask for any further comments. Invariably there were none. After half an hour or less of this we would have a short presentation on some aspect of LR business and a bit of discussion, and then we repaired to the dining room for lunch which seemed to be the main item of the day. It was a very good lunch and I always enjoyed the banana with ginger to end up with.

The form of meeting gradually changed in the 1990s and I like to think I encouraged it in a little way. Members of the committee, particularly those from overseas, began to be more vocal and actually make comments, and even offer criticism, and it surely made the exercise more realistic. One real problem was that a very large percentage of the members did not understand the derivations of the 'Rules' which decree the structural integrity and safety of a ship, so opaque and convoluted had the exercise become. Lloyd's Rules, the bible expressing the thoughts and the will of LR, were becoming like the Blue Funnel ship specifications – enormous to the point of being disheartening to wade into, or digest, or to comprehend as to their logic. One or two of us members of the technical committee were so concerned about the way other disciplines such as civil engineering were moving forward in their methods of designing for safety and efficiency, that we managed to persuade LR to set up a sub-committee in 1993 to review the current Rules and consider changes in their format to incorporate current technology. Professor John Caldwell, always a leader on these matters, was chairman, and I was appointed together with David Chalmers RCNC (*the* authority on naval ship structures) and Philip Bulson an 'outsider' structural engineer with great experience. The whole exercise was done against the background of real public concern about ship safety following the disasters such as *Herald of Free Enterprise*, *Estonia*, and the continuing losses of bulk carriers.

We examined the trends in the designing of aircraft, offshore structures and warships as well as civil engineering structures. We argued that there should be real changes to Lloyd's Rules. For the more technically minded, we recommended the application of what is called a 'limit state approach' to the design and assessment of structures. We claimed this would be more rational and transparent than the current prescriptive type of rules. It just meant that design should be based on ensuring certain margins between the expected operating conditions and the 'limit' where structures become unsafe. We quite agreed it would be a major task to swing LR thinking into this more modern direction, and it would cost money, but we believed it was the way to go. We could not help noticing the number of bright young LR staff in the junior echelons who understood and welcomed our suggestions. As to the seniors in the establishment and the technical committee itself, they thanked us copiously when we submitted our report in 1994 and assured us that our sub-committee's work was much appreciated. As far as any of us on the sub-committee can detect even to this day, nothing happened – a refrain you will be accustomed to hearing from me. There were mumbles about not wanting to go too far ahead of the shipyards. It was a good thing there were by now very few UK shipyards otherwise progress would have been negative.

I shall be referring again to Lloyd's Register when I tell of the *Derbyshire* Formal Investigation but I must say I have always been ambivalent concerning this historic British institution. It has a long pedigree and is internationally recognized. It has great strengths such as its world-wide network of surveyors. It has weaknesses such as lack of direction, and too great an attachment to tradition. On the other hand LR people have always been deferential to Blue Funnel and most respectful to me. I ought not perhaps to be critical, and I am glad to note that there is now a more progressive attitude within the society under the new chairman David Moorhouse.

CHAPTER 24

Forensic affairs

EVERY FEW YEARS I have been asked to serve in some capacity at formal investigations and these have been absorbing occasions. A Panel of Nautical Assessors existed showing names that could be called on to serve, and I was invited by the Secretary of State at the Home Office to join it in 1974. I was kicked out by the Lord Chancellor promptly when I reached my sixtieth birthday in 1985. Actually he was very much on the ball and notified me a day or so before – which I found a little hurtful.

My first investigation was held in Aberdeen, so it was under Scottish law, with full wigs and robes, and it was by far the best conducted I have experienced. The judge was G.S. Gimson QC, Sheriff Principal of Grampian and the Highlands and Islands. It lasted only eleven working days. The report is slim, concise and cogent. The casualty was a fishing vessel named *Trident*, a seine-net trawler of 68 tons, and she sank with the loss of all seven hands off Duncansby Head in 1974. It was my first experience close-up of the fishing industry and I was struck by how casual these men were about safety compared with ocean-going practice – and especially Blue Funnel practice. Most of the interest attached to the stability of the boat which, from all the data we considered, was suspect and the evidence of the designer was unsatisfactory and unreliable. There has been much study of fishing vessel safety since then, and fresh regulation, but it is difficult to alter the ingrained culture of the industry. What impressed me greatly was the careful and studied way the case was handled in court. All the lines of enquiry and the cross-examinations were carefully crafted and no words were wasted. When compared with all I have seen and heard in English courts since then, I am convinced that time and money is wasted needlessly by counsel meandering through their examinations without any clear line in mind, apparently in the hope that something vital will turn up, and it all takes twice as long.

Sheriff Principal Gimson took me and his other two assessors (who were the experts in fishing) to dinner one night during the Inquiry at the Aberdeen Conservative Club and I discovered he had been in the Japanese prison camps during World War II. Over these cruel years he had done painstaking drawings on scraps of paper or other materials recording what he saw around him, and eventually smuggled them out. They have been published in various of the histories of those times. It was especially interesting to me because I have had several friends and colleagues who were also imprisoned, but in particular Colonel Philip Toosey who was a fellow director in Blue Funnel, coming into the group with the Elder Dempster merger. A gentle, reserved man when I knew him, he had been renowned and greatly respected as the senior British officer in those camps where he stood up for his troops so effectively against the harsh treatment by the Japanese.

Next came *Boston Sea Ranger*, another fishing vessel built in 1976 which sank off Cornwall in 1977 with three of the crew saved and five lost. Here again the lack of discipline in observing the regulations and lack of enforcement of company requirements were evident, and also the crew's sloppy operation of the vessel at sea. As I have found so often in fishing circles there was no real understanding of stability, which is just as crucial in these small craft as in large ocean-going ships. To make things worse the freeboard is smaller to make loading of the catch easier, there is less reserve buoyancy since deck-houses are kept to a minimum, and there is a much greater likelihood that hatches and other entry points for water may be left open. It was not difficult for us assessors to help the Judge to conclude that *Boston Sea Ranger* sank because the owners were not forcible enough in ensuring that their instructions were met; and they had not seen that the ship was properly fitted out when she changed from boxed mackerel fishing to bulk mackerel. They were therefore censured, and the master had his certificate withdrawn for failing to comply with the owners' instructions. Judge Gerald Darling QC was the Wreck Commissioner. I was to meet him again at the first of the two *Derbyshire* investigations, and to find that serving alongside a judge as assessor is a very good way to establish future relations.

The *Grainville* was a clapped-out ship, carrying a load of scrap metal from Belfast to Bilbao, that came to a miserable end in a storm in the Irish Sea in 1981 with the loss of three lives; and with the master lying scantily clothed and incapable across the galley stove. I was glad this investigation was held in Newcastle (the owners were based in Sunderland) because I was then at British Shipbuilders and so handily placed for attending for all the thirty long days it lasted. Judge Geoffrey Brice was the Wreck Commissioner and the investigation exhibited everything that I find regrettable about such occasions. The submissions and cross-examinations were interminable and the Judge's report, all of fifty-two pages long (and I admit to contributing too many pages myself) is an over-detailed text-book lesson on how not to operate ships. The vessel involved was a flat-iron collier built in 1951 and so was thirty years old. The Judge's report helpfully tells us that a ship is old if she is more than fifteen years. These ships were designed to carry coal from north-east ports to power stations on the Thames, and were built with a low profile to allow them to pass below the Thames bridges – hence the 'flat-iron' nickname.

The ship ran into gales off the Tusker Rock and began to take in water and then developed a list. None of the crew could persuade the master in the state he was in to make for shelter when it became obvious that the seas had damaged the ship and she was clearly sinking. So she sank, and as so often nowadays, it was to be the prompt arrival of helicopters that ensured that eight lives were saved. If Blue Funnel was at the extreme top end of shipping excellence then the *Grainville* represented the very bottom end. Albert le Blond, the owner, had been a ship's engineer and now ran Wear Dockyard as a repair establishment. He obviously had visions of joining that greatly envied caste, the UK shipowning fraternity. He had acquired five coastal vessels before 1981 but when he bought *Grainville* (formerly *Battersea*) for £24,000 from the CEGB she was his only ship. He had to spend many times that to make her seaworthy. I admired the way he helped the court throughout the investigation although he was obviously pained at what had happened. Nothing could hide the fact that as a ship-operating company his was woefully inadequate – no marine superintendent; no formal record of repairs and maintenance; no company visits to inspect the ship; and unbelievably, no vetting of the ship's personnel. Mr le Blond had never seen, interviewed, or spoken to the master. It was a very different world from the one I knew. I was to meet Geoffrey Brice again too at the first *Derbyshire* investigation.

The name of *Derbyshire* will always feature in heavy print in the annals of British shipping because she was a very large, relatively new, well-run ship that was inexplicably lost in a tropical storm in 1980 in the Pacific with all of the forty-four souls aboard. I need not describe in any detail all that happened thereafter when everybody tried to establish the cause of the loss or theorize on it. All of that is well recorded elsewhere and there have been official Reports from the two Formal Investigations into her loss. I give the record of my own involvement.

Bibby Line, the owners of *Derbyshire*, was a highly respected Liverpool shipowning company who occupied premises just across from the Blue Funnel offices. I had met Sir Derek Bibby at various times, and remember particularly his visits to the Christian Business Men's Association when I was involved. I never had any doubt during the ensuing twenty years of discussion about the loss that the ship had been efficiently and capably run and that no fault could be attributed to the company or its people, and so it proved in the end. There had been many studies into the sinking between the years 1980 and 1987 at which time Government decided there should be a Formal Investigation. By then there were just too many parties all either clamouring for information or offering particular views and opinions for an inquiry to be denied.

As soon as the Department of Transport announced an investigation

Lloyd's Register asked me to act as their expert witness and adviser. There followed an exacting and illuminating time. Judge Gerald Darling of the *Boston Sea Ranger* investigation was the Wreck Commissioner and Geoffrey Brice of the *Grainville* investigation represented the dependants of those who were lost in the sinking. Three assessors were appointed to assist the Wreck Commissioner, two of whom were very old friends – Dr Brian Baxter who had been on the committee studying ship strength when I stood in for Harry Flett in 1960, and John Bunnis who had been with Esso and then Common Brothers and whom I knew well through the North East Coast Institution.

I thought Judge Gerald Darling did a very fair job. Perhaps I am biased because when I was called to give evidence he was especially considerate. Other witnesses had a much tougher time. The popular conception was that *Derbyshire* broke up at a point towards the aft end that became generally known as bulkhead 65, although other theories were postulated. Any possible failure of the main hull was of great concern to Lloyd's Register who had 'classed' the vessel and I was close to them as they carried out massive and detailed investigations into the integrity of the structure. I supported them in their rebuttal of any charge of weakness in the hull and said so in my evidence. There had been some defects in the construction and we all had to admit it, but my job was to point out that there was never 100 per cent perfection in building a massive artefact like a ship of 1,000 feet long, and such defects as were being discussed would not have been fatal. During the detailed and rather puerile cross-examination of me by Geoffrey Brice, Judge Darling interrupted in severe terms: 'Mr Brice, you cannot ask such questions of a witness of this calibre.' Geoffrey apologized – and it did wonders for my standing with LR. The final report was inconclusive as to the cause of the loss, rightly so I believe. There was, however, the firm conclusion that failure of the structure at bulkhead 65 was unlikely. Two other possible causes were given – failure of the hatch covers and shift of the cargo. No firm conclusion could be reached on these.

Movement of the cargo was a new proposition from Dr Angus Skinner of Imperial College London, and I supported LR in putting this forward. The cargo was iron ore, not in chunks of metal, but in the form of a heavy sludge, and because it contained moisture the tendency was for the retained water to sink gradually to the floor of the hold. This much was agreed by all but the Judge and his assessors never seemed to understand what Skinner then suggested, namely that a layer of watery material could build up at the bottom of the hold over a period of time, and then the whole lot could suddenly shift as the ship rolled. The ship must have suffered rolling during the typhoon. It was the same mechanism that had caused the landslide at Aberfan years ago, when a very large coal-waste tip had become wet at its base from the long-term existence of quite a small stream underneath. Over the years a slippery layer had developed until the whole pile descended on the little Welsh village and its school with appalling results.

Skinner had an unnecessarily rough passage with the judge who commented, for example, that if the cargo slipped one way as the ship rolled surely it would just slip back as it rolled the other way. He could not be made to see that once the cargo moved, the boundary conditions at the bottom of the hold that started the slip were then destroyed and there could be no return until a similar layer was built up again and that would take time. I am afraid his assessors did not help him understand. We know there was at least 1,000 tons of water held within the cargo of the largest holds and this could only seep downwards. The last letter from the master when he called at Capetown specifically advised his owners that he was having to pump water from the holds. Judge Darling's Report did recommend that cargo slippage should be studied further. When somewhat later I sat on the research committee of the Marine Safety Agency a programme looking into this phenomenon in response to the Report was underway. After several hundred thousand pounds' expenditure it was accepted there *was* a problem with water retained in such cargoes, but the research was never completed. There were no UK ships carrying iron ore to do the final tests on, and so everybody lost interest.

The Formal Investigation lasted for forty-six days and the Report was issued in January 1989. My biggest problem while advising Lloyd's Register was in establishing who was in control and what their thinking was within the organization, and even on how many days I was expected to be present. There seemed to be a strained feeling about the place, everybody rather tense and fearful of some hierarchical eminence whom I never discovered. This was rather perturbing just when LR needed a clear lead as to their stance in court. When the formal report was finally published some parties, including the relatives of the deceased, found the conclusions hard to accept, and over the following years they consistently campaigned for further investigation.

Largely because of their persistence an expedition to try to find *Derbyshire* was organized in 1994, mainly with ITF finance, and to most people's surprise the wreck was located in the Pacific several hundred miles south of Japan and at some two and a half miles below the surface. Representations were then made to Government for assistance in properly examining the wreck and Lord Donaldson, lately Master of the Rolls, was appointed to advise the Department of Transport on the cost and feasibility of a full-scale examination using the most modern techniques. He held a colloquium in London under the auspices of the RINA in 1996 to gather views and help him in his assessment. I suggested at that colloquium that it would indeed be good if a ship could, for once, be examined underwater in the same way that aircraft that were lost were routinely examined – although I pointed out we might not necessarily get all the answers we wanted or expected. Two advisers had been appointed to help Lord Donaldson in his studies. One was Robin Williams, a consultant from South Wales whom I had not met. The other was Professor Douglas Faulkner of Glasgow whom I knew well. I questioned Lord Donaldson by letter about the role of these advisers when it appeared to me from what they were saying at the colloquium that they were already forming conclusions about the loss. In his reply Lord Donaldson explained their duty was only to advise on the various theories on the loss and whether these had sufficient substance to justify their being followed up. I still felt they were exceeding this remit.

Lord Donaldson's advice to Government to spend some £2 million was accepted. In a brilliantly successful expedition the wreck was examined by the Woods Hole Oceanographic Institution in US in 1997–8 and almost 140,000 photographs were taken. It was established that the area of wreckage covered 1.5 kilometres by 1 kilometre and the ship was in at least some 2,500 individual pieces. This was not by any means what had been expected.

By this time the two advisers had been increased to three by the addition of Dr Torchio from Geneva, a European Commission appointee, since they had put up some of the finance. These three were then styled assessors and they issued the Assessors' Report of 1998. In it they apparently felt able to pronounce on the cause; and came out with the clear suggestion that the hatch to the bosun's store at the very fore end of the main deck had inadvertently been left open at sea. One or more compartments below had then flooded and caused a reduction in freeboard forward such that the ship would be endangered. This seemed to me to be pre-empting the Formal Investigation that most people believed must follow. They then went on to recommend a series of design improvements some of which would incur great cost and all of which would normally merit years of international discussions before reaching agreement.

So we had television pictures of John Prescott, Deputy Prime Minister, showing the underwater photographs of the hatch on the fore deck, implying that here lay the cause, and announcing the Formal Investigation which was eventually to get under way in 2000. This time it was to be held in the High Court and not under a Wreck Commissioner. I have always been surprised that the assessors took it upon themselves to imply such incompetence to the crew of a well-run British ship. It caused great offence, and it took hours and hours of valuable court time to get Robin Williams to accept what everyone else soon realized from the evidence in court, namely that the hatch had come open only during the typhoon or the sinking.

By this time the assessors had become witnesses because the Judge, the Honourable Mr Justice Colman, had decided he would not appoint assessors to help in court. Instead, he appointed two technical advisers, a Dr P.S.J. Crofton who was quite unknown to me, and Professor John van Griethuysen of University College London. John I did know as a very proficient and delightful person. But they did not attend regularly in court and so could not contribute in the way that, I believe, assessors should. The Judge tells us in his Report that they took no part in making the ultimate decisions. He also tells us he adopted this procedure in order to achieve as rapid a conclusion as possible – and under the same heading, that 'robes had nothing to contribute and were therefore dispensed with'. The logic escapes me, unless it be that robing and disrobing would have incurred valuable legal time. In the event the hearing lasted for fifty-four rather tedious days – not a very rapid conclusion.

I was asked by Lloyd's Register to act again as adviser and expert immediately the investigation was announced in 1998. It was to be a less agreeable exercise than the first one. There was a dispiriting sense of *déjà vu* since we found all the same parties arrayed – Bibby Line, the ship's owners; the *Derbyshire* Families Association; the ship's builders; and of course Lloyd's Register who had most to lose. The owners were not particularly concerned once the suggestion that the bosun's hatch had been left open was demolished. Swan Hunter, the builders, had long ceased to exist in recognizable form and Government had taken over responsibility. The Families Association were having their costs reimbursed by Government. This encouraged their counsel to pursue an extravagantly extended line of questioning and a limitless series of expensive and often unnecessary studies that was most trying to the other parties who were not favoured financially in the same way. Again it was difficult working with LR. They seemed not to have anyone with sufficient authority to lay down the line they would take. I had no clear brief as to my area of interest. Because much of the evidence related to the design of the main hatch covers this vagueness made it difficult even for their own staff when in the witness box.

I did not cover myself with any glory on this occasion and have to admit I was puzzled all the way through by the questioning. It seemed to be just the ill-directed ramble such as I have already criticized, particularly from the Families' counsel. When technicalities like the fatigue properties of the material, or the alignment of structural members, or welding procedures were referred to, it seemed to be assumed that current standards and practices of the year 2000 applied. But *Derbyshire* was lost in 1980; she had been delivered from the shipyard in 1976; and she was the fifth in a class of six sister ships, the first of which was built in 1971. The ships had therefore been designed in 1969–70, namely thirty years before this inquiry. These thirty years saw tremendous strides in shipbuilding, yet the legal practitioners seemed to ignore this and persevered with questions that seemed to relate to today's practice. I tried to show that it was pointless saying, for example, that fatigue of steelwork had not been taken into account in the design of *Derbyshire*. Fatigue as something to be considered in ship construction was not generally recognized as important until the 1970s.

The final conclusion from the investigation was that ventilators and air-pipes had been carried away and the stores and tank spaces in the fore-end were flooded by waves sweeping over the ship and this made the forward hatches to the cargo holds more vulnerable. Once the number one hatch was destroyed the sequence of flooding meant inevitable loss. There is still much I would want to question, but what came through very clearly and was accepted by the court was that the ship did *not* break up at bulkhead 65. This was of major import. As to the main hatch covers, if the ship had been built today the hatch covers would have been stronger. The regulations have been tightened up since *Derbyshire* was built, and long before this investigation.

My own view has not changed from when first I saw and read the results of the underwater photographs. I think the disputed bosun's store hatch cover was blown off from the underside in the same way that other similar hatches along the ship were blown open under the explosion-implosion effects during sinking. It has been accepted that under this effect most of the ship structure had disintegrated into many pieces as it sank. The argument in court tended to be that the fore-end, because it was already at least part-filled with sea-water, did not suffer damage in the same way as the rest of the ship. I believe it did, but the evidence is less catastrophic because of the less rigidly enclosed construction and the many openings such as vents and airpipes which absorbed much of that same force as blew open the bosun's store hatch and ripped holes in the deck and bulkhead. I still think these explosive forces destroyed the windlass and some of the vent and air-pipes and other structures on the deck, rather than that the seas carried away all these items, as the report says. I find it hard to believe that air-pipes tucked in behind a perfectly normal bulwark were destroyed by the sea while the bulwark was not, and that a windlass with an anchor chain over it was literally fragmented by the seas. Everybody was too anxious to accept that the fore-end had materially flooded before the sinking. It suited each of the parties to have it so. I am not so sure that it was.

Professor Douglas Faulkner had parted company with his fellow assessors by the time of the Formal Investigation, which did not surprise me. There had obviously been disagreements between the original assessors when they were engaged on the underwater search. The problem I suspect (and I have in mind particularly the record in Hansard of a debate on the loss of *Derbyshire* in the House of Lords) was that Douglas was minded to make his own statements on the causes of the loss. Hansard tells us that the minister, Glenda Jackson, advised Lord Dixon that Professor Faulkner 'had been written to to convey the Department's displeasure in his untimely interventions'. Unsurprisingly, 'he submitted his resignation for personal reasons', according to Baroness Hayman, the Government spokeswoman. He then proceeded to produce a barrage of technical papers in support of his theories at the same time as the re-opened investigation was taking place. My view in the end was that the format and the conduct of this investigation, so different from the usual Wreck Commissioner's inquiry, was not as effective as it should have been.

CHAPTER 25

Argonautics

MY LAST APPOINTMENT in a professional sense was to become chairman of Argonautics in 1995. I had been retired, supposedly, for nine years but was invited out of the blue, as so many of my jobs have been, to take an interest in a new 'cluster' proposal for the Tyne. A group of smaller companies all engaged in marine design found themselves in the same area of Wallsend, all facing similar problems of competing in the maritime market, and all left to battle on once the larger shipbuilding and repair companies like Swan Hunter had closed down. Fortuitously, the local North Tyneside Council had become aware of them while they themselves were rather desperately seeking ways of encouraging business in what was now an industrial area in decline. One particular member of their business development team, Nathan Pellow, having seen the success of clustering companies of like businesses in Italy, persuaded the Council to support the formation of a local marine cluster. I was asked to lead this and was chairman for seven years throughout an interesting period. Prime Minister John Major was at the time forever inveighing against local authorities (and trade unions) but I found North Tyneside Council to be a progressive set-up that genuinely seemed out to help, maintain and improve local businesses, and as far as I could see were doing so effectively. They certainly found public monies to assist our new cluster for which we adopted the name Argonautics Limited, which was pleasing to me remembering Alfred Holt's affection for Greek names.

Our cluster covers the whole spectrum of marine consultancy starting with concept and design by Armstrong Technology, a phoenix-like Swan Hunter design team led by the very effective David Hewitt, rescued out of the ashes of the former shipbuilding company; a similar small-ship company, Wilson Ross MacDougall, under Alan MacDougall; Contract Design (Northern) under Peter Douglas, looking after the stage where design turns into detailing and manufacture; a consultancy called AIMMS running project management and port and ship facility design and building. Peter Rossiter of Isherwoods handles the logistics of maintaining the ships in service. Peter Allan of SeTech specializes in sea-bed work; Christopher Souter of Souter Trading provides spares and equipment; and David Cairns looks after the IT side. So we have available a whole cradle-to-grave marine business for ships and offshore structures.

It is difficult to measure the value of working together in this way in monetary terms, but I have watched the companies begin to share joint projects and gradually develop that mutual trust over the years that is essential if they are to get the benefit of what has been invested in the cluster. I am sure that they are better off now than they would have been operating as individual SMEs.

We had no sooner formed this marine cluster than others began to follow. Now there is a whole batch on Tyneside, culminating in a super-cluster called Northern Defence Industries Limited. It concentrates on defence work and includes Argonautics in its marine division. Our success in forming Argonautics Limited encouraged North Tyneside Council to envisage a dedicated company and a new building which would act as a focal point for new industries. I felt at the time that this was a flight of fancy on the part of these public servants. Thanks to a slab of European money acquired by North Tyneside Council added to what was provided locally, we now have a magnificent six-storey building called the Centre for Advanced Industry (CAI). Members of my Argonautics cluster occupy the top half, and it has been a great cheer to them to have such modern accommodation. The rest of the building is devoted to smaller companies working in the IT and micro-electronics sector – which has had its ups and downs. The Japanese giants Fujitsu and the German Siemens had moved into the North East in the late 1990s with the help of public monies and many smaller companies started out bravely on the back of those big names. But they pulled out after only a year or two, as globally based companies are wont to do. It was another severe blow to our area. Nevertheless NEMI (North of England Microelectronics Institute), which was set up to manage our CAI investment, has done remarkably well in attracting and supporting a lot of new and rather arcane IT companies. I was a director for seven years and I pay tribute to John Williams the general manager who has done wonders – a Blue Funnel trained marine engineer of course. We have only had one serious disappointment, a joint venture with Durham and Newcastle Universities into testing micro-chips where NEMI put real money in. It failed amid acrimony. I have never found universities easy partners. They always seem to want other people's money.

The North East is making heavy weather so far in the struggle to replace the traditional heavy industries that have gone from the area. These disappointments with the micro-electronics ventures are only one example. Newcastle seems to be losing out to Leeds in the push for commerce and business. The undoubted attractions of a city which has handsomely renewed its inner areas particularly around the river Tyne, has excellent communications, and beautiful hinterland both north and south of the river, do not seem to be enough to get things moving. I tend to share the view that the whole area has an ingrained culture that looks for man-size and even ruthless leadership such as prevailed in the days of Lord Armstrong and subsequent powerful industrial leaders, and then is happy to follow rather than take the initiative as individuals. There is still admiration for T. Dan Smith, the forceful council leader of some years ago. The remarkable results of his activities are seen in the city to this day. Of course he ended up in disgrace alongside his architect Poulson, but in his heyday he made things happen, and people here like that.

CHAPTER 26

RSA and RDI

IN 1959, back in Harry Flett's day, I was packed off on a rare visit to London to attend a lecture at the RSA (the Royal Society for the Encouragement of Arts, Manufactures and Commerce.) The subject was the River Thames and its water. Blue Funnel interest came from the fact that the rivets in the hulls of our ships using the river were selectively corroding excessively. The ships did have to sit around in Thames water rather longer than they should have done, which was suspected to be part of the problem. The speaker told us about anaerobic corrosion and like problems. As a brash youngster I asked what was going wrong with our ships, but got no satisfactory answer. The lecturer was more a biologist than a metallurgist. My association with the RSA lapsed thereafter until I was elected a Fellow in 1968 at the instigation of Neville Ward, the interior architect who was advising us on ships' accommodation design at the time.

There were once very close ties between the RINA and RSA. These started with the meeting held at the RSA in John Adam Street on 20 January 1860 when the INA was first established. The *Journal* of the RSA carried the reports of our meetings and recorded progress of our fledgling institution for many years until the INA began to publish its own transactions. John Scott Russell FRS, one of our founder stalwarts, was secretary of the RSA; and the first offices of INA were handily placed in Adelphi Terrace across the street from RSA.

The attraction of the RSA for me has been its broad range of interests and the diversity of its lectures. There are ten regions up and down the country, each running a programme of lectures and events, and I used to attend these with Elfrida on Merseyside. When we moved to the North East I was invited to join the local committee, and then became its chairman for five years, which I greatly enjoyed. In due course and in a system of rotation I became a member of the council of RSA – and fell out with Prue Leith who was chairman. RSA has no real money of its own and is always looking for funds. I dared to suggest that they could acquire income from judicious and appropriate advertising in the *RSA Journal*, and pointed out that most other institutions (like the RINA) covered the cost of their publications in this way. I was quickly made to realize such a practice would be wholly distasteful to this erudite society. Now, some seven years later, I find just one or two very discreet advertisements have been allowed to appear –

Sir Peter Baldwin (right), chairman of the RSA, confers the title of RDI on MM, 1986.

Rothschilds, Mercedes, Mikimoto and English National Ballet in one of the latest issues.

The trouble with the RSA is that it does not know any longer what it is for. In its early days it comfortably embraced science and technology as well as the arts (although the word 'technology' had not been invented), giving prizes and awards for the design of hydraulic machinery and mechanical devices as easily as it recognized prowess in literature or sculpture. The title 'The Royal Society for the Encouragement of Arts, Manufactures and Commerce' is far too long for these days. People get wearied before the end of reading or quoting it, and just think of it as the Royal Society of *Arts*. To some extent they are right because 'Manufactures and Commerce' have tended to be relegated to second place. Nevertheless RSA lectures at John Adam Street, and now increasingly in the regions, are always of the highest quality and there seems to be no difficulty in attracting the top names as speakers; although I feel the discussions following the lectures are seldom allowed enough time to develop any definite conclusion or line of follow-up. Meantime, in the regions we Fellows hold our own events and have our own lectures which we hope have some bearing on the Society's objectives; and we enjoy each other's company very much.

The RSA does have a co-existence with industry, although I sometimes wonder if it sees that particular link as more of a burden than an asset. In 1936 the RSA council decided there should be an award to those who have 'attained eminence in creative design for industry', and the Faculty of Royal Designers for Industry was formed. The objective was 'to further excellence in design and its application to industrial purposes'. There was imposed a maximum number of thirty names. This was raised as the breadth of design activity increased in later years to forty, then fifty, then seventy and finally to one hundred in 1966. There are well-known names on the roll – Lord Foster, Betty Jackson, Zandra Rhodes, Ronald Searle and lots of others equally well recognized; and those now gone – Hardy Amies, Frank Whittle, Barnes Wallis, Gordon Russell. I had the title of Royal Designer for Industry (RDI) conferred on me in 1986. It recognized my contribution to ship design, and the containerships in particular.

But I have experienced a feeling of vague dissatisfaction with the Faculty. In the first place I did not believe that the limit of one hundred members could be appropriate after more than thirty years during which the understanding, application and practice of design had expanded dramatically. Secondly, the Faculty membership was to my mind steered too much towards those disciplines where the visual aspect was dominant. The representation from the vast engineering sector for example was deficient. When I became (to my alarm) master of the Faculty in 1997, I determined to try and correct this, having been greatly encouraged and supported by Jean Muir, the legendary dress designer, when she was master. She had a remarkable appreciation of engineering and proclaimed that her dress design work was 'engineering for the body' – which to me was most enlightening; and she disliked the word 'fashion' unless it was used as a verb.

When Jean discovered I lived in Northumberland she invited Elfrida and me to her secret Northumberland home from time to time – a place of wondrous delight, everything from wallpaper and carpets to statuettes having been specially designed, often by fellow RDIs. She died soon after, which we found desperately sad.

Because RDIs were a fractious lot, 'prima donnas' to many people, and were super-cautious about whom they admitted, I had a distinct impression that the RSA tended to leave them to their own machinations, even though the parent body was the ultimate bestower of the honour of RDI. I tried to involve the RSA council in influencing the raising of the maximum number of members, and in adjusting the overall representation of the various disciplines where there was a marked superiority in the numbers of graphic, film, theatre, exhibition, book and textile designers. I was successful in at least starting the process of increasing the maximum number, and the Privy Council have recently given permission to breach our current figure of 100 maximum. But I failed in attracting council's attention to the imbalance in

MM giving the master's address to the Faculty of RDIs, 1997, on the subject of how a containership twists at sea.

types of member – perhaps not surprisingly since I saw Sir Stuart Hampson, chairman of council, jump out of his skin when someone pointed out in the discussion of my proposal that he was actually president of the Faculty. He hadn't realized it – and so could hardly be expected to spearhead my cause. The eminent theatre designer Tim O'Brien followed me as master of the Faculty. He has been kind enough to suggest it was my prodding that encouraged him to break with the minimal action attitude, and he very successfully initiated a series of annual Summer Schools in design particularly directed at younger folk.

During one of the fraught annual discussions within the Faculty on who might qualify for membership, I was horrified to find a document from a very illustrious graphic designer. He was prepared to accept car designers he said (we already had one or two Formula One car designers on the roll), but not engineers. What hope for my efforts if such was the level of understanding? Just as we came to the successful end of a long consideration at another meeting of the admission of the principal Rolls Royce aero-engine designer, an eminent designer of chairs and seating asked if this man had really considered sufficiently the visual aspects of his products. I had with me a *Sunday Times* photograph taken a little earlier of Jean Muir standing in the actual entry nacelle of a Rolls Royce jet engine. I thought what was good enough for her should be good enough for the rest of us.

Having unburdened myself of my minor disquiet about the Faculty I readily confess it has been most gratifying to serve alongside such engineers as we have – Alex Moulton mechanical engineer par excellence; Jim Randle likewise; Bill Brown master bridge designer; John Barnard racing car designer; Philip Ruffle the father of the remarkable Rolls Royce Trent engine; Colin Mudie the yacht designer, and several others who formed a like-minded circle of friends in what sometimes feels a slightly alien milieu. As we sit round the table it is startlingly evident that the engineers tend to wear jacket and tie and the others do not. Perhaps some sort of psychological treatise is called for?

When I became master of the Faculty I automatically became a vice-president of the RSA and so found myself on the RSA council for a further two years. The general level of intellect and sense of *divina particula aurae* was, as ever, overpowering – but nobody seemed to be able to show the entry point to the sort of vast funds and other resources that would propel the RSA to the kind of success it had enjoyed at the Great Exhibition of 1851. HRH Prince Philip, Duke of Edinburgh has been the president of the RSA ever since the Queen relinquished the position in 1953. He has given incredible support over the whole period. For the two years of my mastership I served on his Duke of Edinburgh Prize for Designers selection panel, the work being done in the Centre Room in Buckingham Palace – from the balcony of which room kings and queens wave to their subjects. The prize is given to the best designer of the year, so selection is really quite difficult and the role of Prince Philip as chairman is crucial, and is effective. If the Faculty of RDIs were as truly representative of the best designers as it should be, the Duke of Edinburgh's Prize would regularly find a home with one of our members, but it does not.

I am proud to be a Royal Designer for Industry but at the same time I think we are too exclusive and pernickety in our selection, processing and acceptance of candidates. And the honour is not well recognized nationally in the way I am sure was intended at its institution. It is not surprising that in the obituaries of our fellow RDIs there is often no mention of the conferment of the honour. I still hope that the RSA council will take a grip and effect change so that the award is recognized and respected more widely, because the Faculty as presently constituted cannot.

PART VII

Last Entries in the Log

Chapter 27

The anchorage

I AM WRITING exactly sixty years on from the wartime Monday in December when I started my apprenticeship at the Caledon shipyard in Dundee. I am in Rothbury, a nicely sized village in the middle of Northumberland and here Elfrida and I enjoy panoramic views over the Coquet Valley, and wonder how long it will be before we need some sort of stair-lift to deal with the slope we live on. The nine-hole golf course, which used to be the race-course, is just below us and it becomes completely flooded several times a year, but fortunately drains extremely rapidly. To see it flooded like this was rare until a year or two ago. Something is changing in our climate. Our village is very much a product of the success of the first Lord Armstrong and his Tyneside shipbuilding and armaments companies. His mansion of Cragside (now National Trust property) is just over the hill from our back door, and there are marks of his wealth and his influence in the housing and layout both of the village and the countryside all around. 'His' branch railway that wandered through the county from Morpeth (fondly known as the 'Wannie' line for it followed the Wansbeck river) and 'his' Rothbury station have gone. There just remain a series of unexpectedly severe humpy bridges at unexpected places which catch out speedsters. Beyond is vast, quiet and lovely Northumberland with farms everywhere – farms that have suffered traumatic change in a very short time – once the backbone of the county, now a fragile element of its well-being.

I wrote years ago in my inaugural presidential address to the NE Coast Institution on first coming to the North East from Liverpool, that I found the people here are over-modest. Like everyone else my secretary at British Shipbuilders always said 'we' did something when she meant 'I' did something. The first person pronoun was just too bumptious. It's the same here in Northumberland. The people are too reticent; they don't look askance at incomers like us so much; it's just that they don't easily feel at home with strangers whom they too readily assume are superior in some way. It takes rather long before we intruders have the joy of finding new local friends. Because until recently I spent so much time on semi-professional affairs in London, it is only now that I have been able to link in a little more with local folk. The Alnwick Probus Club is a great help. After our short stay in the busy and crowded Winchester area before I formally retired from BMT and moved back to Northumberland, we found the peace and quiet here starkly different. The ambulance and the fire engine sometimes pass through the village with sirens blaring. The noise isn't really necessary. If we go west to the Lakes on a summer morning over the old Roman road by Hadrian's Wall, I can almost guarantee we shall see no more than a dozen cars in the first forty miles.

Hazel and Arthur with two of our grandchildren are at present in Papworth near Cambridge, and Ursula, with three, is on the outskirts of Newcastle and so is quite near. Angela is nearest of all for she has decided to sell her flat and move in with us here. Just how temporary a stay it is to be is not clear. When we moved here from Redstacks near Morpeth we attended a long-standing Brethren fellowship in the neighbouring village of Thropton for a few years, but more recently we have made our place of worship the Evangelical church still known as 'the Mission', at Longhorsley, some eight miles down the Coquet Valley. It started up 125 years ago in what is quite a small Northumberland village but it draws its congregation from all around and has prospered over the years. It belongs to the Fellowship of Independent Evangelical Churches and we are happy there.

Harking back to the 1960s for a moment when we broke free from the ultra-restrictive religious system we had known, we experienced a great feeling of freedom. Suddenly there was no end of useful activities that we could get involved in. I joined the Liverpool branch of the Christian Business Men's Association. We had good times and enjoyed hearing some great Christian speakers. I was disappointed that we could never attract Bishop David Sheppard who was making such a notable contribution to the welfare and morale of Liverpool in difficult and depressing times. He considered we were too elitist, I think. A highlight shortly before we moved to Newcastle was holding the national CBMA convention in Liverpool while I was chairman. We took the nautical theme of 'Christ at the Helm', and Blue Funnel did us proud by decking out the conference hall in full nautical regalia – with the Alfred Holt flag prominent. Admiral Sir Horace Law, retired, and a former gunnery expert, a delightful and modest speaker, was principal guest and memorably addressed us on 'Chart and Compass'. He was a predecessor of mine as president of the RINA so I had seen him in action – in the Council chamber.

To find oneself alongside fellow businessmen in these surroundings was most heartening because we all came from so many different churches. There were those like me, ex brethren; John Williamson, general manager of Royal Insurance (whose headquarters were in Liverpool); Gordon Spratt, marketing manager of Unilever; Gordon Read, curator of the Liverpool Museum who was to do so much to inaugurate the Liverpool Maritime Museum (the Philip Holt Trust had laid money by for years in the hope that someday it would happen). But there were others too, like Kenneth Maude,

MM's 70th birthday: (back row) Elfrida, Ursula, Arthur, Hazel and Angela, (front row) Victoria, Charles, Aaron, and MM holding Natasha.

a solicitor and member of the Synod of the Church of England, and Victor Roberts a Blue Funnel fellow director of mine from the merger with Corys.

If the CBMA was elitist and meant that I moved among the business people of Merseyside, I had my taste of the other extreme as well. I was invited to join the committee of the Liverpool City Mission. Here was the raw reality of deprivation and need, both practical and spiritual, a world away from the businessmen's scene. The Liverpool City Mission is the oldest City Mission in England and was about to celebrate its 150th anniversary when I left for Newcastle. The gripping story of its work over these years, *A Voice in the City*, was well written up for that anniversary by my museum curator friend Gordon Read and shows how it was formed in order to try and counter the poverty, wretchedness and disease that characterized Liverpool in the early 1800s. The work was just as necessary in the 1970s and, unsurprisingly, several fellow committee members were colleagues in the CBMA. But it was the full-time staff (David Jebsen and seven other men) who, working at the coal face, carried the burden of getting close to people, preaching the gospel of Christ and bringing practical help and cheer to those at the bottom end of society.

Although Elfrida and I have experienced some disillusionments along the way in our assembly and church fellowships we have never had occasion to waver from our commitment to our basic Christian faith. The choice I made as a student sitting in the little meeting room in Dens Road just along from the Dundee Football Club ground still stands, although I am painfully aware of personal failings that may, or may not, have surprised friends and colleagues. I have vaingloriously referred to my career as a tapestry. It might more honestly be regarded as a rather worn carpet with too many dark blots and discoloured stains on it. Yet underneath there has thankfully been a strong backing, not of my making.

Since retirement here in Northumberland I have become a member of Gideons International in the British Isles. I had been approached many times to join, both here in the North East and while on Merseyside, but had always pleaded too many other commitments. I think I lost opportunities by leaving it as late as this because it is most rewarding. Here again I have found in this thoroughly national (and international) body a high proportion of ex-brethren. With their background of perseverance, discipline and firm beliefs, they have found in the Gideon ministry, as I have, a welcome avenue of service. For the Gideon work is often referred to as a 'disciplined ministry', and everything that has been achieved has come from men and women working steadily together year in year out, with a strong sense of responsibility, a willingness to accept order and ready to devote time to the job.

Most people will recognize the name from seeing the Gideon Bible in the hotel bedroom, or perhaps from seeing their children bring a red 'youth testament' home from school. The movement has been active in this country for just over fifty years but it started in US over 100 years ago when one or two commercial travellers, as we used to call them, formed an association to place bibles in the hotels they frequented. Its history has been well written up to 1987 in *The Gideons* by Phyllis Thompson. I am chairman, for the second time round, of the Mid Northumberland branch, one of the 271 branches in UK. Headquarters are in Lutterworth, and international HQ is in US from where the work in 176 different countries is co-ordinated. The scale of the operation can be appreciated if I say that we distribute one million copies of the scriptures every eight days. It is clear that if we in the UK do not value the Bible so much nowadays, other nations do, many increasingly so. Somewhere last year a student at one of our schools received the twenty-five millionth copy of our youth testament given since we started in UK.

The first time I came across a Gideon Bible was when I visited Liverpool in 1953 for my interview for the job with the naval architects of Alfred Holt. The Stork Hotel was a horsey outfit in the city centre, much favoured by punters attending Aintree, and full of equine pictures. There I first became acquainted with, not just the Bible in the bedroom, but at the front of it the all-important 'Introduction' which has always been a feature of Gideon scriptures.

Although I had been broadly familiar with the Bible from early days it was from that Gideon Bible introduction that I began to realize just what a strange but remarkable book the Bible is – a mini-library of sixty-six separate books and letters written over a period of 1,500 years by many different writers. I quote from the introduction:

> They lived and wrote in different countries and came from different walks of life and different social positions. One wrote history, another biography; another wrote on theology, another poetry, another prophecy. Some wrote on philosophy, and some stories of adventure, travel and romance. Most of them had no contact with each other and no means of knowing that when their writings were all put together as one book it would be complete, all parts agreeing in doctrine, teaching and prophecy.

So I am glad that all the schools in Northumberland welcome us each year to an assembly where we give a little talk and give the young people of about eleven to thirteen years of age their copy of the New Testament. In visiting the schools over the years we have seen the atmosphere change as new Government policies are continually directed at them. Things are much more unsettled than they were a few years ago, there is obviously more hassle and the time they can devote to our visits is always tightening. Hotels and homes for the elderly, bed and breakfast places and hospitals all need our attention. The latter are high consumption establishments as to scriptures and we have to keep replacing copies of the hospital testaments. When you are ill, unhappy, fearful or distressed you read your Bible, and obviously a good many patients keep theirs. We don't mind, for we are ready with more. We visit churches and explain our work, we make sure lifeboat-men and police and fire-fighters are not forgotten. In approaching all these bodies and individuals, asking permission to place bibles and testaments, we hardly ever get a refusal. It is most encouraging.

Then we have HM Prison at Acklington, deep in Northumberland. I find this a difficult but compelling assignment. I go every few weeks to help at the Sunday morning service in the chapel. One gets accustomed to the eerie business of gaining entry, and the prison chaplains are usually wonderful and dedicated people. Barry Cooper the current senior chaplain is a Liverpool man. Intriguingly, he had a grandfather who was a Blue Funnel engineer officer who retired, from a shore position, just as I joined the company in 1953. He had been one of the crew rushed across to Copenhagen just as the German army was about to invade Denmark at the start of World War II.

The intention was to try and sail out our *Glengarry* which was being built there and was almost complete. They were too late and were taken into captivity for the duration, as was the ship.

One of Barry's predecessors as chaplain at Acklington used to confide that 'you cannot work wonders in a prison, you just have to be wise and listen, sympathize and offer comfort in distress'. There are of course noteworthy examples of moral and spiritual change during imprisonment, whether it is Chuck Colson of Watergate or apparently our own Jonathan Aitken. But it is not easy to make an impact. Prison governors here do not readily allow us to give out our Gideon testaments to all the cells. I think they do not like to see them desecrated and made into cigarette papers, although we do not really mind and have always more available. The governors leave it to the chaplain to distribute them from a stock we provide. On the normal Sunday morning the first service is for the ordinary prisoners, nearly always younger men, and only a few come along. They invariably ask urgently for prayers for friends and families and are quite willing to talk after the service and tell us why they are there, how long they have to go before release and what hopes for parole.

The second service follows immediately and is the troubling one. It is for the VPs, the vulnerable prisoners who because of their crimes are liable to hurt from their fellows, and so are accompanied more closely by the officers. We don't have a chance to speak much with them as they are escorted away rapidly at the end of the service, but they come in droves and fill the chapel. They listen intently, the singing is resounding and there is always somebody able and ready to play the organ. These are mainly older men and because I often talk on ship topics I have been asked time and again by them to speak on the subject of life's voyage, where I remind them we are either outward bound or homeward bound – much more evocative terms than the 'outward' and 'return' of the train or airline. It seems to strike some sort of chord. I still find the visits disconcerting because all the men seem so normal and friendly, yet they have been convicted and are here in prison. Unlike the other run-of-the-mill prisoners there is never any reference to what they have done. It is difficult to shed the feeling 'there but for the grace of God goes – Marshall Meek'.

I go back to Liverpool each October to attend the annual dinner of the Nestorians Association, the Blue Funnel old boys' get-together. Two years ago, the Stork Hotel having long since gone, I stayed in a hotel where for the first time I found someone had written in the Gideon Bible in the bedroom. Gideons almost automatically check that the Bible is in or on the bedside locker. In this one, where on the first page it says the Bible is not to be taken away or sold, someone had written in ink 'just ignore it'. Then the book of Proverbs had been singled out for study. There were various annotations.

One for example questioned the statement that 'the wages of the righteous bring them life but the income of the wicked brings punishment'. 'Not always', added the reader in the margin. But on the front page someone else had differed and written in ink 'you are wrong', and then provided a selection of verses to correct our anonymous critic, such as 'we fix our eyes not on what is seen but what is unseen. For what is seen is temporary, but what is unseen is eternal.' Then as a Gideon I added my own little comment. It's the only time I have seen such entries.

What encourages us as Gideons to go on with our labours is the steady flow of letters to headquarters in Lutterworth recording how one and another have been comforted, or indeed had their lives changed, by looking into the Gideon Bible. Our quarterly *Gideon News* gives a continual record of these. I am convinced that many intelligent, attractive and thoughtful people who shy away from the Bible, or harbour sceptical or even antagonistic views about it, are somehow a little afraid of it and try to avoid it. They have just not read this vital, mysteriously potent, never-to-be-destroyed book.

Chapter 28

Signing off

IN PENNING THIS CHRONICLE, a fusion of the personal and the technical, I have been striving not just to record my own modest part in the nation's maritime affairs, but also to paste my experiences on to the more extensive maritime scenario that my span of days has covered. In my early years with Blue Funnel we reached the stage where ships' officers were not so keen to leave the rather confined teak-built wheelhouse to keep their look-out in the open. Larger steel wheelhouses made it possible to keep a look-out in greater comfort, but it meant providing the man on the bridge with all-round, or as near all-round vision as possible. My personal field of vision over these years has probably covered more points of the compass than most of my colleagues were afforded. I didn't exactly seek that; it just happened – providentially I believe. But I have only been able to enter in the log what I observed on my watch – a one-man view and one man's record. There are a host of others who saw these things from another angle as they stood their watch. They probably experienced far rougher waters than I ever did, and could tell a different and better story. It is the magnitude of the change in every aspect of my adventures that leaves the biggest impression. But then almost anybody whose working span has covered the same era can say the same.

The title of my volume reflects the irony. Merchant ships in all their glory and with all their traditions, necessary as they were and still are to our livelihoods (because we still live by exporting and importing), have been lost to Britain. Yet people all around me still talk of the sea, remember our maritime history (whether it be in building ships or sailing them), take comfort in our Royal Navy's presence, and take pride in every seagoing achievement whether it is rowing the Atlantic or circumnavigating the globe. I was in Halifax a few years ago at the opening of the new RSA Centre at Dean Clough by HRH Prince Philip, Duke of Edinburgh. Round the walls were arrayed the plaques illustrating the work of the Royal Designers for Industry. Jean Muir was master at the time and she insisted I accompany her when she guided Prince Philip round the display. When we arrived at my exhibit, mounted next to hers, depicting my containerships and displaying the familiar words 'They that go down to the sea in ships, and do business in great waters; these see the works of the Lord, and his wonders in the deep', he said 'Ah, Psalm 107! – you should read Psalm 104.' I went home and did

Jean Muir, HRH Duke of Edinburgh and MM at the RDI exhibition in Halifax, 1984, where I found the title for my book.

so, and found 'So is this great and wide sea, wherein are things creeping innumerable, both small and great beasts. *There go the ships*: there is that leviathan whom thou hast made to play therein.'

I think much of this country's problems, and perhaps especially those in the maritime sphere, can be blamed on too respectful an adherence to tradition. We feel instinctively that we did things rather well in the past, whether building the ships or sailing them, and we have not readily changed the way we do these things even to this very day. My inaugural address to the NE Coast Institution in 1984 focused on this subject and I suggested that our great traditions should not just provide a soft pillow of self-congratulation or complacency. Our traditions should be a coiled spring set to energize our forward planning and execution, incorporating all that we have learnt and experienced in the past. But in our calmer moments we could probably accept that in the first part of the twentieth century we really did have an oversize share of 'world maritime inc.'. That dominance was almost bound to weaken as other nations gauged their strategic needs and their capabilities and set about acquiring their share. But it is the speed with which we allowed our industries to succumb that still rankles.

It was the conjunction of managers who never looked abroad or outside their own narrow historical practices, and a militant work-force who totally failed to see how short-sighted their antagonisms were, that sealed the fate of our shipbuilding industry. Nationalizing the industry in 1977–8 afforded what was certainly the last opportunity to rescue something of it, but in the way it was organized with a totally inept top management, there was not the slightest hope of success.

As for the shipowners, they had a more rounded type of management but with some curious and disappointing attitudes – a reluctance to act individually outside the consensual Chamber of Shipping; a kind of arrogance that partly came from being largely independent of Government support, until they realized it might have been a good thing to cultivate ministers to some degree; almost as bad a reputation latterly as the shipyards in not adopting modern technology, *vide* the refusal to take any real interest in the Efficient Ship Programme. And they would never, on any account, be associated with or linked to UK shipbuilders. Not altogether surprising, but other countries like Norway and Denmark generated strength from their maritime industries working together.

In the end they all succumbed in a sort of gadarene competition to get out, the only brave soul from the major shipping companies who made a real fight to stay in business being Jeffrey (now Lord) Sterling of P&O. He, to his lasting credit, took on the mammoth endeavour of trying to influence Mrs Thatcher towards helping. Success was rather minimal and it took years before a somewhat beneficial 'tonnage tax' was introduced, by which time it was much too late. Blue Funnel, in spite of their long and glorious history, were no better than the others. The carefully groomed student-princes had no answer to the problem of running a fleet of ships economically in the newer and harsher economic climate of the 1980s; and so the descendants of Alfred Holt's high-minded traditions saw their great company, along with almost all the others in UK, forced out of the business. Very few of these proud managers made any impact on UK business once they were shaken out of the safety of the shipowning web.

Now shipping is largely in the hands of foreign powers who lack the sort of tradition we knew and respected. The Alfred Holt concept of creating a better ship, and sailing it noticeably more efficiently and safely than competitors did, has been lost under the general pressure for increased economic retuns. Our great containerships of the 1960s with their novel design and carefully designed crew quarters have been superseded. In a damning book published in 2000, *Ships, Slaves and Competition*, my old Elder Dempster colleague James Bell and his fellows of the International Commission on Shipping tell us of sub-standard ships, sub-standard practices and operations; and state: 'For thousands of today's international seafarers life at sea is modern slavery and their workplace is a slave ship.' Daily we buy goods made in the far-flung countries of the world – perhaps they form the greater part of all our purchases. This has happened partly because the cost of carriage by sea is so indescribably small a proportion of the total cost. International competition in shipping is ruthless.

Although we can point to overall improvement in ship safety over the last few decades, and the industry compares reasonably with other forms of transportation, too often expense on proper standards of safety and efficiency is skimped and we find major accidents happening. Some may claim these are isolated events that become over-emphasized, but we should not find in 2002 a modern ship full to the gunwhale with expensive motor cars capsizing a few miles off a Channel coast, and then within days being run into twice by two other ships.

There are, thankfully, happier elements within the maritime scene. When I say that our universities, our research establishments, our marine consultancies and our professional maritime institutions are going fairly strongly, it comes as some form of reassurance that not everything has dissolved. None of these activities is an easy money-spinner and they are all having to adapt continuously to the market place, but they are still there, competing successfully internationally and proving, it seems to me, that as a nation we seem to be better at the intellectual and inventive jobs than at making or doing.

One regret I have is that by having to leave the active scene in the 1980s, I missed out on direct involvement with the exciting development of very fast ships such as the catamarans and twin-hull wave-piercing craft, and the whole gamut of new high-speed ferries that were appearing. I must admit as well, of course, that I have never been a small boat enthusiast or practitioner, never indulging in the wet and the cold of the yachtsman, although I do admire and appreciate their prowess, their continually developing technology and the way their designs have always led from one fascinating naval architecture development to another.

So – *there went the ships*! What remains are the records of my and my colleagues' achievements that I have written into the transactions of our learned societies in the hope that others might still build on them and even now advance our remaining maritime businesses. But more especially there are the memories of the people I met all along the way. I have mentioned by name a few of those who worked alongside me. There were ten times as many whose lives touched mine in one way or another over these sixty plus years. I can only say a heartfelt thank you to them all for their help, loyalty and companionship.

Appendix

Major Contributions to Professional Institutions

RINA	Royal Institution of Naval Architects
NECIES	North East Coast Institution of Engineers & Shipbuilders
IESS	Institution of Engineers & Engineers in Scotland
IMechE	Institution of Mechanical Engineers
HCMM	Honourable Company of Master Mariners
SNAME	Society of Naval Architects & Marine Engineers (US, SA, China)
IMarE	Institute of Marine Engineers (now IMarEST)

Note: *written jointly with other authors

*Stress Investigations on a Tanker during Launching**	NECIES 1954
Design and Operation of Fast Cargo Liners – 'Glenlyon' Class	RINA 1964
*Priam Class Cargo Liners – Design & Operation**	RINA 1969
The First OCL Containerships	RINA 1970
*The Structural Design of the OCL Containerships**	RINA 1971
The Ship Designer's Response from the Owner's Side	Royal Soc 1972
*Accommodation in Ships**	RINA 1973
*All Gas and Freighters – The LNG Ship Comes of Age**	HCMM 1975
Operating Experience with Large Containerships	IESS 1975
*Some Failures and Associated Metallurgical Matters**	RINA 1976
Developments in Merchant Ships over the Last Decade	Thomas Low Gray Lecture IMechE 1979
*UK Research on Propeller Hull Interaction and Ship Vibration**	RINA 1979
Future Fuels for Marine Purposes	HCMM 1981
*Coal Burning Ships up to Panamax Size**	SNAME Durban SA 1981
Energy Saving in Ship Design and Operation	SNAME Beijing 1982

Design Considerations in Developing the Fuel Economic Ship★	RINA/IMarE 1982
Safety in Ships – the Shipbuilder's Viewpoint★	Glasgow University Centenary 1983
Design and Construction for Safety	RINA/RAeroSoc 1983
Ship Performance and Contractual Requirements★	NECIES 1984
Taking Stock – Marine Technology and UK Maritime Performance	RINA 1984
Traditions – Helping or Hindering	President's Address to the NECIES 1984
The UK Efficient Ship Project	Department of Trade and Industry Conference 1985
Design Construction and Initial Certification of Ships★	RAeroSoc/RINA 1990
'They that go down to the sea in ships'	Master's Address to the Faculty of Royal Designers for Industry 1997

Index